A Short Course in
Differential
Equations

By Earl D. Rainville

Elementary Differential Equations, Third edition

A Short Course in Differential Equations, Third edition

Special Functions

The Laplace Transform: An Introduction

Unified Calculus and Analytic Geometry

Analytic Geometry, Fifth edition
(with the late CLYDE E. LOVE)

Differential and Integral Calculus, Sixth edition
(with the late CLYDE E. LOVE)

Intermediate Differential Equations, Second edition

EARL D. RAINVILLE

Professor of Mathematics, The University of Michigan

A SHORT COURSE IN

Differential

Equations THIRD EDITION

The Macmillan Company, New York
Collier-Macmillan Limited, London

Library of Congress catalog card number 64-10580

THE MACMILLAN COMPANY, NEW YORK
COLLIER-MACMILLAN CANADA, LTD., TORONTO, ONTARIO

Printed in the United States of America

This book appears as the first 19 chapters of *Elementary
Differential Equations*, Third edition, © Copyright 1964 by
The Macmillan Company.

Some material in this book is from *The Laplace Transform:
An Introduction*, © Copyright 1963 by Earl D. Rainville.

Preface to
the Third Edition

This edition includes two new chapters devoted to the Laplace transform. Three other chapters have been rewritten with emphasis on the use of the transform in certain applications. A new section is devoted to the transverse displacements of a beam. There is a slight increase in the space devoted to some of the material included in earlier editions.

Altogether about one third of the text and exercises is new. The number of exercises has been increased to more than 1,400. More than half of my recently published book on the Laplace transform is included here.

I am disturbed at the recent increase in the number of students whose large vocabulary of advanced mathematical terms, ideas, and theorems is matched only by their complete inability to solve any but the simplest of specific problems. At a recent mathematics meeting I heard one speaker express alarm at the manipulative skill being developed by the students. Such fears have not yet caused me any loss of sleep. As in all my texts, I have made a serious attempt to aid the reader in developing a considerable skill in solving problems using the mathematical concepts and tools presented.

As in the earlier editions, I have tried to exhibit both the techniques for obtaining solutions and the basic ideas and theories behind these techniques. The numerous exercises have been constructed carefully with the double aim of developing the student's skill and adding to his understanding. Definitions and statements of fact are made with care.

The omission of infinite series methods has made possible, even within the bounds of a small book, a thorough treatment of topics essential to a first course. A longer book, my *Elementary Differential Equations*, Third edition, contains an extensive treatment of both power series and Fourier series methods and an introduction to application of the Laplace transform technique to boundary value problems involving partial differential equations.

I am grateful for the comments and suggestions received from many of my colleagues here at Michigan and from instructors and students in other colleges and universities. I am pleased to acknowledge in particular the aid and encouragement I received from Professors Jack R. Britton and L. C. Snively and Dean C. A. Hutchinson of the University of Colorado; Professor William N. Huff of the University of Oklahoma; Professor Phillip E. Bedient of Franklin and Marshall College; Professor Ralph L. Shively of Swarthmore College; and Professors D. G. Dickson, R. V. Churchill, R. C. F. Bartels, and G. E. Hay, of the University of Michigan.

I wish also to express my gratitude to Professor Bedient for his independent reading of the proof sheets for this book.

EARL D. RAINVILLE

Ann Arbor, Michigan

Contents

A Short Course in Differential Equations

CHAPTER 1

Definitions, Elimination of

Arbitrary Constants

1. Examples of differential equations

A differential equation is one that involves at least one derivative of an unknown function. As in equation (3) below, a derivative may be involved implicitly through the presence of differentials. Our aim is to solve differential equations; that is, to find the unknown function, or functions, which occur.

Differential equations arise frequently in physics, engineering, and chemistry, and on occasion in such subjects as biology, physiology, and economics. The solution of differential equations plays an important role in the study of the motions of heavenly bodies such as planets, moons, and artificial satellites.

The following are examples of differential equations:

$$(1) \qquad \frac{dy}{dx} = \cos x,$$

$$(2) \qquad \frac{d^2y}{dx^2} + k^2y = 0,$$

(3) $$(x^2 + y^2)\,dx - 2xy\,dy = 0,$$

(4) $$\frac{\partial u}{\partial t} = h^2 \left(\frac{\partial^2 u}{\partial x^2} + \frac{\partial^2 u}{\partial y^2} \right),$$

(5) $$L\frac{d^2 i}{dt^2} + R\frac{di}{dt} + \frac{1}{C}i = E\omega \cos \omega t,$$

(6) $$\frac{\partial^2 V}{\partial x^2} + \frac{\partial^2 V}{\partial y^2} = 0,$$

(7) $$\left(\frac{d^2 w}{dx^2}\right)^3 - xy\frac{dw}{dx} + w = 0,$$

(8) $$\frac{d^3 x}{dy^3} + x\frac{dx}{dy} - 4xy = 0,$$

(9) $$\frac{d^2 y}{dx^2} + 7\left(\frac{dy}{dx}\right)^3 - 8y = 0,$$

(10) $$\frac{d^2 y}{dt^2} + \frac{d^2 x}{dt^2} = x,$$

(11) $$x\frac{\partial f}{\partial x} + y\frac{\partial f}{\partial y} = nf.$$

When an equation involves one or more derivatives with respect to a particular variable, that variable is called an *independent* variable. A variable is called *dependent* if a derivative of that variable occurs.

In the equation

(5) $$L\frac{d^2 i}{dt^2} + R\frac{di}{dt} + \frac{1}{C}i = E\omega \cos \omega t$$

i is the dependent variable, t the independent variable, and L, R, C, E, and ω are called parameters. The equation

(6) $$\frac{\partial^2 V}{\partial x^2} + \frac{\partial^2 V}{\partial y^2} = 0$$

has one dependent variable V and two independent variables.

Since the equation

(3) $$(x^2 + y^2)\,dx - 2xy\,dy = 0$$

may be written

$$x^2 + y^2 - 2xy\frac{dy}{dx} = 0$$

or

$$(x^2 + y^2) \frac{dx}{dy} - 2xy = 0,$$

we may consider either variable to be dependent, the other being the independent one.

Oral Exercise

Identify the independent variables, the dependent variables, and the parameters in the equations given as examples in this section.

2. Definitions

A relation defining an explicit function is called a solution of a differential equation if it satisfies that equation in the ordinary sense of checking upon direct substitution. For example, let us verify that

$$y = e^{2x}$$

is a solution of the equation

(1) $$\frac{d^2y}{dx^2} + \frac{dy}{dx} - 6y = 0.$$

We substitute our tentative solution into the left member of equation (1) and find that

$$\frac{d^2y}{dx^2} + \frac{dy}{dx} - 6y = 4e^{2x} + 2e^{2x} - 6e^{2x} \equiv 0,$$

which completes the desired verification.

Consider, however, the differential equation

(2) $$(4x^3 - y^3)\,dx + (2y - 3xy^2)\,dy = 0$$

and the relation

(3) $$x^4 - xy^3 + y^2 = c,$$

in which c is a constant. It is surely not convenient to solve equation (3) for either x or y. But differentiation of both members of (3) produces

$$4x^3\,dx - y^3\,dx - 3xy^2\,dy + 2y\,dy = 0,$$

which is merely a rearrangement of (2). If x and y are related by equation (3), then x, y, dx, and dy are related by (2). Therefore we wish to call the relation (3) a solution of equation (2). This suggests a broader definition of the term solution, which we now state.

Any relation, free from derivatives, that involves one or more of the variables and that is consistent with the differential equation will be called a solution of the equation.

An equation involving partial derivatives is called a *partial differential equation;* one involving ordinary derivatives is called an *ordinary differential equation.*

The *order* of a differential equation is the order of the highest-ordered derivative appearing in the equation. For instance,

$$(4) \qquad \frac{d^2y}{dx^2} + 2b\left(\frac{dy}{dx}\right)^3 + y = 0$$

is an equation of "order two." It is also referred to as a "second-order equation."

The *degree* of an ordinary differential equation is the algebraic degree in the highest-ordered derivative in the equation.

The equation

$$\left(\frac{d^2y}{dx^2}\right)^3 + \frac{d^2y}{dx^2}\left(\frac{dy}{dx}\right)^4 - x^7y = \sin x$$

is of degree three, because in so far as the second derivative alone is concerned, the equation is a cubic. Equation (4) is of degree one.

Any equation of the form

$$(5) \qquad M(x, y)\, dx + N(x, y)\, dy = 0$$

is of order one and degree one. All the equations which we shall solve in Chapter 2 may be written in the form (5).

A very important concept is that of the linearity or nonlinearity of a differential equation. An equation is said to be *linear* if each term of the equation is either linear in all the dependent variables and their various derivatives or does not contain any of them. Otherwise the equation is said to be *nonlinear.* The term $y\dfrac{dy}{dx}$ is of degree two in y and its derivative together and is therefore nonlinear. Every linear equation is of degree one, but not every equation of degree one is linear. Note that equation (4) above is nonlinear.

The equation

$$x^2y'' + xy' + (x^2 - n^2)y = 4x^3$$

is linear in y. The manner in which the independent variable enters the equation has nothing to do with the property of linearity.

Oral Exercises

For each of the following, state whether the equation is ordinary or partial, linear or nonlinear, and give its order and degree.

1. $\dfrac{d^2x}{dt^2} + k^2x = 0.$

2. $\dfrac{\partial^2 w}{\partial t^2} = a^2 \dfrac{\partial^2 w}{\partial x^2}.$

3. $(x^2 + y^2)\,dx + 2xy\,dy = 0.$

4. $y' + P(x)y = Q(x).$

5. $y''' - 3y' + 2y = 0.$

6. $yy'' = x.$

7. $\dfrac{\partial^2 u}{\partial x^2} + \dfrac{\partial^2 u}{\partial y^2} + \dfrac{\partial^2 u}{\partial z^2} = 0.$

8. $\dfrac{d^4y}{dx^4} = w(x).$

9. $x\dfrac{d^2y}{dt^2} - y\dfrac{d^2x}{dt^2} = c_1.$

10. $L\dfrac{di}{dt} + Ri = E.$

11. $(x + y)\,dx + (3x^2 - 1)\,dy = 0.$

12. $x(y'')^3 + (y')^4 - y = 0.$

13. $\left(\dfrac{d^3w}{dx^3}\right)^2 - 2\left(\dfrac{dw}{dx}\right)^4 + yw = 0.$

14. $\dfrac{dy}{dx} = 1 - xy + y^2.$

15. $y'' + 2y' - 8y = x^2 + \cos x.$

16. $a\,da + b\,db = 0.$

3. The elimination of arbitrary constants

In practice, differential equations arise in many ways, some of which we shall encounter later. There is one way of arriving at a differential equation which is useful in that it gives us a feeling for the kinds of solutions to be expected. In this section we shall start with a relation (the solution) involving arbitrary constants, and, by elimination of those arbitrary constants, come to a differential equation satisfied by the original relation. In a sense we start with the answer and find the problem.

Methods for the elimination of arbitrary constants vary with the way in which the constants enter the given relation. A method which is efficient for one problem may be poor for another. One fact persists throughout. Since each differentiation yields a new relation, the number of derivatives that need be used is the same as the number of arbitrary

constants to be eliminated. We shall in each case determine the differential equation that is:

(a) Of order equal to the number of arbitrary constants in the given
relation;

(b) Consistent with that relation;

(c) Free from arbitrary constants.

EXAMPLE (a): Eliminate* the arbitrary constants c_1 and c_2 from
the relation

(1) $$y = c_1 e^{-2x} + c_2 e^{3x}.$$

Since two constants are to be eliminated, obtain the two derivatives,

(2) $$y' = -2c_1 e^{-2x} + 3c_2 e^{3x},$$
(3) $$y'' = 4c_1 e^{-2x} + 9c_2 e^{3x}.$$

The elimination of c_1 from equations (2) and (3) yields

$$y'' + 2y' = 15c_2 e^{3x};$$

the elimination of c_1 from equations (1) and (2) yields

$$y' + 2y = 5c_2 e^{3x}.$$

Hence

$$y'' + 2y' = 3(y' + 2y),$$

or

$$y'' - y' - 6y = 0.$$

Another method for obtaining the differential equation in this example
proceeds as follows. We know from a theorem in elementary algebra that
the three equations (1), (2), and (3) considered as equations in the two
unknowns c_1 and c_2 can have solutions only if

(4) $$\begin{vmatrix} -y & e^{-2x} & e^{3x} \\ -y' & -2e^{-2x} & 3e^{3x} \\ -y'' & 4e^{-2x} & 9e^{3x} \end{vmatrix} = 0.$$

Since e^{-2x} and e^{3x} cannot be zero, equation (4) may be rewritten, with the
factors e^{-2x} and e^{3x} removed, as

$$\begin{vmatrix} y & 1 & 1 \\ y' & -2 & 3 \\ y'' & 4 & 9 \end{vmatrix} = 0$$

---

* By differentiations and pertinent legitimate mathematical procedures. Elimination by erasure, for instance, is not permitted.

from which the differential equation

$$y'' - y' - 6y = 0$$

follows immediately.

This latter method has the advantage of making it easy to see that the elimination of the constants $c_1, c_2, \cdots, c_n$ from a relation of the form

$$y = c_1 e^{m_1 x} + c_2 e^{m_2 x} + \cdots + c_n e^{m_n x}$$

will always lead to a linear differential equation

$$a_0 \frac{d^n y}{dx^n} + a_1 \frac{d^{n-1}y}{dx^{n-1}} + \cdots + a_{n-1}\frac{dy}{dx} + a_n y = 0,$$

in which the coefficients $a_0, a_1, \cdots, a_n$ are constants. The study of such differential equations will receive much of our attention.

EXAMPLE (b): Eliminate the constant a from the equation

$$(x - a)^2 + y^2 = a^2.$$

Direct differentiation of the relation yields

$$2(x - a) + 2yy' = 0,$$

from which

$$a = x + yy'.$$

Therefore, using the original equation, we find that

$$(yy')^2 + y^2 = (x + yy')^2,$$

or

$$y^2 = x^2 + 2xyy',$$

which may be written in the form

$$(x^2 - y^2)\,dx + 2xy\,dy = 0.$$

Another method will be used in this example as an illustration of a device which is frequently helpful. The method is based upon the isolation of an arbitrary constant.

The equation

$$(x - a)^2 + y^2 = a^2$$

may be put in the form

$$x^2 + y^2 - 2ax = 0,$$

or

$$\frac{x^2 + y^2}{x} = 2a.$$

Then differentiation of both members leads to

$$\frac{x(2x\,dx + 2y\,dy) - (x^2 + y^2)\,dx}{x^2} = 0,$$

or

$$(x^2 - y^2)\,dx + 2xy\,dy = 0,$$

as desired.

EXAMPLE (c): Eliminate B and α from the relation

(5) $$x = B \cos (\omega t + \alpha),$$

in which ω is a parameter (not to be eliminated).

First we obtain two derivatives of x with respect to t:

(6) $$\frac{dx}{dt} = -\omega B \sin (\omega t + \alpha),$$

(7) $$\frac{d^2x}{dt^2} = -\omega^2 B \cos (\omega t + \alpha).$$

Comparison of equations (5) and (7) shows at once that

$$\frac{d^2x}{dt^2} + \omega^2 x = 0.$$

EXAMPLE (d): Eliminate c from the equation

$$cxy + c^2x + 4 = 0.$$

At once we get

$$c(y + xy') + c^2 = 0.$$

Since $c \neq 0$,

$$c = -(y + xy')$$

and substitution into the original equation leads us to the result

$$x^3(y')^2 + x^2yy' + 4 = 0.$$

Exercises

In each of the following, eliminate the arbitrary constants.

1. $x^3 - 3x^2y = c.$ 　　　　　　　ANS. $(x - 2y)\,dx - x\,dy = 0.$

2. $y \sin x - xy^2 = c.$ 　ANS. $y(\cos x - y)\,dx + (\sin x - 2xy)\,dy = 0.$

3. $PV = C$.

4. $x^2y = 1 + cx$.   ANS. $(x^2y + 1)\, dx + x^3\, dy = 0$.

5. $cy^2 = x^2 + y$.   ANS. $2xy\, dx - (y + 2x^2)\, dy = 0$.

6. $x = A \sin(\omega t + \beta)$: ω a parameter, not to be eliminated.

$$\text{ANS.} \quad \frac{d^2x}{dt^2} + \omega^2 x = 0.$$

7. $x = c_1 \cos \omega t + c_2 \sin \omega t$; ω a parameter.   ANS. $\dfrac{d^2x}{dt^2} + \omega^2 x = 0$.

8. $y = cx + c^2 + 1$.   ANS. $y = xy' + (y')^2 + 1$.

9. $y = mx + \dfrac{h}{m}$; h a parameter, m to be eliminated.

$$\text{ANS.} \quad y = xy' + \frac{h}{y'}.$$

10. $y^2 = 4ax$.   ANS. $2x\, dy - y\, dx = 0$.

11. $y = ax^2 + bx + c$.   ANS. $y''' = 0$.

12. $y = c_1 + c_2 e^{2x}$.   ANS. $y'' - 2y' = 0$.

13. $y = 4 + c_1 e^{2x}$.   ANS. $y' - 2y = -8$.

14. $y = c_1 + c_2 e^{-3x}$.   ANS. $y'' + 3y' = 0$.

15. $y = c_1 e^{-x} + c_2 e^{-3x}$.   ANS. $y'' + 4y' + 3y = 0$.

16. $y = x + c_1 e^{-x} + c_2 e^{-3x}$.   ANS. $y'' + 4y' + 3y = 4 + 3x$.

17. $y = c_1 e^x + c_2 e^{-2x}$.   ANS. $y'' + y' - 2y = 0$.

18. $y = x^2 + c_1 e^x + c_2 e^{-2x}$.   ANS. $y'' + y' - 2y = 2(1 + x - x^2)$.

19. $y = c_1 e^{-x} + c_2 x e^{-x}$.   ANS. $y'' + 2y' + y = 0$.

20. $y = A e^{2x} + B x e^{2x}$.   ANS. $y'' - 4y' + 4y = 0$.

21. $y = c_1 e^{2x} \cos 3x + c_2 e^{2x} \sin 3x$.   ANS. $y'' - 4y' + 13y = 0$.

22. $y = c_1 e^{ax} \cos bx + c_2 e^{ax} \sin bx$; a and b are parameters.

$$\text{ANS.} \quad y'' - 2ay' + (a^2 + b^2)y = 0.$$

23. $y = c_1 x + c_2 e^{-x}$.   ANS. $(x + 1)y'' + xy' - y = 0$.

24. $y = x^2 + c_1 x + c_2 e^{-x}$.   ANS. $(x + 1)y'' + xy' - y = x^2 + 2x + 2$.

25. $y = c_1 x^2 + c_2 e^{2x}$.

$$\text{ANS.} \quad x(1 - x)y'' + (2x^2 - 1)y' - 2(2x - 1)y = 0.$$

4. Families of curves

A relation involving a parameter, as well as one or both of the coordinates of a point in a plane, represents a family of curves, one curve corresponding to each value of the parameter. For instance, the equation

$$(1) \qquad\qquad (x - c)^2 + (y - c)^2 = 2c^2,$$

or

(2) $x^2 + y^2 - 2c(x + y) = 0,$

may be interpreted as the equation of a family of circles, each having its center on the line $y = x$ and each passing through the origin. Figure 1 shows several elements, or members, of this family.

If the constant c in equation (1) or in equation (2) is treated as an arbitrary constant and eliminated as in the preceding section, the result is called the *differential equation of the family represented by equation* (1). In this example, the elimination of c is easily performed by isolating c,

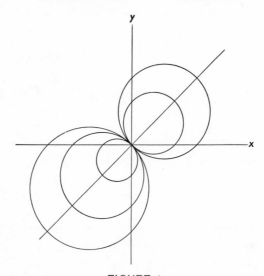

FIGURE 1

then differentiating throughout the equation with respect to x. Thus, from

$$\frac{x^2 + y^2}{x + y} = 2c$$

we find that

$$\frac{(x + y)(2x\,dx + 2y\,dy) - (x^2 + y^2)(dx + dy)}{(x + y)^2} = 0.$$

Therefore

(3) $(x^2 + 2xy - y^2)\,dx - (x^2 - 2xy - y^2)\,dy = 0$

is the differential equation of the family of circles represented by equation (1).

Note that equation (3) associates with each point (x, y) in the plane a definite slope

(4)
$$\frac{dy}{dx} = \frac{x^2 + 2xy - y^2}{x^2 - 2xy - y^2},$$

except where the denominator on the right in (4) vanishes. An examination of the method that was used to get (4) from (1) shows that at any point (x, y), equation (4) gives the slope of that curve of the family (1) which passes through the point in question.

A simple and convenient check is now revealed. When the denominator on the right of equation (4) vanishes, the curve passing through that point must have a vertical tangent. From

$$x^2 - 2xy - y^2 = 0$$

we see that

(5)
$$y = (\sqrt{2} - 1)x$$

or

(6)
$$y = -(\sqrt{2} + 1)x.$$

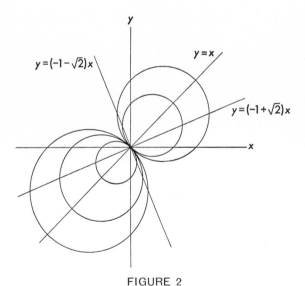

FIGURE 2

In Figure 2, the straight lines (5) and (6) appear along with the family (1). It is seen that the lines (5) and (6) cut the members of the family of circles in precisely those points of vertical tangency.

For a two-parameter family of curves, the differential equation will be of order two, and such a simple geometric interpretation is not available.

EXAMPLE (a): Find the differential equation of the family of parabolas (Figure 3), having their vertices at the origin and their foci on the y-axis.

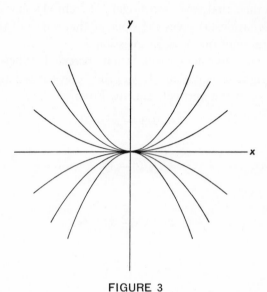

FIGURE 3

From analytic geometry, we find the equation of this family of parabolas to be

(7) $$x^2 = 4ay.$$

Then from

$$\frac{x^2}{y} = 4a$$

the a may be eliminated by differentiation. Thus it follows that

(8) $$2xy\,dx - x^2\,dy = 0.$$

We may write the differential equation of the family (7) as

(9) $$2y\,dx - x\,dy = 0,$$

because $x = 0$ is still a solution of (9), and nothing is lost in removing the factor x from the left member of (8).

EXAMPLE (b): Find the differential equation of the family of circles (Figure 4) having their centers on the y-axis.

Since a member of the family of circles of this example may have its center anywhere on the y-axis and its radius of any magnitude, we are dealing with the two-parameter family

(10) $x^2 + (y - b)^2 = r^2.$

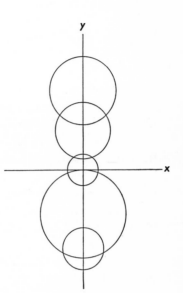

We shall eliminate both b and r and arrive, of course, at a second-order differential equation for the family (10).

At once

$$x + (y - b)y' = 0,$$

from which

$$\frac{x + yy'}{y'} = b.$$

Then

$$\frac{y'[1 + yy'' + (y')^2] - y''(x + yy')}{(y')^2} = 0,$$

so the desired differential equation is

$$xy'' - (y')^3 - y' = 0.$$

FIGURE 4

Exercises

In each exercise, obtain the differential equation of the family of plane curves described and sketch several representative members of the family.

1. Straight lines through the origin.   ANS. $y\,dx - x\,dy = 0.$
2. Straight lines through the fixed point (h, k). The h and k are not to be eliminated.   ANS. $(y - k)\,dx - (x - h)\,dy = 0.$
3. Straight lines with slope and y-intercept equal.
     ANS. $y\,dx - (x + 1)\,dy = 0.$
4. Straight lines with slope and x-intercept equal.
     ANS. $(y')^2 = xy' - y.$
5. Straight lines with algebraic sum of the intercepts fixed as k.
     ANS. $(xy' - y)(y' - 1) + ky' = 0.$
6. Straight lines at a fixed distance p from the origin.
     ANS. $(xy' - y)^2 = p^2[1 + (y')^2].$
7. Circles with center at the origin.   ANS. $x\,dx + y\,dy = 0.$

8. Circles with center on the x-axis.   ANS. $yy'' + (y')^2 + 1 = 0$.

9. Circles with fixed radius r and tangent to the x-axis.

ANS. $(y \pm r)^2 (y')^2 + y^2 \pm 2ry = 0$.

10. Circles tangent to the x-axis.

ANS. $[1 + (y')^2]^3 = [yy'' + 1 + (y')^2]^2$.

11. Circles with center on the line $y = -x$, and passing through the origin·

ANS. $(x^2 - 2xy - y^2)\, dx + (x^2 + 2xy - y^2)\, dy = 0$.

12. Circles of radius unity. Use the fact that the radius of curvature is one.

ANS. $(y'')^2 = [1 + (y')^2]^3$.

13. All circles. Use the curvature.   ANS. $y'''[1 + (y')^2] = 3y'(y'')^2$.

14. Parabolas with vertex on the x-axis, with axis parallel to the y-axis, and with distance from focus to vertex fixed as a.   ANS. $a(y')^2 = y$.

15. Parabolas with vertex on the y-axis, with axis parallel to the x-axis, and with distance from focus to vertex fixed as a.   ANS. $x(y')^2 = a$.

16. Parabolas with axis parallel to the y-axis and with distance from vertex to focus fixed as a.   ANS. $2ay'' = 1$.

17. Parabolas with axis parallel to the x-axis and with distance from vertex to focus fixed as a.   ANS. $2ay'' + (y')^3 = 0$.

18. Work Ex. 17, using differentiation with respect to y.

ANS. $2a \dfrac{d^2x}{dy^2} = 1$.

19. Use the fact that

$$\frac{d^2x}{dy^2} = \frac{d}{dy}\left(\frac{dx}{dy}\right) = \frac{dx}{dy}\frac{d}{dx}\left(\frac{dx}{dy}\right) = \frac{dx}{dy}\frac{d}{dx}\left(\frac{dy}{dx}\right)^{-1} = \frac{-y''}{(y')^3}$$

to prove that the answers to Exs. 17 and 18 are equivalent.

20. Parabolas with vertex and focus on the x-axis.   ANS. $yy'' + (y')^2 = 0$.

21. Parabolas with axis parallel to the x-axis.   ANS. $y'y''' - 3(y'')^2 = 0$.

22. Central conics with center at the origin and vertices on the coordinate axes.   ANS. $xyy'' + x(y')^2 - yy' = 0$.

23. The confocal central conics

$$\frac{x^2}{a^2 + \lambda} + \frac{y^2}{b^2 + \lambda} = 1$$

with a and b held fixed.   ANS. $(xy' - y)(yy' + x) = (a^2 - b^2)y'$.

24. The cubics $cy^2 = x^2(x - a)$ with a held fixed.

ANS. $2x(x - a)y' = y(3x - 2a)$.

25. The cubics of Ex. 24 with c held fixed and a to be eliminated.

ANS. $2cy(xy' - y) = x^3$.

26. The quartics $c^2y^2 = x(x - a)^3$ with a held fixed.

ANS. $2x(x - a)y' = y(4x - a)$.

27. The quartics of Ex. 26 with c held fixed and a to be eliminated.

ANS. $c^2(2xy' - y)^3 = 27x^4y$.

28. The strophoids $y^2 = \dfrac{x^2(a + x)}{a - x}$.

ANS. $(x^4 - 4x^2y^2 - y^4)\, dx + 4x^3y\, dy = 0$.

29. The cissoids $y^2 = \dfrac{x^3}{a - x}$.   ANS. $2x^3y' = y(y^2 + 3x^2)$.

30. The trisectrices of Maclaurin $y^2(a + x) = x^2(3a - x)$.

ANS. $(3x^4 - 6x^2y^2 - y^4)\, dx + 8x^3y\, dy = 0$.

31. Circles through the intersections of the circle $x^2 + y^2 = 1$ and the line $y = x$. Use the "$u + kv$" form; that is, the equation

$$x^2 + y^2 - 1 + k(y - x) = 0.$$

ANS. $(x^2 - 2xy - y^2 + 1)\, dx + (x^2 + 2xy - y^2 - 1)\, dy = 0$.

32. Circles through the fixed points $(a, 0)$ and $(-a, 0)$. Use the method of Ex. 31.   ANS. $2xy\, dx + (y^2 + a^2 - x^2)\, dy = 0$.

33. The circles $r = 2a(\sin \theta - \cos \theta)$.

ANS. $(\cos \theta - \sin \theta)\, dr + r(\cos \theta + \sin \theta)\, d\theta = 0$.

34. The cardioids $r = a(1 - \sin \theta)$.

ANS. $(1 - \sin \theta)\, dr + r \cos \theta\, d\theta = 0$.

35. The cissoids $r = a \sin \theta \tan \theta$. (See Ex. 29.)

ANS. $\sin \theta \cos \theta\, dr - r(1 + \cos^2 \theta)\, d\theta = 0$.

36. The strophoids $r = a(\sec \theta + \tan \theta)$.   ANS. $\dfrac{dr}{d\theta} = r \sec \theta$.

37. The trisectrices of Maclaurin $r = a(4 \cos \theta - \sec \theta)$. (See Ex. 30.)

ANS. $\cos \theta(4 \cos^2 \theta - 1)\, dr + r \sin \theta(4 \cos^2 \theta + 1)\, d\theta = 0$.

CHAPTER **2**

Equations of Order One
and Degree One

5. General solutions of ordinary differential equations

An ordinary differential equation of the nth order has, in general, a solution containing n arbitrary constants.* We shall call such a solution the general solution. Other terms frequently used are complete solution, complete primitive, and complete integral.

6. Separation of variables

The general equation of the first order and first degree is

$$(1) \qquad M\,dx + N\,dy = 0,$$

where M and N may be functions of both x and y. Some equations of the type (1) are so simple that they can be put in the form

---

* A proof and a precise statement appear, for example, in E. L. Ince, *Ordinary Differential Equations* (London: Longmans, Green and Co., 1927).

(2) $$A(x)\, dx + B(y)\, dy = 0;$$

that is, the variables can be separated. Then the solution can be written at once. For it is only a matter of finding a function F whose total differential is the left member of (2). Then $F = c$, where c is an arbitrary constant, is the desired result.

EXAMPLE (a): Solve the equation

(3) $$2(y + 3)\, dx - xy\, dy = 0.$$

Separation of the variables leads to

$$\frac{2\, dx}{x} - \frac{y\, dy}{y + 3} = 0,$$

or

(4) $$\frac{2\, dx}{x} - \left[1 - \frac{3}{y + 3}\right] dy = 0.$$

Hence we could write the solution as

(5) $$2 \ln x - y + 3 \ln (y + 3) = c.$$

Although (5) is a correct solution, the presence of two logarithmic terms suggests that we put the arbitrary constant in logarithmic form also. Thus, directly from (4) we may write the solution as

(6) $$2 \ln x - y + 3 \ln (y + 3) + \ln c_1 = 0,$$

where c_1 is an arbitrary constant different from the c of (5).
From (6) we get

$$y = 2 \ln x + 3 \ln (y + 3) + \ln c_1,$$

from which it follows that

(7) $$e^y = c_1 x^2 (y + 3)^3,$$

which is more compact than (5).

Of course, (5) can be transformed into (7) quite easily. From (5)

$$y + c = 2 \ln x + 3 \ln (y + 3),$$

or

$$e^{y+c} = x^2 (y + 3)^3.$$

Now we put

$$e^c = \frac{1}{c_1}$$

and arrive at (7).

The problem of changing one form of solution into another form is one which arises frequently when two or more persons solve the same differential equation and a check on the results is desired. Unless the use to which the solution will be put is known, there is little reason for preference for one form over another, except for considerations of compactness, symmetry, and other esthetic qualities. It is essentially a matter of individual inclination. Section 7 contains further remarks on the form of solutions.

EXAMPLE (b): Solve the equation

$$(8) \qquad (1 + y^2)\, dx + (1 + x^2)\, dy = 0,$$

with the "boundary condition" that when $x = 0$, $y = -1$.

From the differential equation we get

$$\frac{dx}{1 + x^2} + \frac{dy}{1 + y^2} = 0$$

from which it follows at once that

$$(9) \qquad \text{Arctan } x + \text{Arctan } y = c.$$

In the solution (9), each "Arctan" stands for the principal value of the inverse tangent and is subject to the restriction

$$-\tfrac{1}{2}\pi < \text{Arctan } x < \tfrac{1}{2}\pi.$$

The boundary condition that $y = -1$ when $x = 0$ permits us to determine the value of c that must be used to obtain the particular solution desired here. Since Arctan $0 = 0$ and Arctan $(-1) = -\tfrac{1}{4}\pi$, the solution of the boundary value problem is

$$(10) \qquad \text{Arctan } x + \text{Arctan } y = -\tfrac{1}{4}\pi.$$

Suppose next that we wish to sketch the curve (10). Resorting to a device of trigonometry, we take the tangent of each side of (10). Since

$$\tan (\text{Arctan } x) = x$$

and

$$\tan (A + B) = \frac{\tan A + \tan B}{1 - \tan A \tan B},$$

we are led to the equation

$$\frac{x + y}{1 - xy} = -1,$$

or

(11) $$xy - x - y - 1 = 0.$$

Now (11) is the equation of an equilateral hyperbola with asymptotes $x = 1$ and $y = 1$. But if we turn to (10), we see from

$$\text{Arctan } x = -\tfrac{1}{4}\pi - \text{Arctan } y$$

that, since $(- \text{Arctan } y) < \tfrac{1}{2}\pi$,

$$\text{Arctan } x < \tfrac{1}{4}\pi.$$

Hence $x < 1$, and equation (10) represents only one branch of the hyperbola (11). In Figure 5, the solid curve is the graph of equation (10); the solid curve and the dotted curve together are the graph of equation (11).

Each branch of the hyperbola (11) is a solution of the differential equation, one branch for $x < 1$, the other for $x > 1$. In this problem we were forced onto the left branch, equation (10), by the boundary condition that $y = -1$ when $x = 0$.

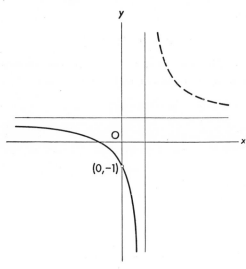

FIGURE 5

One distinction between the solutions (10) and (11) can be seen by noting that a computing machine, given the differential equation (8) and seeking a solution that passes through the point $(0, -1)$, would draw only the left branch of the curve in Figure 5. The barrier (asymptote) at $x = 1$ would prevent the machine from learning of the existence of the other branch of the hyperbola (11).

7. On the form of solutions

Consider the equation

(1) $2x(y + 1)\, dx - y\, dy = 0.$

Separating the variables in equation (1), we obtain

(2) $2x\, dx = \left(1 - \dfrac{1}{y + 1}\right) dy.$

Therefore, the general solution of equation (1) is

(3) $x^2 = y - \ln\,(y + 1) + c.$

Suppose, however, that we wish to solve a boundary value problem consisting of the differential equation (1) and the condition that when $x = 0$, $y = -2$. Putting $y = -2$ into the right member of equation (3) would lead to the use of $\ln\,(-1)$. Since (-1) has no real logarithm, we prefer to avoid this complication. Hence we seek other forms for the general solution of equation (1).

Since

$$d\ln\,(-y - 1) = \frac{-dy}{-y - 1} = \frac{dy}{y + 1},$$

it is possible to write the general solution of equation (2) in the form

(4) $x^2 = y - \ln\,(-y - 1) + c_1.$

Substituting $x = 0$ and $y = -2$ into equation (4) causes no trouble. It leads us to the equation

$$0 = -2 - \ln\,(1) + c_1,$$

from which we find $c_1 = 2$. Thus the desired solution of the boundary value problem is

$$x^2 = y + 2 - \ln\,(-y - 1), \quad \text{for } y < -1.$$

It can be seen that the solution (3) is useful for the range $y > -1$, while the solution (4) is useful for $y < -1$. In at least two ways it is possible to write a solution combining the advantages of (3) with those of (4).

Since

$$d\ln\,[c_2(y + 1)] = \frac{c_2\, dy}{c_2(y + 1)} = \frac{dy}{y + 1},$$

the general solution of equation (1) may be written in the form

(5) $x^2 = y - \ln [c_2(y + 1)].$

In adjusting the solution (5) to our immediate purpose, we place $x = 0$, $y = -2$ and find that

$$0 = -2 - \ln (-c_2),$$

so that $\ln (-c_2) = -2$, or $c_2 = -e^{-2}$. Hence the desired solution is

$$x^2 = y - \ln [-e^{-2}(y + 1)],$$

or

$$x^2 = y + 2 - \ln [-(y + 1)].$$

In equation (5), c_2 will turn out to be negative when a boundary condition requires that $y < -1$ and positive when it is required that $y > -1$.

From equation (5) it is not difficult to obtain the relation

(6) $(y + 1)e^{x^2} = c_3 e^y$

as another form of the solution of the differential equation (1).

In this book we shall usually leave solutions in forms similar to (5) or (6) above. Whenever an answer such as equation (3) is given, it is implied that the user will adjust its form to his particular purpose. The result should be verified by direct appeal to the differential equation so the validity of the transition from one solution to another does not enter the argument.

8. The exp u notation

The function e^u enters our work frequently, and sometimes the exponent u is complicated. Even a simple example such as $e^{x^{\frac{1}{2}}}y^2$ may be undesirable in print, because exponents are usually set in small type. It is customary in advanced mathematics to use the notation

(1) $\exp u = e^u.$

That is, exp is used to denote the exponential function in much the same way that sin is used to denote the sine function.

EXAMPLE (a): For $e^{x^{\frac{1}{2}}}y^2$ we write $\exp (x^{\frac{1}{2}}y^2)$.

EXAMPLE (b): Equation (6) of the preceding section may be written as

(2) $(y + 1) \exp (x^2) = c_3 \exp (y).$

Most people retain the notation e^u when u is simple, even though in the same equation the exp notation may have been used elsewhere. Equation (2) is sometimes written in the form

$$(3) \qquad (y + 1) \exp (x^2) = c_3 e^y.$$

A few minutes of practice should make the reader feel at home with the symbol exp u. Some familiarity with this notation will result from verification of simple identities such as the following:

$$(4) \qquad \exp (x) \cdot \exp (y) = \exp (x + y),$$
$$(5) \qquad [\exp (x)]^k = \exp (kx),$$
$$(6) \qquad \exp (\ln y) = y,$$
$$(7) \qquad \exp \left(\frac{x}{y}\right) \exp \left(\frac{y}{x}\right) = \exp \left(\frac{x^2 + y^2}{xy}\right),$$
$$(8) \qquad \exp (3 \ln x) = [\exp (\ln x)]^3 = x^3,$$
$$(9) \qquad \exp (x - 2 \ln x) = x^{-2} e^x.$$

We shall use the exp notation whenever it seems to add to the clarity of the printed result.

Exercises

In Exs. 1–26, obtain the general solution.

1. $(4 + x)y' = y^3$. ANS. $2y^2 \ln [c(4 + x)] = -1$.

2. $\exp (y^2) \, dx + x^2 y \, dy = 0$. ANS. $x \exp (-y^2) + 2 = cx$.

3. $\cos x \cos y \, dx + \sin x \sin y \, dy = 0$. ANS. $\sin x = c \cos y$.

4. $3y \, dx = 2x \, dy$. ANS. $x^3 = cy^2$.

5. $my \, dx = nx \, dy$. ANS. $x^m = cy^n$.

6. $y' = xy^2$. ANS. $y(x^2 + c) + 2 = 0$.

7. $\dfrac{dV}{dP} = \dfrac{-V}{P}$. ANS. $PV = C$.

8. $e^x(y - 1) \, dx + 2(e^x + 4) \, dy = 0$. ANS. $(y - 1)^2(e^x + 4) = c^2$.

9. $dr = e(r \sin \theta \, d\theta - \cos \theta \, dr)$. ANS. $r(1 + e \cos \theta) = c$.

10. $(xy - x) \, dx + (xy + y) \, dy = 0$.
ANS. $(y - 1) \exp (x + y) = c(x + 1)$.

11. $(y + 1) \, dx = 2xy \, dy$. ANS. $e^{2y} = cx(y + 1)^2$.

12. $x^2 \, dx + y(x - 1) \, dy = 0$.

13. $(xy + x) \, dx = (x^2 y^2 + x^2 + y^2 + 1) \, dy$.
ANS. $\ln (x^2 + 1) = y^2 - 2y + 4 \ln [c(y + 1)]$.

14. $x \cos^2 y \, dx + \tan y \, dy = 0$. ANS. $x^2 + \tan^2 y = c^2$.

15. $x^2 yy' = e^y$. ANS. $x(y + 1) = (1 + cx)e^y$.

16. $\tan^2 y \, dy = \sin^3 x \, dx.$ ANS. $\cos^3 x - 3 \cos x = 3(\tan y - y + c).$

17. $y' = \cos^2 x \cos y.$ ANS. $4 \ln (\sec y + \tan y) = 2x + \sin 2x + c.$

18. $y' = y \sec x.$ ANS. $y = c(\sec x + \tan x).$

19. $dx = t(1 + t^2) \sec^2 x \, dt.$ ANS. $2x + \sin 2x = c + (1 + t^2)^2.$

20. $(e^{2x} + 4)y' = y.$ ANS. $y^8(1 + 4e^{-2x}) = c^2.$

21. $\alpha \, d\beta + \beta \, d\alpha + \alpha\beta(3 \, d\alpha + d\beta) = 0.$ ANS. $c\alpha\beta = \exp(-3\alpha - \beta).$

22. $(1 + \ln x) \, dx + (1 + \ln y) \, dy = 0.$ ANS. $x \ln x + y \ln y = c.$

23. $x \, dx - \sqrt{a^2 - x^2} \, dy = 0.$

     ANS. $y - c = -\sqrt{a^2 - x^2}$, the lower half of the circle $x^2 + (y - c)^2 = a^2.$

24. $x \, dx + \sqrt{a^2 - x^2} \, dy = 0.$

     ANS. $y - c = \sqrt{a^2 - x^2}$, the upper half of the circle $x^2 + (y - c)^2 = a^2.$

25. $a^2 \, dx = x \sqrt{x^2 - a^2} \, dy.$ ANS. $x = a \sec \dfrac{y + c}{a}.$

26. $y \ln x \ln y \, dx + dy = 0.$ ANS. $x \ln x + \ln \ln y = x + c.$

In Exs. 27–33, obtain the particular solution satisfying the boundary condition indicated.

27. $\dfrac{dr}{dt} = -4rt$; when $t = 0$, $r = r_0.$ ANS. $r = r_0 \exp(-2t^2).$

28. $2xyy' = 1 + y^2$; when $x = 2$, $y = 3.$ ANS. $y^2 = 5x - 1.$

29. $xyy' = 1 + y^2$; when $x = 2$, $y = 3.$ ANS. $5x^2 - 2y^2 = 2.$

30. $y' = x \exp(y - x^2)$; when $x = 0$, $y = 0.$

     ANS. $2e^{-y} = 1 + \exp(-x^2).$

31. $xy^2 \, dx + e^x \, dy = 0$; when $x \to \infty$, $y \to \frac{1}{2}.$

     ANS. $y = e^x/(2e^x - x - 1).$

32. $(2a^2 - r^2) \, dr = r^3 \sin \theta \, d\theta$; when $\theta = 0$, $r = a.$

33. $v \dfrac{dv}{dx} = g$; when $x = x_0$, $v = v_0.$ ANS. $v^2 - v_0^2 = 2g(x - x_0).$

9. Homogeneous functions

Polynomials in which all terms are of the same degree, such as

$$x^2 - 3xy + 4y^2,$$
(1)
$$x^3 + y^3,$$
$$x^4y + 7y^5,$$

are called *homogeneous* polynomials. We wish now to extend that concept of homogeneity so it will apply to functions other than polynomials.

If we assign a physical dimension, say length, to each variable x and y in the polynomials in (1), then each polynomial itself also has a physical dimension, length to some power. This suggests the desired generalization. If, when certain variables are thought of as lengths, a function has physical dimension length to the kth power, then we shall call that function homogeneous of degree k in those variables. For example, the function

$$(2) \qquad f(x, y) = 2y^3 \exp\left(\frac{y}{x}\right) - \frac{x^4}{x + 3y}$$

is of dimension (length)^3 when x and y are lengths. Therefore that function is said to be homogeneous of degree 3 in x and y.

We permit the degree k to be any number. The function $\sqrt{x + 4y}$ is called homogeneous of degree $\frac{1}{2}$ in x and y. The function

$$\frac{x}{\sqrt{x^2 + y^2}}$$

is homogeneous of degree zero in x and y.

A formal definition of homogeneity is: *The function $f(x, y)$ is said to be homogeneous of degree k in x and y if, and only if,*

$$(3) \qquad f(\lambda x, \lambda y) = \lambda^k f(x, y).$$

The definition is easily extended to functions of more than two variables.

For the function $f(x, y)$ of equation (2), the formal definition of homogeneity leads us to consider

$$f(\lambda x, \lambda y) = 2\lambda^3 y^3 \exp\left(\frac{\lambda y}{\lambda x}\right) - \frac{\lambda^4 x^4}{\lambda x + 3\lambda y}.$$

But we see at once that

$$f(\lambda x, \lambda y) = \lambda^3 f(x, y);$$

hence $f(x, y)$ is homogeneous of degree 3 in x and y, as stated previously.

The following theorems prove useful in the next section.

THEOREM 1: *If $M(x, y)$ and $N(x, y)$ are both homogeneous and of the same degree, the function $\dfrac{M(x, y)}{N(x, y)}$ is homogeneous of degree zero.*

THEOREM 2: *If $f(x, y)$ is homogeneous of degree zero in x and y, $f(x, y)$ is a function of $\dfrac{y}{x}$ alone.*

Proof of Theorem 1 is left to the student.

Proof of Theorem 2: Let us put $y = vx$. Then Theorem 2 states that if $f(x, y)$ is homogeneous of degree zero, $f(x, y)$ is a function of v alone. Now

(4) $$f(x, y) = f(x, vx) = x^0 f(1, v) = f(1, v),$$

in which the x is now playing the role taken by λ in the definition (3) above. By (4), $f(x, y)$ depends on v alone as stated in Theorem 2.

Oral Exercises

Determine in each exercise whether the function is homogeneous or not. If it is homogeneous, state the degree of the function.

1. $4x^2 - 3xy + y^2$.

2. $x^3 - xy + y^3$.

3. $2y + \sqrt{x^2 + y^2}$.

4. $\sqrt{x - y}$.

5. e^x.

6. $\tan x$.

7. $\exp\left(\dfrac{x}{y}\right)$.

8. $\tan \dfrac{3y}{x}$.

9. $(x^2 + y^2) \exp\left(\dfrac{2x}{y}\right) + 4xy$.

10. $x \sin \dfrac{y}{x} - y \sin \dfrac{x}{y}$.

11. $\dfrac{x^2 + 3xy}{x - 2y}$.

12. $\dfrac{x^5}{x^2 + 2y^2}$.

13. $(u^2 + v^2)^{\frac{1}{2}}$.

14. $(u^2 - 4v^2)^{-\frac{1}{2}}$.

15. $y^2 \tan \dfrac{x}{y}$.

16. $\dfrac{(x^2 + y^2)^{\frac{1}{2}}}{(x^2 - y^2)^{\frac{1}{2}}}$.

17. $\dfrac{a + 4b}{a - 4b}$.

18. $\ln \dfrac{x}{y}$.

19. $x \ln x - y \ln y$.

20. $x \ln x - x \ln y$.

10. Equations with homogeneous coefficients

Suppose the coefficients M and N in an equation of order one and degree one,

(1) $$M(x, y)\, dx + N(x, y)\, dy = 0,$$

are both homogeneous functions and are of the *same degree* in x and y. By Theorems 1 and 2 of Section 9, the ratio M/N is a function of y/x alone. Hence equation (1) may be put in the form

(2) $$\frac{dy}{dx} + g\left(\frac{y}{x}\right) = 0.$$

This suggests the introduction of a new variable v by putting $y = vx$. Then (2) becomes

$$(3) \qquad x\frac{dv}{dx} + v + g(v) = 0,$$

in which the variables are separable. We can obtain the solution of (3) by the method of Section 6, insert y/x for v, and thus arrive at the solution of (1). We have shown that the substitution $y = vx$ will transform equation (1) into an equation in v and x in which the variables are separable.

The above method would have been equally successful had we used $x = vy$ to obtain from (1) an equation in y and v. See Example (b) below.

EXAMPLE (a): Solve the equation

$$(4) \qquad (x^2 - xy + y^2)\, dx - xy\, dy = 0.$$

Since the coefficients in (4) are both homogeneous and of degree two in x and y, let us put $y = vx$. Then (4) becomes

$$(x^2 - x^2v + x^2v^2)\, dx - x^2v(v\, dx + x\, dv) = 0,$$

from which the factor x^2 should be removed at once. That done, we have to solve

$$(1 - v + v^2)\, dx - v(v\, dx + x\, dv) = 0,$$

or

$$(1 - v)\, dx - xv\, dv = 0.$$

Hence we separate variables to get

$$\frac{dx}{x} + \frac{v\, dv}{v - 1} = 0.$$

Then from

$$\frac{dx}{x} + \left[1 + \frac{1}{v - 1}\right] dv = 0$$

the solution is seen to be

$$\ln x + v + \ln (v - 1) = \ln c,$$

or

$$x(v - 1)e^v = c.$$

In terms of the original variables, the solution is

$$x\left(\frac{y}{x} - 1\right)\exp\left(\frac{y}{x}\right) = c,$$

or

$$(y - x) \exp\left(\frac{y}{x}\right) = c.$$

EXAMPLE (b): Solve the equation

(5) $$xy \, dx + (x^2 + y^2) \, dy = 0.$$

Again the coefficients in the equation are homogeneous and of degree two. We could use $y = vx$, but the relative simplicity of the dx term in (5) suggests that we put

$$x = vy.$$

Then $dx = v \, dy + y \, dv$, and equation (5) is replaced by

$$vy^2(v \, dy + y \, dv) + (v^2y^2 + y^2) \, dy = 0,$$

or

$$v(v \, dy + y \, dv) + (v^2 + 1) \, dy = 0.$$

Hence we need to solve

(6) $$vy \, dv + (2v^2 + 1) \, dy = 0,$$

which leads at once to

$$\ln (2v^2 + 1) + 4 \ln y = \ln c,$$

or

$$y^4(2v^2 + 1) = c.$$

Thus the desired solution is

$$y^4\left(\frac{2x^2}{y^2} + 1\right) = c;$$

that is,

(7) $$y^2(2x^2 + y^2) = c.$$

Since the left member of the solution (7) cannot be negative, we may, for symmetry's sake, change the arbitrary constant to c_1^4, writing

$$y^2(2x^2 + y^2) = c_1^4.$$

It is worth-while for the student to attack equation (5) using $y = vx$. That method leads directly to the equation

$$(v^3 + 2v) \, dx + x(v^2 + 1) \, dv = 0.$$

Frequently in equations with homogeneous coefficients, it is quite immaterial whether one uses $y = vx$ or $x = vy$.

Exercises

In Exs. 1–19 obtain the general solution.

1. $(x - 2y) \, dx + (2x + y) \, dy = 0.$

               ANS. $\ln (x^2 + y^2) + 4 \, \text{Arctan} \, (y/x) = c.$

2. $2(2x^2 + y^2) \, dx - xy \, dy = 0.$ ANS. $x^4 = c^2(4x^2 + y^2).$

3. $xy \, dx - (x^2 + 3y^2) \, dy = 0.$ ANS. $x^2 = 6y^2 \ln (y/c).$

4. $x^2 y' = 4x^2 + 7xy + 2y^2.$ ANS. $x^2(y + 2x) = c(y + x).$

5. $3xy \, dx + (x^2 + y^2) \, dy = 0.$

6. $(x - y)(4x + y) \, dx + x(5x - y) \, dy = 0.$

               ANS. $x(y + x)^2 = c(y - 2x).$

7. $(5v - u) \, du + (3v - 7u) \, dv = 0.$ ANS. $(3v + u)^2 = c(v - u).$

8. $(x^2 + 2xy - 4y^2) \, dx - (x^2 - 8xy - 4y^2) \, dy = 0.$

               ANS. $x^2 + 4y^2 = c(x + y).$

9. $(x^2 + y^2) \, dx - xy \, dy = 0.$ ANS. $y^2 = 2x^2 \ln (x/c).$

10. $v^2 \, dx + x(v - 4x) \, dv = 0.$ ANS. $xv^2 = c(v - 2x).$

11. $(2x + y)^2 \, dx = xy \, dy.$ ANS. $x^3(x + y) = c \exp (y/x).$

12. $y \, dx = (x + \sqrt{y^2 - x^2}) \, dy.$ ANS. $\text{Arcsin} \, (x/y) = \ln (y/c).$

13. $(3x^2 - 2xy + 3y^2) \, dx = 4xy \, dy.$ ANS. $(y - x)(y + 3x)^3 = cx^3.$

14. $[x \csc (y/x) - y] \, dx + x \, dy = 0.$ ANS. $\ln (x/c) = \cos (y/x).$

15. $x \, dx + \sin^2 (y/x)[y \, dx - x \, dy] = 0.$

          ANS. $4x \ln (x/c) - 2y + x \sin (2y/x) = 0.$

16. $(x - y \ln y + y \ln x) \, dx + x(\ln y - \ln x) \, dy = 0.$

           ANS. $(x - y) \ln x + y \ln y = cx + y.$

17. $[x - y \, \text{Arctan} \, (y/x)] \, dx + x \, \text{Arctan} \, (y/x) \, dy = 0.$

          ANS. $2y \, \text{Arctan} \, (y/x) = x \ln [c^2(x^2 + y^2)/x^4].$

18. $v(v^2 + u^2) \, du + u(v^2 - u^2) \, dv = 0.$

19. $(y^3 - 4xy^2 - 2x^3) \, dx + x^2(2y + x) \, dy = 0.$

           ANS. $x^2(y - 2x)^2 = c^2(x^2 + y^2).$

20. Prove that with the aid of the substitution $y = vx$, you can solve any equation of the form

$$y^n f(x) \, dx + H(x, y)(y \, dx - x \, dy) = 0,$$

where $H(x, y)$ is homogeneous in x and y.

In Exs. 21–33 find the solution indicated.

21. $(x - y) \, dx + (3x + y) \, dy = 0;$ when $x = 2, \, y = -1.$

          ANS. $2(x + 2y) + (x + y) \ln (x + y) = 0.$

22. $(y - \sqrt{x^2 + y^2}) \, dx - x \, dy = 0;$ when $x = \sqrt{3}, \, y = 1.$

          ANS. $x^2 = 9 - 6y.$

23. $(y + \sqrt{x^2 + y^2})\, dx - x\, dy = 0$; when $x = \sqrt{3}$, $y = 1$.

ANS. $x^2 = 2y + 1$.

24. $[x \cos^2 (y/x) - y]\, dx + x\, dy = 0$; when $x = 1$, $y = \pi/4$.

ANS. $\tan (y/x) = \ln (e/x)$.

25. $(y^2 + 7xy + 16x^2)\, dx + x^2\, dy = 0$; when $x = 1$, $y = 1$.

ANS. $x - y = 5(y + 4x) \ln x$.

26. $y^2\, dx + (x^2 + 3xy + 4y^2)\, dy = 0$; when $x = 2$, $y = 1$.

ANS. $4(2y + x) \ln y = 2y - x$.

27. $xy\, dx + 2(x^2 + 2y^2)\, dy = 0$; when $x = 0$, $y = 1$.

ANS. $y^4(3x^2 + 4y^2) = 4$.

28. $y(2x^2 - xy + y^2)\, dx - x^2(2x - y)\, dy = 0$; when $x = 1$, $y = \frac{1}{2}$.

ANS. $y^2 \ln x = 2y^2 + xy - x^2$.

29. $y(9x - 2y)\, dx - x(6x - y)\, dy = 0$; when $x = 1$, $y = 1$.

ANS. $3x^3 - x^2y - 2y^2 = 0$.

30. $y(x^2 + y^2)\, dx + x(3x^2 - 5y^2)\, dy = 0$; when $x = 2$, $y = 1$.

ANS. $2y^5 - 2x^2y^3 + 3x = 0$.

31. $(16x + 5y)\, dx + (3x + y)\, dy = 0$; the curve to pass through the point $(1, -3)$.   ANS. $y + 3x = (y + 4x) \ln (y + 4x)$.

32. $v(3x + 2v)\, dx - x^2\, dv = 0$; when $x = 1$, $v = 2$.

ANS. $2x^3 + 2x^2v - 3v = 0$.

33. $(3x^2 - 2y^2)y' = 2xy$; when $x = 0$, $y = -1$. ANS. $x^2 = 2y^2(y + 1)$.

34. From Theorems 1 and 2, page 24, it follows that if F is homogeneous of degree k in x and y, F can be written in the form

(A) $$F = x^k\, \varphi\left(\frac{y}{x}\right).$$

Use (A) to prove Euler's theorem that if F is a homogeneous function of degree k in x and y,

$$x\, \frac{\partial F}{\partial x} + y\, \frac{\partial F}{\partial y} = kF.$$

11. Exact equations

In Section 6 it was noted that when an equation can be put in the form

$$A(x)\, dx + B(y)\, dy = 0,$$

the general solution can be determined by integration; that is, by finding a function whose differential is $A(x)\, dx + B(y)\, dy$.

That idea can be extended to some equations of the form

(1) $M(x, y) \, dx + N(x, y) \, dy = 0$

in which separation of variables may not be possible. Suppose that a function $F(x, y)$ can be found that has for its total differential the expression $M \, dx + N \, dy$; that is,

(2) $dF = M \, dx + N \, dy.$

Then certainly

(3) $F(x, y) = c$

is the general solution of (1). For, from (3) it follows that

$$dF = 0,$$

or, in view of (2),

$$M \, dx + N \, dy = 0,$$

as desired.

Two things, then, are needed: first, to find out under what conditions on M and N a function F exists such that its total differential is exactly $M \, dx + N \, dy$; second, if those conditions are satisfied, actually to determine the function F. If there exists a function F such that

$$M \, dx + N \, dy$$

is exactly the total differential of F, we call equation (1) an *exact equation.*

If the equation

(1) $M \, dx + N \, dy = 0$

is exact, then by definition F exists such that

$$dF = M \, dx + N \, dy.$$

But, from calculus,

$$dF = \frac{\partial F}{\partial x} \, dx + \frac{\partial F}{\partial y} \, dy,$$

so

$$M = \frac{\partial F}{\partial x}, \quad N = \frac{\partial F}{\partial y}.$$

These two equations lead to

$$\frac{\partial M}{\partial y} = \frac{\partial^2 F}{\partial y \, \partial x}$$

and

$$\frac{\partial N}{\partial x} = \frac{\partial^2 F}{\partial x\, \partial y}.$$

Again from calculus

$$\frac{\partial^2 F}{\partial y\, \partial x} = \frac{\partial^2 F}{\partial x\, \partial y},$$

provided these partial derivatives are continuous. Therefore, if (1) is an exact equation, then

(4) $$\frac{\partial M}{\partial y} = \frac{\partial N}{\partial x}.$$

Thus, for (1) to be exact it is necessary that (4) be satisfied.

Let us now show that if condition (4) is satisfied, then (1) is an exact equation. Let $\varphi(x, y)$ be a function for which

$$\frac{\partial \varphi}{\partial x} = M.$$

The function φ is the result of integrating $M\, dx$ with respect to x while holding y constant. Now

$$\frac{\partial^2 \varphi}{\partial y\, \partial x} = \frac{\partial M}{\partial y};$$

hence, if (4) is satisfied, then also

(5) $$\frac{\partial^2 \varphi}{\partial x\, \partial y} = \frac{\partial N}{\partial x}.$$

Let us integrate both sides of this last equation with respect to x, holding y fixed. In the integration with respect to the x, the "arbitrary constant" may be any function of y. Let us call it $B'(y)$, for ease in indicating its integral. Then integration of (5) with respect to x yields

(6) $$\frac{\partial \varphi}{\partial y} = N + B'(y).$$

Now a function F can be exhibited, namely,

$$F = \varphi(x, y) - B(y),$$

for which

$$dF = \frac{\partial \varphi}{\partial x}\, dx + \frac{\partial \varphi}{\partial y}\, dy - B'(y)\, dy$$
$$= M\, dx + [N + B'(y)]\, dy - B'(y)\, dy$$
$$= M\, dx + N\, dy.$$

Hence, equation (1) is exact. We have completed a proof of the theorem stated below.

THEOREM 3: *If* M, N, $\dfrac{\partial M}{\partial y}$, *and* $\dfrac{\partial N}{\partial x}$ *are continuous functions of* x *and* y,

then a necessary and sufficient condition that

(1) $M\, dx + N\, dy = 0$

be an exact equation is that

(4) $\dfrac{\partial M}{\partial y} = \dfrac{\partial N}{\partial x}.$

Furthermore, the proof contains the germ of a method for obtaining the solution, a method used in Examples (a) and (b) below. It will be found, however, that with a little practice, we can write the solutions of very many exact equations after inspection. See Examples (c) and (d). No matter what method is used, the result should be checked by differentiation.

EXAMPLE (a): Solve the equation

(7) $3x(xy - 2)\, dx + (x^3 + 2y)\, dy = 0.$

First, from the fact that

$$\frac{\partial M}{\partial y} = 3x^2 \quad \text{and} \quad \frac{\partial N}{\partial x} = 3x^2,$$

we conclude that equation (7) is exact. Therefore, its solution is $F = c$, where

(8) $\dfrac{\partial F}{\partial x} = M = 3x^2 y - 6x,$

and

(9) $\dfrac{\partial F}{\partial y} = N = x^3 + 2y.$

Let us attempt to determine F from equation (8). Integration of both sides of (8) with respect to x, holding y constant, yields

(10) $F = x^3 y - 3x^2 + T(y),$

where the usual arbitrary constant in indefinite integration is now necessarily a function $T(y)$, as yet unknown. To determine $T(y)$, we use the fact that the function F of equation (10) must also satisfy equation (9).

Hence

$$x^3 + T'(y) = x^3 + 2y,$$
$$T'(y) = 2y.$$

No arbitrary constant is needed in obtaining $T(y)$, since one is being introduced on the right in the solution $F = c$. Then

$$T(y) = y^2,$$

and from (10)

$$F = x^3y - 3x^2 + y^2.$$

Finally, the solution of equation (7) is seen to be

$$x^3y - 3x^2 + y^2 = c.$$

EXAMPLE (b): Solve the equation

(11) $(2x^3 - xy^2 - 2y + 3)\, dx - (x^2y + 2x)\, dy = 0.$

Here

$$\frac{\partial M}{\partial y} = -2xy - 2 = \frac{\partial N}{\partial x},$$

so equation (11) is exact.

The solution of (11) is $F = c$, where

(12) $$\frac{\partial F}{\partial x} = 2x^3 - xy^2 - 2y + 3$$

and

(13) $$\frac{\partial F}{\partial y} = -x^2y - 2x.$$

Because (13) is simpler than (12), and for variety's sake, let us start the determination of F from equation (13).

At once, from (13)

$$F = -\tfrac{1}{2}x^2y^2 - 2xy + Q(x),$$

where $Q(x)$ will be determined from (12). The latter yields

$$-xy^2 - 2y + Q'(x) = 2x^3 - xy^2 - 2y + 3,$$
$$Q'(x) = 2x^3 + 3.$$

Therefore

$$Q(x) = \tfrac{1}{2}x^4 + 3x,$$

and the desired solution of (11) is

$$-\tfrac{1}{2}x^2y^2 - 2xy + \tfrac{1}{2}x^4 + 3x = \tfrac{1}{2}c,$$

or

$$x^4 - x^2y^2 - 4xy + 6x = c.$$

EXAMPLE (c): Solve the equation of Example (a) by inspection.
Suppose that we have tested

$$(7) \qquad\qquad 3x(xy - 2)\,dx + (x^3 + 2y)\,dy = 0$$

and found that it is exact. Then we may write the general solution by inspection; that is, by careful observation of the left member of (7), we shall find a function of which it is the total differential.

First, the term $3x^2y\,dx$ suggests the differential of x^3y. Hence we search (7) for the necessary companion term $x^3\,dy$ and group the two terms. Any term such as $-6x\,dx$, which contains only one variable, is an exact differential as it stands. Thus we are led to rewrite equation (7) as

$$(3x^2y\,dx + x^3\,dy) - 6x\,dx + 2y\,dy = 0,$$

from which it follows that

$$x^3y - 3x^2 + y^2 = c.$$

EXAMPLE (d): Solve the equation

$$(11) \qquad (2x^3 - xy^2 - 2y + 3)\,dx - (x^2y + 2x)\,dy = 0$$

of Example (b) by inspection.
The grouping

$$2x^3\,dx - (xy^2\,dx + x^2y\,dy) - (2y\,dx + 2x\,dy) + 3\,dx = 0$$

leads at once to the result

$$\tfrac{1}{2}x^4 - \tfrac{1}{2}x^2y^2 - 2xy + 3x = \tfrac{1}{2}c,$$
$$x^4 - x^2y^2 - 4xy + 6x = c.$$

Exercises

Test each of the following equations for exactness and solve the equation. The equations which are not exact may, of course, be solved by methods discussed in the preceding sections.

1. $(x + y)\,dx + (x - y)\,dy = 0.$ ANS. $x^2 + 2xy - y^2 = c.$

2. $(6x + y^2)\,dx + y(2x - 3y)\,dy = 0.$ ANS. $3x^2 + xy^2 - y^3 = c.$

3. $(2xy - 3x^2)\,dx + (x^2 + y)\,dy = 0.$ ANS. $x^2y - x^3 + \tfrac{1}{2}y^2 = c.$

4. $(y^2 - 2xy + 6x) \, dx - (x^2 - 2xy + 2) \, dy = 0.$
   ANS. $xy^2 - x^2y + 3x^2 - 2y = c.$

5. $(2xy + y) \, dx + (x^2 - x) \, dy = 0.$ ANS. $y = cx(x - 1)^{-3}.$

6. $(x - 2y) \, dx + 2(y - x) \, dy = 0.$ ANS. $x^2 + 2y^2 = 4xy + c.$

7. Do Ex. 6 by another method.

8. $(2x - 3y) \, dx + (2y - 3x) \, dy = 0.$ ANS. $x^2 + y^2 = 3xy + c.$

9. Do Ex. 8 by another method.

10. $v(2uv^2 - 3) \, du + (3u^2v^2 - 3u + 4v) \, dv = 0.$
    ANS. $v(u^2v^2 - 3u + 2v) = c.$

11. $(\cos 2y - 3x^2y^2) \, dx + (\cos 2y - 2x \sin 2y - 2x^3y) \, dy = 0.$
    ANS. $\frac{1}{2} \sin 2y + x \cos 2y - x^3y^2 = c.$

12. $(1 + y^2) \, dx + (x^2y + y) \, dy = 0.$
    ANS. $2 \operatorname{Arctan} x + \ln (1 + y^2) = c.$

13. $(1 + y^2 + xy^2) \, dx + (x^2y + y + 2xy) \, dy = 0.$
    ANS. $2x + y^2(1 + x)^2 = c.$

14. $(w^3 + wz^2 - z) \, dw + (z^3 + w^2z - w) \, dz = 0.$
    ANS. $(w^2 + z^2)^2 = 4wz + c.$

15. $(2xy - \tan y) \, dx + (x^2 - x \sec^2 y) \, dy = 0.$ ANS. $x^2y - x \tan y = c.$

16. $(\cos x \cos y - \cot x) \, dx - \sin x \sin y \, dy = 0.$
    ANS. $\sin x \cos y = \ln (c \sin x).$

17. $(r + \sin \theta - \cos \theta) \, dr + r(\sin \theta + \cos \theta) \, d\theta = 0.$
    ANS. $r^2 + 2r(\sin \theta - \cos \theta) = c.$

18. $x(3xy - 4y^3 + 6) \, dx + (x^3 - 6x^2y^2 - 1) \, dy = 0.$
    ANS. $x^3y - 2x^2y^3 + 3x^2 - y = c.$

19. $(\sin \theta - 2r \cos^2 \theta) \, dr + r \cos \theta(2r \sin \theta + 1) \, d\theta = 0.$
    ANS. $r \sin \theta - r^2 \cos^2 \theta = c.$

20. $[2x + y \cos (xy)] \, dx + x \cos (xy) \, dy = 0.$ ANS. $x^2 + \sin (xy) = c.$

21. $2xy \, dx + (y^2 + x^2) \, dy = 0.$ ANS. $y(3x^2 + y^2) = c.$

22. $2xy \, dx + (y^2 - x^2) \, dy = 0.$ ANS. $x^2 + y^2 = cy.$

23. $(xy^2 + y - x) \, dx + x(xy + 1) \, dy = 0.$ ANS. $x^2y^2 + 2xy - x^2 = c.$

24. $3y(x^2 - 1) \, dx + (x^3 + 8y - 3x) \, dy = 0;$ when $x = 0, \ y = 1.$
    ANS. $xy(x^2 - 3) = 4(1 - y^2).$

25. $(1 - xy)^{-2} \, dx + [y^2 + x^2(1 - xy)^{-2}] \, dy = 0;$ when $x = 2, \ y = 1.$
    ANS. $xy^4 - y^3 + 5xy - 3x = 5.$

26. $(3 + y + 2y^2 \sin^2 x) \, dx + (x + 2xy - y \sin 2x) \, dy = 0.$
    ANS. $y^2 \sin 2x = c + 2x(3 + y + y^2).$

27. $2x[3x + y - y \exp (-x^2)] \, dx + [x^2 + 3y^2 + \exp (-x^2)] \, dy = 0.$
    ANS. $x^2y + y^3 + 2x^3 + y \exp (-x^2) = c.$

28. $(xy^2 + x - 2y + 3) \, dx + x^2y \, dy = 2(x + y) \, dy;$ when $x = 1, \ y = 1.$
    ANS. $(xy - 2)^2 + (x + 3)^2 = 2y^2 + 15.$

12. Methods of solution

Many texts present the material covered in Chapters 2 and 4 of this book as a collection of methods for solving equations of order one and degree one. A reader sometimes gets the impression that such techniques are isolated devices, a "bag of tricks." Actually, the only techniques presented here are the method of integrating an exact equation and two procedures for trying to make an equation exact if it is not exact in its original form. We already (Section 11) know how to handle an exact equation.

If an equation is not exact, it is natural to attempt to make it exact by the introduction of an appropriate factor, which is then called an *integrating factor*. Separation of variables (Section 6) is a simple example of the integrating factor technique. In Section 13 we shall solve the general linear equation of order one by first obtaining an integrating factor. Sections 17 and 18 contain additional developments of the same basic idea.

A second method for converting some equations into exact ones is to introduce a new variable, or variables, chosen by intelligent reaction to the form of the equation. Section 10 contains a simple instance in which the homogeneity of the coefficients suggests the ratio of the original variables as a new one because of Theorem 2, page 24. Chapter 4 contains other examples of appropriately chosen changes of variable.

13. The linear equation of order one

An equation that is linear and of order one in the dependent variable y must by definition (page 4) be of the form

(1) $$A(x)\, dy + B(x)y\, dx = C(x)\, dx.$$

By dividing each member of equation (1) by $A(x)$, we obtain

(2) $$dy + P(x)y\, dx = Q(x)\, dx,$$

which we choose as the standard form for the linear equation of order one.

For the moment, suppose that there exists for equation (2) an integrating factor $v(x)$, a function of x alone. Then

(3) $$v\, dy + vP(x)y\, dx = vQ(x)\, dx$$

must be an exact equation. But (3) is easily put into the form

$$M \, dx + N \, dy = 0$$

with

$$M = vPy - vQ,$$

and

$$N = v,$$

in which v, P, and Q are functions of x alone.

Therefore, if equation (3) is to be exact, it follows from the requirement

$$\frac{\partial M}{\partial y} = \frac{\partial N}{\partial x}$$

that v must satisfy the equation

(4) $$vP = \frac{dv}{dx}.$$

From (4), v may be obtained readily, for

$$P \, dx = \frac{dv}{v},$$

so

$$\ln v = \int P \, dx,$$

or

(5) $$v = \exp \left(\int P \, dx \right).$$

That is, if equation (2) has an integrating factor independent of y, then that factor must be as given by equation (5).

It remains to be shown that the v given by equation (5) is actually an integrating factor of

(2) $$dy + P(x)y \, dx = Q(x) \, dx.$$

Let us apply the factor throughout (2), obtaining

(6) $$\exp \left(\int P \, dx \right) dy + P \exp \left(\int P \, dx \right) y \, dx = Q \exp \left(\int P \, dx \right) dx.$$

The left member of (6) is the differential of the product

$$y \exp \left(\int P \, dx \right);$$

the right member of (6) is an exact differential since it is independent of y. Hence equation (6) is exact, which is what we wished to show.

Of course one integrating factor is sufficient. Hence we may use in the exponent $\left(\int P \, dx \right)$ any function whose differential is $P \, dx$.

With an integrating factor at hand, we can lay down the following rule for integrating any linear equation of order one:

(a) Put the equation into standard form:

$$dy + Py\ dx = Q\ dx;$$

(b) Obtain the integrating factor $\exp\left(\int P\ dx\right)$;
(c) Apply the integrating factor to the equation in its standard form;
(d) Solve the resultant exact equation.

Note, in integrating the exact equation, that *the integral of the left member is always the product of the dependent variable and the integrating factor used.*

EXAMPLE (a): Solve the equation

$$2(y - 4x^2)\ dx + x\ dy = 0.$$

The equation is linear in y. When put in standard form it becomes

(7) $$dy + \frac{2}{x} y\ dx = 8x\ dx.$$

Then an integrating factor is

$$\exp\left(\int \frac{2\ dx}{x}\right) = \exp\left(2 \ln x\right) = [\exp\left(\ln x\right)]^2 = x^2.$$

Next we apply the integrating factor to (7), thus obtaining the exact equation

(8) $$x^2\ dy + 2xy\ dx = 8x^3\ dx.$$

The solution of (8) is

(9) $$x^2 y = 2x^4 + c$$

and should be checked, particularly since verification of the result is so easy.

From (9) we get (8) by differentiation. Then the original differential equation follows from (8) by a simple adjustment. Hence (9) is a solution of the original equation.

EXAMPLE (b): Solve the equation

$$y\ dx + (3x - xy + 2)\ dy = 0.$$

Since the product $y\,dy$ occurs here, the equation is not linear in y. It is, however, linear in x. Therefore we arrange the terms as in

$$y\,dx + (3 - y)x\,dy = -2\,dy$$

and pass to the standard form,

$$(10) \qquad dx + \left(\frac{3}{y} - 1\right)x\,dy = -\frac{2}{y}\,dy.$$

Now

$$\int \left(\frac{3}{y} - 1\right)dy = 3\ln y - y + c_1,$$

so that an integrating factor for equation (10) is

$$\exp(3\ln y - y) = \exp(3\ln y)\cdot e^{-y} = [\exp(\ln y)]^3 \cdot e^{-y} = y^3 e^{-y}.$$

Application of this integrating factor to equation (10) leads to the exact equation

$$y^3 e^{-y}\,dx + y^2(3 - y)e^{-y}x\,dy = -2y^2 e^{-y}\,dy,$$

from which we get

$$xy^3 e^{-y} = -2\int y^2 e^{-y}\,dy$$
$$= 2y^2 e^{-y} + 4ye^{-y} + 4e^{-y} + c.$$

Thus we may write the solution as

$$xy^3 = 2y^2 + 4y + 4 + ce^y.$$

Exercises

In Exs. 1–25, find the general solution.

1. $(x^5 + 3y)\,dx - x\,dy = 0.$ 　　　　　ANS. $2y = x^5 + cx^3.$

2. $2(2xy + 4y - 3)\,dx + (x + 2)^2\,dy = 0.$

ANS. $y = 2(x + 2)^{-1} + c(x + 2)^{-4}.$

3. $y' = x - 2y.$ 　　　　　ANS. $4y = 2x - 1 + ce^{-2x}.$

4. $(y + 1)\,dx + (4x - y)\,dy = 0.$

ANS. $20x = 4y - 1 + c(y + 1)^{-4}.$

5. $u\,dx + (1 - 3u)x\,du = 3u^2 e^{3u}\,du.$ 　　ANS. $xu = (u^3 + c)e^{3u}.$

6. $u\,dx + (1 - 3u)x\,du = 3u\,du.$ 　　ANS. $xu = ce^{3u} - u - \frac{1}{3}.$

7. $y' = x - 4xy.$ Solve by two methods.

ANS. $4y = 1 + c\exp(-2x^2).$

8. $y' = \csc x + y\cot x.$ 　　　　　ANS. $y = c\sin x - \cos x.$

9. $y' = \csc x - y\cot x.$ 　　　　　ANS. $y\sin x = x + c.$

10. $(2xy + x^2 + x^4)\, dx - (1 + x^2)\, dy = 0.$

ANS. $y = (1 + x^2)(c + x - \text{Arctan } x).$

11. $(y - \cos^2 x)\, dx + \cos x\, dy = 0.$

ANS. $y(\sec x + \tan x) = c + x - \cos x.$

12. $y' = x - 2y \cot 2x.$ ANS. $4y \sin 2x = c + \sin 2x - 2x \cos 2x.$

13. $(y - x + xy \cot x)\, dx + x\, dy = 0.$

ANS. $xy \sin x = c + \sin x - x \cos x.$

14. $\dfrac{dy}{dx} - my = c_1 e^{mx},$ where c_1 and m are constants.

ANS. $y = (c_1 x + c_2)e^{mx}.$

15. $\dfrac{dy}{dx} - m_2 y = c_1 e^{m_1 x},$ where $c_1,\, m_1,\, m_2$ are constants and $m_1 \neq m_2.$

ANS. $y = c_3 e^{m_1 x} + c_2 e^{m_2 x},$ where $c_3 = \dfrac{c_1}{m_1 - m_2}.$

16. $v\, dx + (2x + 1 - vx)\, dv = 0.$ ANS. $xv^2 = v + 1 + ce^v.$

17. $x(x^2 + 1)y' + 2y = (x^2 + 1)^3.$

ANS. $x^2 y = \tfrac{1}{4}(x^2 + 1)^3 + c(x^2 + 1).$

18. $2y(y^2 - x)dy = dx.$ ANS. $x = y^2 - 1 + c \exp(-y^2).$

19. $(1 + xy)\, dx - (1 + x^2)\, dy = 0.$ ANS. $y = x + c(1 + x^2)^{\frac{1}{2}}.$

20. $2y\, dx = (x^2 - 1)(dx - dy).$

ANS. $(x - 1)y = (x + 1)[c + x - 2 \ln(x + 1)].$

21. $dx - (1 + 2x \tan y)\, dy = 0.$

ANS. $2x \cos^2 y = y + c + \sin y \cos y.$

22. $(1 + \cos x)y' = \sin x(\sin x + \sin x \cos x - y).$

ANS. $y = (1 + \cos x)(c + x - \sin x).$

23. $y' = 1 + 3y \tan x.$ ANS. $3y \cos^3 x = c + 3 \sin x - \sin^3 x.$

24. $(x + a)y' = bx - ny;\ a,\ b,\ n$ are constants with $n \neq 0,\ n \neq -1.$

ANS. $n(n + 1)y = b(nx - a) + c(x + a)^{-n}.$

25. Solve the equation of Ex. 24 for the exceptional cases $n = 0$ and $n = -1.$

ANS.   If $n = 0,\ y = bx + c - ab \ln(x + a).$

If $n = -1,\ y = ab + c(x + a) + b(x + a) \ln(x + a).$

26. In the standard form $dy + Py\, dx = Q\, dx$ put $y = vw$, thus obtaining

$$w(dv + Pv\, dx) + v\, dw = Q\, dx.$$

Then, by first choosing v so that

$$dv + Pv\, dx = 0$$

and later determining w, show how to complete the solution of

$$dy + Py\, dx = Q\, dx.$$

In Exs. 27–33 find the particular solution indicated.

27. $(2x + 3)y' = y + (2x + 3)^{\frac{1}{2}}$; when $x = -1$, $y = 0$.

ANS. $2y = (2x + 3)^{\frac{1}{2}} \ln (2x + 3)$.

28. $y' = x^3 - 2xy$; when $x = 1$, $y = 1$.

ANS. $2y = x^2 - 1 + 2 \exp (1 - x^2)$.

29. $L\dfrac{di}{dt} + Ri = E$, where L, R, and E are constants; when $t = 0$, $i = 0$.

ANS. $i = \dfrac{E}{R}\left[1 - \exp\left(-\dfrac{Rt}{L}\right)\right]$.

30. $\dfrac{di}{dt} + Ri = E \sin \omega t$; when $t = 0$, $i = 0$.

ANS.   Let $Z^2 = R^2 + \omega^2 L^2$. Then

$$i = EZ^{-2}\left[R \sin \omega t - \omega L \cos \omega t + \omega L \exp\left(-\dfrac{Rt}{L}\right)\right].$$

31. Find that solution of $y' = 2(2x - y)$ which passes through the point $(0, -1)$.   ANS. $y = 2x - 1$.

32. Find that solution of $y' = 2(2x - y)$ which passes through the point $(0, 1)$.   ANS. $y = 2x - 1 + 2e^{-2x}$

33. $(1 + t^2)\, ds + 2t[st^2 - 3(1 + t^2)^2]\, dt = 0$; when $t = 0$, $s = 2$.

ANS. $s = (1 + t^2)[3 - \exp (-t^2)]$.

Miscellaneous Exercises

In each exercise, find the general solution, unless the statement of the exercise stipulates otherwise.

1. $y' = \exp (2x - y)$.   ANS. $2e^y = e^{2x} + c$.

✗**2.** $(x + y)\, dx + x\, dy = 0$.   ANS. $x(x + 2y) = c$.

3. $y^2\, dx - x(2x + 3y)\, dy = 0$.   ANS. $y^2(x + y) = cx$.

∪**4.** $(x^2 + 1)\, dx + x^2 y^2\, dy = 0$.   ANS. $xy^3 = 3(1 + cx - x^2)$.

5. $(x^3 + y^3)\, dx + y^2(3x + ky)\, dy = 0$; k is constant.

ANS. $ky^4 + 4xy^3 + x^4 = c$.

✓**6.** $y' = x^3 - 2xy$; when $x = 1$, $y = 2$.

ANS. $2y = x^2 - 1 + 4 \exp (1 - x^2)$.

7. $\dfrac{dy}{dx} - \cos x = \cos x \tan^2 y$.   ANS. $2 \sin x = y + \sin y \cos y + c$.

∪**8.** $\cos x \dfrac{dy}{dx} = 1 - y - \sin x$.   ANS. $y(1 + \sin x) = (x + c) \cos x$.

9. $\sin \theta \dfrac{dr}{d\theta} = -1 - 2r \cos \theta$.   ANS. $r \sin^2 \theta = c + \cos \theta$.

10. $y(x + 3y)\, dx + x^2\, dy = 0.$ ANS. $x^2y = c(2x + 3y).$

11. $\dfrac{dy}{dx} = \sec^2 x \sec^3 y.$ ANS. $3 \tan x + c = 3 \sin y - \sin^3 y.$

12. $y(2x^3 - x^2y + y^3)\, dx - x(2x^3 + y^3)\, dy = 0.$

ANS. $2x^2y \ln (cx) = 4x^3 - y^3.$

13. $(1 + x^2)y' = x^4y^4.$ ANS. $x^3y^3 + 1 = y^3(c + 3x - 3 \text{ Arctan } x).$

14. $y(3 + 2xy^2)\, dx + 3(x^2y^2 + x - 1)\, dy = 0.$

ANS. $x^2y^3 = 3(c + y - xy).$

15. $(2x^2 - 2xy - y^2)\, dx + xy\, dy = 0.$ ANS. $x^3 = c(y - x) \exp (y/x).$

16. $y(x^2 + y^2)\, dx + x(3x^2 - 5y^2)\, dy = 0$; when $x = 2$, $y = 1.$

ANS. $2y^5 - 2x^2y^3 + 3x = 0.$

17. $y' + ay = b$; a and b are constants. Solve by two methods.

ANS. $y = b/a + ce^{-ax}.$

18. $(x - y)\, dx - (x + y)\, dy = 0.$ Solve by two methods.

ANS. $x^2 - 2xy - y^2 = c.$

19. $\dfrac{dx}{dt} = \cos x \cos^2 t.$ ANS. $4 \ln (\sec x + \tan x) = 2t + \sin 2t + c.$

20. $(\sin y - y \sin x)\, dx + (\cos x + x \cos y)\, dy = 0.$

ANS. $x \sin y + y \cos x = c.$

21. $(1 + 4xy - 4x^2y)\, dx + (x^2 - x^3)\, dy = 0$; when $x = 2$, $y = \frac{1}{4}.$

ANS. $2x^4y = x^2 + 2x + 2 \ln (x - 1).$

22. $3x^3y' = 2y(y - 3).$ ANS. $y = c(y - 3) \exp (x^{-2}).$

23. $(2y \cos x + \sin^4 x)\, dx = \sin x\, dy$; when $x = \frac{1}{2}\pi$, $y = 1.$

ANS. $y = 2 \sin^2 x \sin^2 \frac{1}{2}x.$

24. $xy(dx - dy) = x^2\, dy + y^2\, dx.$ ANS. $x = y \ln (cxy).$

25. $a^2(dy - dx) = x^2\, dy + y^2\, dx$; a is constant.

ANS. $2 \text{ Arctan } (y/a) = \ln [c(x + a)/(x - a)].$

26. $(y - \sin^2 x)\, dx + \sin x\, dy = 0.$

ANS. $y(\csc x - \cot x) = x + c - \sin x.$

27. $(x - y)\, dx + (3x + y)\, dy = 0$; when $x = 2$, $y = -1.$

ANS. $2(x + 2y) + (x + y) \ln (x + y) = 0.$

28. $y\, dx = (2x + 1)(dx - dy).$ ANS. $3y = (2x + 1) + c(2x + 1)^{-\frac{1}{2}}.$

In solving Exs. 29–33, recall that the principal value Arcsin x of the inverse sine function is restricted as follows:

$$-\tfrac{1}{2}\pi \leq \text{Arcsin } x \leq \tfrac{1}{2}\pi.$$

29. $\sqrt{1 - y^2}\, dx + \sqrt{1 - x^2}\, dy = 0.$

ANS.   Arcsin x + Arcsin $y = c$, or a part of the ellipse $x^2 + 2c_1xy + y^2 + c_1^2 - 1 = 0$, where $c_1 = \cos c.$

30. Solve the equation of Ex. 29 with the added condition that when $x = 0$, $y = \frac{1}{2}\sqrt{3}$.

ANS. Arcsin x + Arcsin $y = \frac{1}{3}\pi$, or that arc of the ellipse $x^2 + xy + y^2 = \frac{3}{4}$ that is indicated by a heavy solid line in Figure 6.

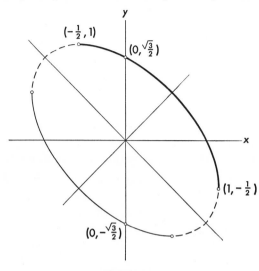

FIGURE 6

31. Solve the equation of Ex. 29 with the added condition that when $x = 0$, $y = -\frac{1}{2}\sqrt{3}$.

ANS. Arcsin x + Arcsin $y = -\frac{1}{3}\pi$, or that arc of the ellipse $x^2 + xy + y^2 = \frac{3}{4}$, that is indicated by a light solid line in Figure 6.

32. Show that after the answers to Exs. 30 and 31 have been deleted, the remaining arcs of the ellipse

$$x^2 + xy + y^2 = \frac{3}{4}$$

are not solutions of the differential equation

$$\sqrt{1 - y^2}\, dx + \sqrt{1 - x^2}\, dy = 0.$$

For this purpose consider the sign of the slope of the curve.

33. For the equation

$$\sqrt{1 - y^2}\, dx - \sqrt{1 - x^2}\, dy = 0$$

state and solve four problems analogous to Exs. 29–32 above.

34. $v\, du = (e^v + 2uv - 2u)\, dv.$ ANS. $v^2 u = ce^{2v} - (v + 1)e^v.$

35. $y\, dx = (3x + y^3 - y^2)\, dy$; when $x = 1$, $y = -1$.

ANS. $x = y^2\left[1 + y \ln\left(-y\right)\right].$

36. $y^2\,dx - (xy + 2)\,dy = 0.$ ANS. $xy = cy^2 - 1.$

37. $(x^2 - 2xy - y^2)\,dx - (x^2 + 2xy - y^2)\,dy = 0.$

ANS. $(x + y)(x^2 - 4xy + y^2) = c^3.$

38. $y^2\,dx + (xy + y^2 - 1)\,dy = 0$; when $x = -1,\ y = 1.$

ANS. $y^2 + 2xy + 1 = 2\ln y.$

39. $y(y^2 - 3x^2)\,dx + x^3\,dy = 0.$ ANS. $2x^6 = y^2(x^4 + c).$

40. $y' = \cos x - y \sec x$; when $x = 0,\ y = 1.$

ANS. $y(1 + \sin x) = \cos x(x + 2 - \cos x).$

41. Find that solution of $y' = 3x + y$ which passes through the point $(-1, 0).$ ANS. $y = -3(x + 1).$

42. Find that solution of $y' = 3x + y$ which passes through the point $(-1, 1).$ ANS. $y = \exp(x + 1) - 3(x + 1).$

43. $y' = y \tan x + \cos x.$ ANS. $2y = \sin x + (x + c)\sec x.$

44. $(x^2 - 1 + 2y)\,dx + (1 - x^2)\,dy = 0$; when $x = 2,\ y = 1.$

ANS. $(x + 1)y = (x - 1)[x + 1 + 2\ln(x - 1)].$

45. $(x^3 - 3xy^2)\,dx + (y^3 - 3x^2y)\,dy = 0.$ ANS. $x^4 - 6x^2y^2 + y^4 = c.$

46. $(1 - x^2)y' = 1 - xy - 3x^2 + 2x^4.$ ANS. $y = x - x^3 + c(1 - x^2)^{\frac{3}{2}}.$

47. $(y^2 + y)\,dx - (y^2 + 2xy + x)\,dy = 0$; when $x = 3,\ y = 1.$

ANS. $2y^2 + y = x.$

48. $(y^3 - x^3)\,dx = xy(x\,dx + y\,dy).$

ANS. $2x^2\ln(x + y) = cx^2 + 2xy - y^2.$

49. $y' = \sec x - y \tan x.$ ANS. $y = \sin x + c \cos x.$

50. $x^2y' = y(1 - x).$ ANS. $x\ln(cxy) = -1.$

51. $xy' = x - y + xy \tan x.$ ANS. $xy \cos x = c + \cos x + x \sin x.$

52. $(3x^4y - 1)\,dx + x^5\,dy = 0$; when $x = 1,\ y = 1.$

ANS. $x^4y = 2x - 1.$

53. $y^2\,dx + x^2\,dy = 2xy\,dy.$ ANS. $y^2 = x(y + c).$

54. $(\sin x \sin y + \tan x)\,dx - \cos x \cos y\,dy = 0.$

ANS. $\cos x \sin y = \ln(c \sec x).$

55. $(3xy - 4y - 1)\,dx + x(x - 2)\,dy = 0$; when $x = 1,\ y = 2.$

ANS. $2x^2(x - 2)y = x^2 - 5.$

CHAPTER 3

Elementary Applications

14. Velocity of escape from the earth

Many physical problems involve differential equations of order one and degree one.

Consider the problem of determining the velocity of a particle projected in a radial direction outward from the earth and acted upon by only one force, the gravitational attraction of the earth.

We shall assume an initial velocity in a radial direction so that the motion of the particle takes place entirely on a line through the center of the earth.

According to the Newtonian law of gravitation, the acceleration of the particle will be inversely proportional to the square of the distance from the particle to the center of the earth. Let r be that variable distance, and let R be the radius of the earth. If t represents time, v the velocity of the particle, a its acceleration, and k the constant of proportionality in the Newtonian law, then

$$a = \frac{dv}{dt} = \frac{k}{r^2}.$$

The acceleration is negative because the velocity is decreasing. Hence the constant k is negative. When $r = R$, then $a = -g$, the acceleration of gravity at the surface of the earth. Thus

45

$$-g = \frac{k}{R^2},$$

from which

$$a = -\frac{gR^2}{r^2}.$$

We wish to express the acceleration in terms of the velocity and the distance. We have $a = \frac{dv}{dt}$ and $v = \frac{dr}{dt}$. Hence

$$a = \frac{dv}{dt} = \frac{dr}{dt}\frac{dv}{dr} = v\frac{dv}{dr},$$

so the differential equation for the velocity is now seen to be

(1) $$v\frac{dv}{dr} = -\frac{gR^2}{r^2}.$$

The method of separation of variables applies to equation (1) and leads at once to the solution

$$v^2 = \frac{2gR^2}{r} + C.$$

Suppose the particle leaves the earth's surface with the velocity v_0. Then $v = v_0$ when $r = R$, from which the constant C is easily determined to be

$$C = v_0{}^2 - 2gR.$$

Thus a particle projected in a radial direction outward from the earth's surface with an initial velocity v_0 will travel with a velocity v given by the equation

(2) $$v^2 = \frac{2gR^2}{r} + v_0{}^2 - 2gR.$$

It is of considerable interest to determine whether the particle will escape from the earth. Now at the surface of the earth, at $r = R$, the velocity is positive, $v = v_0$. An examination of the right member of equation (2) shows that the velocity of the particle will remain positive if, and only if,

(3) $$v_0{}^2 - 2gR \geqq 0.$$

For, if the inequality (3) is satisfied, the velocity given by equation (2) will remain positive, since it cannot vanish, is continuous, and is positive at $r = R$. On the other hand, if the inequality (3) is not satisfied, then

$v_0{}^2 - 2gR < 0$, and there will be a critical value of r for which the right member of equation (2) is zero. That is, the particle would stop, the velocity would change from positive to negative, and the particle would return to the earth.

A particle projected from the earth with a velocity v_0 such that $v_0 \geqq \sqrt{2gR}$ will escape from the earth. Hence, the minimum such velocity of projection,

$$(4) \qquad\qquad v_e = \sqrt{2gR},$$

is called the *velocity of escape*.

The radius of the earth is approximately $R = 3960$ miles. The acceleration of gravity at the surface of the earth is approximately $g = 32.16$ feet per second per second, or $g = 6.09(10)^{-3}$ miles per second per second. For the earth, the velocity of escape is easily found to be $v_e = 6.95$ miles per second.

Of course, the gravitational pull of other celestial bodies, the moon, the sun, Mars, Venus, etc. has been neglected in the idealized problem treated here. It is not difficult to see that such approximations are justified, since we are interested in only the critical initial velocity v_e. Whether the particle actually recedes from the earth forever or becomes, for instance, a satellite of some heavenly body, is of no consequence in the present problem.

If in this study we happen to be thinking of the particle as an idealization of a ballistic-type rocket, then other elements must be considered. Air resistance in the first few miles may not be negligible. Methods for overcoming such difficulties are not suitable topics for discussion here.

It must be realized that the formula $v_e = \sqrt{2gR}$ applies equally well for the velocity of escape from the other members of the solar system, as long as R and g are given their appropriate values.

15. Newton's law of cooling

Experiment has shown that under certain conditions, a good approximation to the temperature of an object can be obtained by using Newton's law of cooling: The temperature of a body changes at a rate which is proportional to the difference in temperature between the outside medium and the body itself. We shall assume here that the constant of proportionality is the same whether the temperature is increasing or decreasing.

Suppose, for instance, that a thermometer, which has been at the reading 70 °F inside a house, is placed outside where the air temperature is 10 °F. Three minutes later it is found that the thermometer reading is 25 °F. We wish to predict the thermometer reading at various later times.

Let u (°F) represent the temperature of the thermometer at time t (min.), the time being measured from the instant the thermometer is placed outside. We are given that when $t = 0$, $u = 70$ and when $t = 3$, $u = 25$.

According to Newton's law, the time rate of change of temperature, du/dt, is proportional to the temperature difference $(u - 10)$. Since the thermometer temperature is decreasing, it is convenient to choose $(-k)$ as the constant of proportionality. Thus the u is to be determined from the differential equation

(1) $$\frac{du}{dt} = -k(u - 10),$$

and the conditions that

(2) $$\text{when } t = 0, u = 70$$

and

(3) $$\text{when } t = 3, u = 25.$$

We need to know the thermometer reading at two different times because there are two constants to be determined, the k in equation (1) and the "arbitrary" constant which occurs in the solution of the differential equation (1).

From equation (1) it follows at once that

$$u = 10 + Ce^{-kt}.$$

Then condition (2) yields $70 = 10 + C$ from which $C = 60$, so we have

(4) $$u = 10 + 60e^{-kt}.$$

The value of k will be determined now by using the condition (3). Putting $t = 3$ and $u = 25$ into equation (4) we get

$$25 = 10 + 60e^{-3k},$$

from which $e^{-3k} = \frac{1}{4}$, so $k = \frac{1}{3} \ln 4$.

Thus, the temperature is given by the equation

(5) $$u = 10 + 60 \exp\left(-\tfrac{1}{3}t \ln 4\right).$$

Since $\ln 4 = 1.39$, equation (5) may be replaced by

(6) $$u = 10 + 60 \exp(-0.46t),$$

which is convenient when a table of values of e^{-x} is available.

16. Simple chemical conversion

It is known from the results of chemical experimentation that, in certain reactions in which a substance A is being converted into another substance, the time rate of change of the amount x of unconverted substance is proportional to x.

Let the amount of unconverted substance be known at some specified time; that is, let $x = x_0$ at $t = 0$. Then the amount x at any time $t > 0$ is determined by the differential equation

(1) $$\frac{dx}{dt} = -kx$$

and the condition that $x = x_0$ when $t = 0$. Since the amount x is decreasing as time increases, the constant of proportionality in equation (1) is taken to be $(-k)$.

From equation (1) it follows that

$$x = Ce^{-kt}.$$

But $x = x_0$ when $t = 0$. Hence $C = x_0$. Thus we have the result

(2) $$x = x_0 e^{-kt}.$$

Let us now add another condition, which will enable us to determine k. Suppose it is known that at the end of half a minute, at $t = 30$ (sec.), two-thirds of the original amount x_0 has already been converted. Let us determine how much unconverted substance remains at $t = 60$ (sec.).

When two-thirds of the substance has been converted, one-third remains unconverted. Hence $x = \frac{1}{3}x_0$ when $t = 30$. Equation (2) now yields the relation

$$\tfrac{1}{3}x_0 = x_0 e^{-30k}$$

from which k is easily found to be $\frac{1}{30}\ln 3$. Then with t measured in seconds, the amount of unconverted substance is given by the equation

(3) $$x = x_0 \exp(-\tfrac{1}{30}t \ln 3).$$

At $t = 60$,

$$x = x_0 \exp(-2\ln 3) = x_0(3)^{-2} = \tfrac{1}{9}x_0.$$

Exercises

1. The radius of the moon is roughly 1080 miles. The acceleration of gravity at the surface of the moon is about $0.165g$, where g is the acceleration of gravity at the surface of the earth. Determine the velocity of escape for the moon.   ANS.   1.5 mi./sec.

2. Determine to two significant figures the velocity of escape for each of the celestial bodies listed below. The data given are rough and g may be taken to be $6.1(10)^{-3}$ mi./sec².

	Accel. of gravity *at surface*	*Radius* *in miles*	*Ans. in* *mi./sec.*
Venus	$0.85g$	3,800	6.3
Mars	$0.38g$	2,100	3.1
Jupiter	$2.6g$	43,000	37
Sun	$28g$	432,000	380
Ganymede	$0.12g$	1,780	1.6

3. A thermometer reading 18 °F is brought into a room the temperature of which is 70 °F. One minute later the thermometer reading is 31 °F. Determine the temperature reading as a function of time and in particular, find the temperature reading five minutes after the thermometer is first brought into the room.
ANS. $u = 70 - 52 \exp(-0.29t)$; when $t = 5$, $u = 58$.

4. A thermometer reading 75 °F is taken out where the temperature is 20 °F. The reading is 30 °F four minutes later. Find (a) the thermometer reading seven minutes after the thermometer was brought outside, and (b) the time taken for the reading to drop from 75 °F to within a half degree of the air temperature.   ANS.   (a) 23 °F; (b) 11.5 min.

5. At 1:00 P.M., a thermometer reading 70 °F is taken outside where the air temperature is −10 °F, ten below zero. At 1:02 P.M., the reading is 26 °F. At 1:05 P.M., the thermometer is taken back indoors where the air is at 70 °F. What is the thermometer reading at 1:09 P.M.?

6. At 9 A.M., a thermometer reading 70 °F is taken outdoors where the temperature is 15 °F. At 9:05 A.M., the thermometer reading is 45 °F. At 9:10 A.M., the thermometer is taken back indoors where the temperature is fixed at 70 °F. Find (a) the reading at 9:20 A.M. and (b) when the reading, to the nearest degree, will show the correct (70 °F) indoor temperature.   ANS.   (a) 58 °F; (b) 9:46 A.M.

7. At 2:00 P.M., a thermometer reading 80 °F is taken outside where the air temperature is 20 °F. At 2:03 P.M., the temperature reading yielded by the thermometer is 42 °F. Later, the thermometer is brought inside

where the air is at 80 °F. At 2:10 P.M., the reading is 71 °F. When was the thermometer brought indoors?   ANS.   At 2:05 P.M.

8. Suppose that a chemical reaction proceeds according to the law given in Section 16 above. If half the substance A has been converted at the end of ten seconds, find when nine-tenths of the substance will have been converted.   ANS.   33 sec.

9. The conversion of a substance B follows the law used in Section 16 above. If only a fourth of the substance has been converted at the end of ten seconds, find when nine-tenths of the substance will have been converted.   ANS.   80 sec.

10. For a substance C, the time rate of conversion is proportional to the square of the amount x of unconverted substance. Let k be the numerical value of the constant of proportionality and let the amount of unconverted substance be x_0 at time $t = 0$. Determine x for all $t \geqq 0$.
ANS. $x = x_0/(1 + x_0kt)$.

11. Two substances, A and B, are being converted into a single compound C. In the laboratory it has been shown that, for these substances, the following law of conversion holds: the time rate of change of the amount x of compound C is proportional to the product of the amounts of unconverted substances A and B. Assume the units of measure so chosen that one unit of the compound C is formed from the combination of one unit of A with one unit of B. If at time $t = 0$ there are a units of substance A, b units of substance B, and none of the compound C, present, show that the law of conversion may be expressed by the equation

$$\frac{dx}{dt} = k(a - x)(b - x).$$

Solve this equation with the given initial condition.

ANS.   If $b \neq a, x = \dfrac{ab[\exp (b - a)kt - 1]}{b \exp (b - a)kt - a}$; if $b = a, x = a^2kt/(akt + 1)$.

12. In the solution of Ex. 11, above assume that $k > 0$ and investigate the behavior of x as $t \to \infty$.   ANS.   If $b \geqq a$, $x \to a$; if $b \leqq a$, $x \to b$.

13. Radium decomposes at a rate proportional to the quantity of radium present. Suppose that it is found that in 25 years approximately 1.1 per cent of a certain quantity of radium has decomposed. Determine approximately how long it will take for one-half the original amount of radium to decompose.   ANS.   1600 years.

14. A certain radioactive substance has a half-life of 38 hours. Find how long it takes for 90% of the radioactivity to be dissipated.
ANS.   126 hrs.

15. A bacterial population B is known to have a rate of growth proportional to B itself. If between noon and 2 P.M. the population triples, at what time, no controls being exerted, should B become 100 times what it was at noon?   ANS.   About 8:22 P.M.

16. In the motion of an object through a certain medium (air at certain pressures is an example), the medium furnishes a resisting force proportional to the square of the velocity of the moving object. Suppose a body falls, due to the action of gravity, through such a medium. Let t represent time, and v represent velocity, positive downward. Let g be the usual constant acceleration of gravity and let w be the weight of the body. Use Newton's law, force equals mass times acceleration, to conclude that the differential equation of the motion is

$$\frac{w}{g}\frac{dv}{dt} = w - kv^2,$$

where kv^2 is the magnitude of the resisting force furnished by the medium.

17. Solve the differential equation of Ex. 16 with the initial condition that $v = v_0$ when $t = 0$. Introduce the constant $a^2 = w/k$ to simplify the formulas.   ANS. $\dfrac{a+v}{a-v} = \dfrac{a+v_0}{a-v_0}\exp\left(\dfrac{2gt}{a}\right).$

18. List a consistent set of units for the dimensions of the variables and parameters of Exs. 16–17 above.

ANS. t in sec. g in ft./sec.^{2}
       v in ft./sec. k in (lb.)(sec.^{2})/(ft.^{2})
       w in lb. a in ft./sec.

19. There are mediums that resist motion through them with a force proportional to the first power of the velocity. For such a medium, state and solve problems analogous to Exs. 16–18 above, except that for convenience a constant $b = w/k$ may be introduced to replace the a^2 of Ex. 17. Show that b has the dimensions of a velocity.

ANS. $v = b +$
$$(v_0 - b)\exp\left(-\frac{gt}{b}\right).$$

FIGURE 7

20. Figure 7 shows a weight, w pounds, sliding down an inclined plane which makes an angle α with the horizontal. Assume that no force other than gravity is acting on the weight; that is, there is no friction, no air resistance, etc. At

time $t = 0$, let $x = x_0$ and let the initial velocity be v_0. Determine x for $t > 0$.   ANS. $x = \frac{1}{2}gt^2 \sin \alpha + v_0 t + x_0$.

21. A long, very smooth board is inclined at an angle of 10° with the horizontal. A weight starts from rest ten feet from the bottom of the board and slides downward under the action of gravity alone. Find how long it will take the weight to reach the bottom of the board and determine the terminal speed.   ANS.   1.9 sec. and 10.5 ft./sec.

22. Add to the conditions of Ex. 20 above a retarding force of magnitude kv, where v is the velocity. Determine v and x under the assumption that the weight starts from rest with $x = x_0$. Use the notation $a = kg/w$.   ANS. $v = a^{-1}g \sin \alpha \, (1 - e^{-at})$;

$$x = x_0 + a^{-2}g \sin \alpha \, (-1 + e^{-at} + at).$$

FIGURE 8

23. A man, standing at O in Figure 8, holds a rope of length a to which a weight is attached, initially at W_0. The man walks to the right dragging the weight after him. When the man is at M, the weight is at W. Find the differential equation of the path (called the tractrix) of the weight and solve the equation.   ANS. $x = a \ln \dfrac{a + \sqrt{a^2 - y^2}}{y} - \sqrt{a^2 - y^2}$.

CHAPTER 4

Additional Topics on Equations of

Order One and Degree One

17. Integrating factors found by inspection

In Section 13 we found that any linear equation of order one can be solved with the aid of an integrating factor. In Section 18 there is some discussion of tests for the determination of integrating factors.

At present we are concerned with equations that are simple enough to enable us to find integrating factors by inspection. The ability to do this depends largely upon recognition of certain common exact differentials and upon experience.

Below are four exact differentials which occur frequently:

(1) $$d(xy) = x \, dy + y \, dx,$$

(2) $$d\left(\frac{x}{y}\right) = \frac{y \, dx - x \, dy}{y^2},$$

(3) $$d\left(\frac{y}{x}\right) = \frac{x \, dy - y \, dx}{x^2},$$

(4) $$d\left(\operatorname{Arctan} \frac{y}{x}\right) = \frac{x \, dy - y \, dx}{x^2 + y^2}.$$

Note the homogeneity of the coefficients of dx and dy in each of these differentials.

A differential involving only one variable, one such as $x^{-2} \, dx$, is an exact differential.

54

EXAMPLE (a): Solve the equation

(5) $y\,dx + (x + x^3y^2)\,dy = 0.$

Let us group the terms of like degree, writing the equation in the form

$$(y\,dx + x\,dy) + x^3y^2\,dy = 0.$$

Now the combination $(y\,dx + x\,dy)$ attracts attention, so we rewrite the equation, obtaining

(6) $d(xy) + x^3y^2\,dy = 0.$

Since the differential of xy is present in equation (6), any factor that is a function of the product xy will not disturb the integrability of that term. But the other term contains the differential dy, hence should contain a function of y alone. Therefore, let us divide by $(xy)^3$ and write

$$\frac{d(xy)}{(xy)^3} + \frac{dy}{y} = 0.$$

The equation above is integrable as it stands. Its solution is

$$-\frac{1}{2x^2y^2} + \ln y = -\ln c,$$

or

$$2x^2y^2 \ln (cy) = 1.$$

EXAMPLE (b): Solve the equation

(7) $y(x^3 - y)\,dx - x(x^3 + y)\,dy = 0.$

Let us regroup the terms of (7) to obtain

(8) $x^3(y\,dx - x\,dy) - y(y\,dx + x\,dy) = 0.$

Recalling that

$$d\left(\frac{x}{y}\right) = \frac{y\,dx - x\,dy}{y^2},$$

we divide the terms of equation (8) throughout by y^2 to get

(9) $x^3\,d\left(\frac{x}{y}\right) - \frac{d(xy)}{y} = 0.$

Equation (9) will be made exact by introducing a factor; if it can be found, to make the coefficient of $d(x/y)$ a function of (x/y) and the coefficient of $d(xy)$ a function of (xy). Some skill in obtaining such factors can be developed with a little practice. When a factor can be found by inspection, that method is frequently the most rapid one.

There is a straightforward attack on equation (9) which has its good points. Assume that the integrating factor desired is $x^k y^n$, where k and n are to be determined. Applying that factor, we obtain

(10) $$x^{k+3} y^n \, d\left(\frac{x}{y}\right) - x^k y^{n-1} \, d(xy) = 0.$$

Since the coefficient of $d(x/y)$ is to be a function of the ratio (x/y), the exponents of x and y in that coefficient must be numerically equal, but of opposite sign. That is,

(11) $$k + 3 = -n.$$

In a similar manner, from the coefficient of $d(xy)$ it follows that we must put

(12) $$k = n - 1.$$

From equations (11) and (12) we conclude that $k = -2$, $n = -1$. The desired integrating factor is $x^{-2} y^{-1}$ and (10) becomes

$$\frac{x}{y} \, d\left(\frac{x}{y}\right) - \frac{d(xy)}{x^2 y^2} = 0$$

of which the solution is

$$\tfrac{1}{2}\left(\frac{x}{y}\right)^2 + \frac{1}{xy} = \frac{c}{2}.$$

Finally, we may write the desired solution of equation (7) as

$$x^3 + 2y = cxy^2.$$

EXAMPLE (c): Solve the equation

$$3x^2 y \, dx + (y^4 - x^3) \, dy = 0.$$

Since two terms in the coefficients of dx and dy are of degree three and the other coefficient is not of degree three, let us regroup the terms to get

$$(3x^2 y \, dx - x^3 \, dy) + y^4 \, dy = 0,$$

or

$$y \, d(x^3) - x^3 \, dy + y^4 \, dy = 0.$$

The form of the first two terms now suggests the numerator in the differential of a quotient, as in

$$d\left(\frac{u}{v}\right) = \frac{v\,du - u\,dv}{v^2}.$$

Therefore, we divide each term of our equation by y^2 and obtain

$$\frac{y\,d(x^3) - x^3\,dy}{y^2} + y^2\,dy = 0,$$

or

$$d\left(\frac{x^3}{y}\right) + y^2\,dy = 0.$$

Hence the solution of the original equation is

$$\frac{x^3}{y} + \frac{y^3}{3} = \frac{c}{3}$$

or

$$3x^3 + y^4 = cy.$$

Exercises

Except when the exercise indicates otherwise, find the general solution.

1. $y(2xy + 1)\,dx - x\,dy = 0.$ ANS. $x(xy + 1) = cy.$

2. $y(y^3 - x)\,dx + x(y^3 + x)\,dy = 0.$ ANS. $2xy^3 - x^2 = cy^2.$

3. $(x^3y^3 + 1)\,dx + x^4y^2\,dy = 0.$ ANS. $x^3y^3 = -3\ln(cx).$

4. $2t\,ds + s(2 + s^2t)\,dt = 0.$ ANS. $1 + s^2t = cs^2t^2.$

5. $y(x^4 - y^2)\,dx + x(x^4 + y^2)\,dy = 0.$ ANS. $y(3x^4 + y^2) = cx^3.$

6. $y(y^2 + 1)\,dx + x(y^2 - 1)\,dy = 0.$ ANS. $x(y^2 + 1) = cy.$

7. Do Ex. 6 by a second method.

8. $y(x^3 - y^5)\,dx - x(x^3 + y^5)\,dy = 0.$ ANS. $x^4 = y^4(c + 4xy).$

9. $y(x^2 - y^2 + 1)\,dx - x(x^2 - y^2 - 1)\,dy = 0.$
          ANS. $x^2 + cxy + y^2 = 1.$

10. $(x^3 + xy^2 + y)\,dx + (y^3 + x^2y + x)\,dy = 0.$
          ANS. $(x^2 + y^2)^2 = c - 4xy.$

11. $y(x^2 + y^2 - 1)\,dx + x(x^2 + y^2 + 1)\,dy = 0.$
          ANS. $xy + \text{Arctan}\,(y/x) = c.$

12. $(x^3 + xy^2 - y)\,dx + (y^3 + x^2y + x)\,dy = 0.$
          ANS. $2\,\text{Arctan}\,(y/x) = c - x^2 - y^2.$

13. $y(x^3e^{xy} - y)\,dx + x(y + x^3e^{xy})\,dy = 0.$ ANS. $2x^2e^{xy} + y^2 = cx^2.$

14. $xy(y^2 + 1)\,dx + (x^2y^2 - 2)\,dy = 0;$ when $x = 1,\ y = 1.$
          ANS. $x^2(y^2 + 1) = 2 + 4\ln y.$

15. $y^2(1 - x^2)\,dx + x(x^2y + 2x + y)\,dy = 0.$
          ANS. $x^2y + x + y = cxy^2.$

16. $y(x^2y^2 - 1)\,dx + x(x^2y^2 + 1)\,dy = 0.$ ANS. $x^2y^2 = 2\ln(cx/y).$

17. $x^4y' = -x^3y - \csc(xy).$ ANS. $2x^2\cos(xy) = cx^2 - 1.$

18. $[1 + y\tan(xy)]\,dx + x\tan(xy)\,dy = 0.$ ANS. $\cos(xy) = ce^x.$

19. $y(x^2y^2 - m)\,dx + x(x^2y^2 + n)\,dy = 0.$ ANS. $x^2y^2 = 2\ln(cx^m/y^n).$

20. $x(x^2 - y^2 - x)\,dx - y(x^2 - y^2)\,dy = 0$; when $x = 2, y = 0.$

ANS. $3(x^2 - y^2)^2 = 4(x^3 + 4).$

21. $y(x^2 + y)\,dx + x(x^2 - 2y)\,dy = 0$; when $x = 1, y = 2.$

ANS. $x^2y - y^2 + 2x = 0.$

22. $y(x^3y^3 + 2x^2 - y)\,dx + x^3(xy^3 - 2)\,dy = 0$; when $x = 1, y = 1.$

ANS. $x^3y^3 + 4x^2 - 7xy + 2y = 0.$

23. $y(2 - 3xy)\,dx - x\,dy = 0.$ ANS. $x^2(1 - xy) = cy.$

24. $y(2x + y^2)\,dx + x(y^2 - x)\,dy = 0.$ ANS. $x(x + y^2) = cy.$

25. $y\,dx + 2(y^4 - x)\,dy = 0.$ ANS. $y^4 + x = cy^2.$

26. $y(3x^3 - x + y)\,dx + x^2(1 - x^2)\,dy = 0.$

ANS. $y\ln(cx) = x(1 - x^2).$

27. $2x^5y' = y(3x^4 + y^2).$ ANS. $x^4 = y^2(1 + cx).$

28. $(x^ny^{n+1} + ay)\,dx + (x^{n+1}y^n + bx)\,dy = 0.$

ANS.   If $n \ne 0$, $x^ny^n = n\ln(cx^{-a}y^{-b}).$
If $n = 0$, $xy = c_1x^{-a}y^{-b}.$

29. $(x^{n+1}y^n + ay)\,dx + (x^ny^{n+1} + ax)\,dy = 0.$

ANS.   If $n \ne 1$, $(n - 1)(xy)^{n-1}(x^2 + y^2 - c) = 2a.$
If $n = 1$, $x^2 + y^2 - c = -2a\ln(xy).$

18. The determination of integrating factors

Let us see what progress can be made on the problem of the determination of an integrating factor for the equation

(1) $M\,dx + N\,dy = 0.$

Suppose u, possibly a function of both x and y, is to be an integrating factor of (1). Then the equation

(2) $uM\,dx + uN\,dy = 0$

must be exact. Therefore, by the result of Section 11,

$$\frac{\partial}{\partial y}(uM) = \frac{\partial}{\partial x}(uN).$$

Hence u must satisfy the partial differential equation

$$u\frac{\partial M}{\partial y} + M\frac{\partial u}{\partial y} = u\frac{\partial N}{\partial x} + N\frac{\partial u}{\partial x},$$

or

(3) $$u\left(\frac{\partial M}{\partial y} - \frac{\partial N}{\partial x}\right) = N\frac{\partial u}{\partial x} - M\frac{\partial u}{\partial y}.$$

Furthermore, by reversing the argument above, it can be seen that if u satisfies equation (3), then u is an integrating factor for equation (1). We have "reduced" the problem of solving the ordinary differential equation (1) to the problem of obtaining a particular solution of the partial differential equation (3).

Not much has been gained, since we have developed no methods for attacking an equation such as (3). Therefore, we turn the problem back into the realm of ordinary differential equations by restricting u to be a function of only one variable.

First let u be a function of x alone. Then $\frac{\partial u}{\partial y} = 0$ and $\frac{\partial u}{\partial x}$ becomes $\frac{du}{dx}$. Then (3) reduces to

$$u\left(\frac{\partial M}{\partial y} - \frac{\partial N}{\partial x}\right) = N\frac{du}{dx},$$

or

(4) $$\frac{1}{N}\left(\frac{\partial M}{\partial y} - \frac{\partial N}{\partial x}\right)dx = \frac{du}{u}.$$

If the left member of the above equation is a function of x alone, then we can determine u at once. Indeed, if

(5) $$\frac{1}{N}\left(\frac{\partial M}{\partial y} - \frac{\partial N}{\partial x}\right) = f(x),$$

then the desired integrating factor is $u = \exp\left(\int f(x)\,dx\right)$.

By a similar argument, assuming that u is a function of y alone, we are led to the conclusion that if

(6) $$\frac{1}{M}\left(\frac{\partial M}{\partial y} - \frac{\partial N}{\partial x}\right) = g(y),$$

then an integrating factor for equation (1) is $u = \exp\left(-\int g(y)\,dy\right)$.

Our two results are expressed in the following rules.

If $\frac{1}{N}\left(\frac{\partial M}{\partial y} - \frac{\partial N}{\partial x}\right) = f(x)$, a function of x alone, then $\exp\left(\int f(x)\,dx\right)$ is an integrating factor for the equation

(1) $$M\,dx + N\,dy = 0.$$

If $\dfrac{1}{M}\left(\dfrac{\partial M}{\partial y} - \dfrac{\partial N}{\partial x}\right) = g(y)$, a function of y alone, then $\exp\left(-\int g(y)\,dy\right)$ is an integrating factor for equation (1).

EXAMPLE (a): Solve the equation

$$(7) \qquad (4xy + 3y^2 - x)\,dx + x(x + 2y)\,dy = 0.$$

Here $M = 4xy + 3y^2 - x$, $N = x^2 + 2xy$, so

$$\frac{\partial M}{\partial y} - \frac{\partial N}{\partial x} = 4x + 6y - (2x + 2y) = 2x + 4y.$$

Hence

$$\frac{1}{N}\left(\frac{\partial M}{\partial y} - \frac{\partial N}{\partial x}\right) = \frac{2x + 4y}{x(x + 2y)} = \frac{2}{x}.$$

Therefore an integrating factor for equation (7) is

$$\exp\left(2\int \frac{dx}{x}\right) = \exp\left(2\ln x\right) = x^2.$$

Returning to the original equation (7), we insert the integrating factor and obtain

$$(8) \qquad (4x^3y + 3x^2y^2 - x^3)\,dx + (x^4 + 2x^3y)\,dy = 0,$$

which we know must be an exact equation. The methods of Section 11 apply. We are then led to put equation (8) in the form

$$(4x^3y\,dx + x^4\,dy) + (3x^2y^2\,dx + 2x^3y\,dy) - x^3\,dx = 0,$$

from which the solution

$$x^4y + x^3y^2 - \tfrac{1}{4}x^4 = \tfrac{1}{4}c,$$

or

$$x^3(4xy + 4y^2 - x) = c$$

follows at once.

EXAMPLE (b): Solve the equation

$$(9) \qquad y(x + y + 1)\,dx + x(x + 3y + 2)\,dy = 0.$$

First we form

$$\frac{\partial M}{\partial y} = x + 2y + 1, \qquad \frac{\partial N}{\partial x} = 2x + 3y + 2.$$

Then we see that

$$\frac{\partial M}{\partial y} - \frac{\partial N}{\partial x} = -x - y - 1,$$

so

$$\frac{1}{N}\left(\frac{\partial M}{\partial y} - \frac{\partial N}{\partial x}\right) = -\frac{x + y + 1}{x(x + 3y + 2)}$$

is not a function of x alone. But

$$\frac{1}{M}\left(\frac{\partial M}{\partial y} - \frac{\partial N}{\partial x}\right) = -\frac{x + y + 1}{y(x + y + 1)} = -\frac{1}{y}.$$

Therefore exp $(\ln y) = y$ is the desired integrating factor for (9).
Using the integrating factor, we write

$$(xy^2 + y^3 + y^2)\,dx + (x^2y + 3xy^2 + 2xy)\,dy = 0,$$

or

$$(xy^2\,dx + x^2y\,dy) + (y^3\,dx + 3xy^2\,dy) + (y^2\,dx + 2xy\,dy) = 0.$$

Then the solution of (9) is found to be

$$\tfrac{1}{2}x^2y^2 + xy^3 + xy^2 = \tfrac{1}{2}c,$$

or

$$xy^2(x + 2y + 2) = c.$$

EXAMPLE (c): Solve the equation

(10) $$y(x + y)\,dx + (x + 2y - 1)\,dy = 0.$$

From $\dfrac{\partial M}{\partial y} = x + 2y$, $\dfrac{\partial N}{\partial x} = 1$, we conclude at once that

$$\frac{1}{N}\left(\frac{\partial M}{\partial y} - \frac{\partial N}{\partial x}\right) = \frac{x + 2y - 1}{x + 2y - 1} = 1.$$

Hence e^x is an integrating factor for (10). Then

$$(xye^x + y^2e^x)\,dx + (xe^x + 2ye^x - e^x)\,dy = 0$$

is an exact equation. Grouping the terms in the following manner,

$$[xye^x\,dx + (xe^x - e^x)\,dy] + (y^2e^x\,dx + 2ye^x\,dy) = 0,$$

leads us at once to the solution

$$e^x(x - 1)y + y^2e^x = c,$$

or

$$y(x + y - 1) = ce^{-x}.$$

Exercises

Solve each of the following equations.

1. $(x^2 + y^2 + 1) \, dx + x(x - 2y) \, dy = 0$.

ANS. $x^2 - y^2 + xy - 1 = cx$.

2. $2y(x^2 - y + x) \, dx + (x^2 - 2y) \, dy = 0$.   ANS. $y(x^2 - y) = ce^{-2x}$.

3. $y(2x - y + 1) \, dx + x(3x - 4y + 3) \, dy = 0$.

ANS. $xy^3(x - y + 1) = c$.

4. $y(4x + y) \, dx - 2(x^2 - y) \, dy = 0$.   ANS. $2x^2 + xy + 2y \ln y = cy$.

5. $(xy + 1) \, dx + x(x + 4y - 2) \, dy = 0$.

ANS. $xy + \ln x + 2y^2 - 2y = c$.

6. $(2y^2 + 3xy - 2y + 6x) \, dx + x(x + 2y - 1) \, dy = 0$.

ANS. $x^2(y^2 + xy - y + 2x) = c$.

7. $y(y + 2x - 2) \, dx - 2(x + y) \, dy = 0$.   ANS. $y(2x + y) = ce^x$.

8. $y^2 dx + (3xy + y^2 - 1) \, dy = 0$.   ANS. $y^2(y^2 + 4xy - 2) = c$.

9. $2y(x + y + 2) \, dx + (y^2 - x^2 - 4x - 1) \, dy = 0$.

ANS. $x^2 + 2xy + y^2 + 4x + 1 = cy$.

10. $2(2y^2 + 5xy - 2y + 4)dx + x(2x + 2y - 1) \, dy = 0$.

ANS. $x^4(y^2 + 2xy - y + 2) = c$.

11. $3(x^2 + y^2) \, dx + x(x^2 + 3y^2 + 6y) \, dy = 0$.

ANS. $x(x^2 + 3y^2) = ce^{-y}$.

12. $y(8x - 9y) \, dx + 2x(x - 3y) \, dy = 0$.   ANS. $x^3y(2x - 3y) = c$.

13. Do Ex. 12 by another method.

14. $y(2x^2 - xy + 1) \, dx + (x - y) \, dy = 0$.

ANS. $y(2x - y) = c \exp(-x^2)$.

15. Euler's theorem (Ex. 34, page 29) on homogeneous functions states that if F is a homogeneous function of degree k in x and y, then

$$x \frac{\partial F}{\partial x} + y \frac{\partial F}{\partial y} = kF.$$

Use Euler's theorem to prove the result that if M and N are homogeneous functions of the same degree, and if $Mx + Ny \neq 0$, then

$$\frac{1}{Mx + Ny}$$

is an integrating factor for the equation

(1) $M \, dx + N \, dy = 0$.

16. In the result to be proved in Ex. 15 above there is an exceptional case, namely, when $Mx + Ny = 0$. Solve equation (1) when $Mx + Ny = 0$.

ANS. $y = cx$.

Use the integrating factor in the result of Ex. 15 above to solve each of the equations in Exs. 17–20. The student should realize, from its position in the exercises instead of in the text, that the method of Ex. 15 is not being strongly recommended.

17. $xy\,dx - (x^2 + 2y^2)\,dy = 0.$ ANS. $x^2 = 4y^2 \ln(y/c).$
18. $v^2\,dx + x(x + v)\,dv = 0.$ ANS. $xv^2 = c(x + 2v).$
19. $v(u^2 + v^2)\,du - u(u^2 + 2v^2)\,dv = 0.$ ANS. $u^2 = 2v^2 \ln(cv^2/u).$
20. $(x^2 + y^2)\,dx - xy\,dy = 0.$ (Ex. 9, page 28.)

19. Substitution suggested by the equation

An equation of the form

$$M\,dx + N\,dy = 0$$

may not yield at once (or at all) to the methods of Chapter 2. Even then the usefulness of those methods is not exhausted. It may be possible by some change of variables to transform the equation into one of a type which we know how to solve.

A natural source of suggestions for useful transformations is the differential equation itself. If a particular function of one or both variables stands out in the equation, then it is worth while to examine the equation after that function has been introduced as a new variable. For instance, in the equation

$$(1) \qquad (x + 2y - 1)\,dx + 3(x + 2y)\,dy = 0$$

the combination $(x + 2y)$ occurs twice and so attracts attention. Hence we put

$$x + 2y = v,$$

and since no other function of x and y stands out, we retain either x or y for the other variable. The solution is completed in Example (a) below.

In the equation

$$(2) \qquad (1 + 3x \sin y)\,dx - x^2 \cos y\,dy = 0,$$

the presence of both $\sin y$ and its differential $\cos y\,dy$, and the fact that y appears in the equation in no other manner, leads us to put $\sin y = w$ and to obtain the differential equation in w and x. See Example (b) below.

EXAMPLE (a): Solve the equation

(1) $$(x + 2y - 1)\, dx + 3(x + 2y)\, dy = 0.$$

As suggested above, put

$$x + 2y = v.$$

Then

$$dx = dv - 2\, dy$$

and equation (1) becomes

$$(v - 1)(dv - 2\, dy) + 3v\, dy = 0,$$

or

$$(v - 1)\, dv + (v + 2)\, dy = 0.$$

Now the variables can be separated. From the equation in the form

$$\frac{v - 1}{v + 2}\, dv + dy = 0,$$

we get

$$\left[1 - \frac{3}{v + 2}\right] dv + dy = 0$$

and then

$$v - 3 \ln (v + 2) + y + c = 0.$$

But $v = x + 2y$, so our final result is

$$x + 3y + c = 3 \ln (x + 2y + 2).$$

EXAMPLE (b): Solve the equation

(2) $$(1 + 3x \sin y)\, dx - x^2 \cos y\, dy = 0.$$

Put $\sin y = w$. Then $\cos y\, dy = dw$ and (2) becomes

$$(1 + 3xw)\, dx - x^2\, dw = 0,$$

an equation linear in w. From the standard form

$$dw - \frac{3}{x} w\, dx = \frac{dx}{x^2}$$

an integrating factor is seen to be

$$\exp (-3 \ln x) = x^{-3}.$$

Application of the integrating factor yields the exact equation

$$x^{-3}\, dw - 3x^{-4}w\, dx = x^{-5}\, dx,$$

from which we get

$$x^{-3}w = -\tfrac{1}{4}x^{-4} + \tfrac{1}{4}c,$$

or

$$4xw = cx^4 - 1.$$

Hence (2) has the solution

$$4x \sin y = cx^4 - 1.$$

20. Bernoulli's equation

A well-known equation which fits into the category of Section 19 is Bernoulli's equation,

$$(1) \qquad y' + P(x)y = Q(x)y^n.$$

If $n = 1$ in (1), the variables are separable, so we concentrate on the case $n \neq 1$. Equation (1) may be put in the form

$$(2) \qquad y^{-n}\, dy + Py^{-n+1}\, dx = Q\, dx.$$

But the differential of y^{-n+1} is $(1 - n)y^{-n}\, dy$, so equation (2) may be simplified by putting

$$y^{-n+1} = z,$$

from which

$$(1 - n)y^{-n}\, dy = dz.$$

Thus the equation in z and x is

$$dz + (1 - n)Pz\, dx = (1 - n)Q\, dx,$$

a linear equation in standard form. Hence any Bernoulli equation can be solved with the aid of the above change of dependent variable (unless $n = 1$, when no substitution is needed).

EXAMPLE (a): Solve the equation

$$(3) \qquad y(6y^2 - x - 1)\, dx + 2x\, dy = 0.$$

First let us group the terms according to powers of y, writing

$$2x\, dy - y(x + 1)\, dx + 6y^3\, dx = 0.$$

Now it can be seen that the equation is a Bernoulli equation, since it involves only terms containing respectively dy, y, and y^n ($n = 3$ here). Therefore, we divide throughout by y^3, obtaining

$$2xy^{-3}\, dy - y^{-2}(x + 1)\, dx = -6\, dx.$$

This equation is linear in y^{-2}, so we put $y^{-2} = v$, obtain $dv = -2y^{-3}\,dy$, and need to solve the equation

$$x\,dv + v(x + 1)\,dx = 6\,dx,$$

or

(4) $$dv + v(1 + x^{-1})\,dx = 6x^{-1}\,dx.$$

Since

$$\exp{(x + \ln x)} = xe^x$$

is an integrating factor for (4), the equation

$$xe^x\,dv + ve^x(x + 1)\,dx = 6e^x\,dx$$

is exact. Its solution

$$xve^x = 6e^x + c,$$

together with $v = y^{-2}$, leads us to the final result

$$y^2(6 + ce^{-x}) = x.$$

EXAMPLE (b): Solve the equation

(5) $$6y^2\,dx - x(2x^3 + y)\,dy = 0.$$

This is a Bernoulli equation with x as the dependent variable, so it can be treated in the manner used in Example (a). That method of attack is left for the exercises.

Equation (5) can equally well be treated as follows. Note that if each member of (5) be multiplied by x^2, the equation becomes

(6) $$6y^2x^2\,dx - x^3(2x^3 + y)\,dy = 0.$$

In (6), the variable x appears only in the combinations x^3 and its differential $3x^2\,dx$. Hence a reasonable choice for a new variable is $w = x^3$. The equation in w and y is

$$2y^2\,dw - w(2w + y)\,dy = 0,$$

an equation with coefficients homogeneous of degree two in y and w. The further change of variable $w = zy$ leads to the equation

$$2y\,dz - z(2z - 1)\,dy = 0,$$
$$\frac{4\,dz}{2z - 1} - \frac{2\,dz}{z} - \frac{dy}{y} = 0.$$

Therefore, we have

$$2\ln{(2z - 1)} - 2\ln z - \ln y = \ln c,$$

or

$$(2z - 1)^2 = cyz^2.$$

But $z = w/y = x^3/y$, so the solution we seek is

$$(2x^3 - y)^2 = cyx^6.$$

Exercises

In Exs. 1–21 obtain the general solution.

1. $(3x - 2y + 1) \, dx + (3x - 2y + 3) \, dy = 0.$
                                        ANS. $5(x + y + c) = 2 \ln (15x - 10y + 11).$

2. $\sin y(x + \sin y) \, dx + 2x^2 \cos y \, dy = 0.$
                                        ANS. $x^3 \sin^2 y = c(3x + \sin y)^2.$

3. $\dfrac{dy}{dx} = (9x + 4y + 1)^2.$ ANS. $3 \tan (6x + c) = 2(9x + 4y + 1).$

4. $y' = y - xy^3 e^{-2x}.$ ANS. $e^{2x} = y^2(x^2 + c).$

5. $\dfrac{dy}{dx} = \sin (x + y).$ ANS. $x + c = \tan (x + y) - \sec (x + y).$

6. $xy \, dx + (x^2 - 3y) \, dy = 0.$ ANS. $x^2 y^2 = 2y^3 + c.$

7. $(3 \tan x - 2 \cos y) \sec^2 x \, dx + \tan x \sin y \, dy = 0.$
                                        ANS. $\cos y \tan^2 x = \tan^3 x + c.$

8. $(x + 2y - 1) \, dx + (2x + 4y - 3) \, dy = 0.$ Solve by two methods.
                                        ANS. $(x + 2y - 1)^2 = 2y + c.$

9. Solve the equation

$$6y^2 \, dx - x(2x^3 + y) \, dy = 0$$

of Example (b) above by treating it as a Bernoulli equation in the dependent variable x.

10. $2x^3 y' = y(y^2 + 3x^2).$ Solve by two methods.   ANS. $y^2(c - x) = x^3.$

11. $(3 \sin y - 5x) \, dx + 2x^2 \cot y \, dy = 0.$
                                        ANS. $x^3(\sin y - x)^2 = c \sin^2 y.$

12. $y' = 1 + 6x \exp (x - y).$ ANS. $\exp (y - x) = 3x^2 + c.$

13. $\dfrac{dv}{du} = (u - v)^2 - 2(u - v) - 2.$

                                        ANS. $(u - v - 3) \exp (4u) = c(u - v + 1).$

14. $2y \, dx + x(x^2 \ln y - 1) \, dy = 0.$ ANS. $y(1 + x^2 - x^2 \ln y) = cx^2.$

15. $\cos y \sin 2x \, dx + (\cos^2 y - \cos^2 x) \, dy = 0.$
                                        ANS. $\cos^2 x(1 + \sin y) = \cos y(y + c - \cos y).$

16. $(ke^{2v} - u) \, du = 2e^{2v}(e^{2v} + ku) \, dv.$
                                        ANS. $2k \operatorname{Arctan} (ue^{-2v}) = \ln [c(u^2 + e^{4v})].$

17. $y' \tan x \sin 2y = \sin^2 x + \cos^2 y$.

ANS. $(\sin^2 x + 3 \cos^2 y) \sin x = c$.

18. $(x + 2y - 1) \, dx - (x + 2y - 5) \, dy = 0$.

19. $y(x \tan x + \ln y) \, dx + \tan x \, dy = 0$.

ANS. $\sin x \ln y = x \cos x - \sin x + c$.

20. $xy' - y = x^k y^n$, where $n \neq 1$ and $k + n \neq 1$.

ANS. $(k + n - 1)y^{1-n} = (1 - n)x^k + cx^{1-n}$.

21. The equation of Ex. 20 for the values of k and n not included there.

ANS.   If $n = 1$ and $k \neq 0$, $x^k = k \ln (cy/x)$.

If $n = 1$ and $k = 0$, $y = cx^2$.

If $n \neq 1$ but $k + n = 1$, $y^{1-n} = (1 - n)x^{1-n} \ln (cx)$.

In Exs. 22–27, find the particular solution required.

22. $4(3x + y - 2) \, dx - (3x + y) \, dy = 0$; when $x = 1$, $y = 0$.

ANS. $7(4x - y - 4) = 8 \ln \dfrac{21x + 7y - 8}{13}$.

23. $y' = 2(3x + y)^2 - 1$; when $x = 0$, $y = 1$.

ANS. $4 \operatorname{Arctan} (3x + y) = 8x + \pi$.

24. $2xyy' = y^2 - 2x^3$. Find the solution that passes through the point $(1, 2)$.   ANS. $y^2 = x(5 - x^2)$.

25. $(y^4 - 2xy) \, dx + 3x^2 \, dy = 0$; when $x = 2$, $y = 1$.

ANS. $x^2 = y^3(x + 2)$.

26. $(2y^3 - x^3) \, dx + 3xy^2 \, dy = 0$; when $x = 1$, $y = 1$. Solve by two methods.   ANS. $5x^2y^3 = x^5 + 4$.

27. $(x^2 + 6y^2) \, dx - 4xy \, dy = 0$; when $x = 1$, $y = 1$. Solve by three methods.   ANS. $2y^2 = x^2(3x - 1)$.

21. Coefficients linear in the two variables

Consider the equation

(1) $(a_1 x + b_1 y + c_1) \, dx + (a_2 x + b_2 y + c_2) \, dy = 0$,

in which the a's, b's, and c's are constants. We know already how to solve the special case in which $c_1 = 0$ and $c_2 = 0$, for then the coefficients in (1) are each homogeneous and of degree one in x and y. It is reasonable to attempt to reduce equation (1) to that situation.

In connection with (1) consider the lines

(2) $a_1 x + b_1 y + c_1 = 0$,

$a_2 x + b_2 y + c_2 = 0$.

They may be parallel or they may intersect. There will not be two lines if a_1 and b_1 are zero, or if a_2 and b_2 are zero, but equation (1) will then be linear in one of its variables.

If the lines (2) intersect, let the point of intersection be (h, k). Then the translation

$$(3) \qquad \begin{aligned} x &= u + h, \\ y &= v + k \end{aligned}$$

will change the equations (2) into equations of lines through the origin of the uv coordinate system, namely,

$$(4) \qquad \begin{aligned} a_1u + b_1v &= 0, \\ a_2u + b_2v &= 0. \end{aligned}$$

Therefore, since $dx = du$ and $dy = dv$, the change of variables

$$\begin{aligned} x &= u + h, \\ y &= v + k, \end{aligned}$$

where (h, k) is the point of intersection of the lines (2), will transform the differential equation (1) into

$$(5) \qquad (a_1u + b_1v)\, du + (a_2u + b_2v)\, dv = 0,$$

an equation which we know how to solve.

If the lines (2) do not intersect, there exists a constant k such that

$$a_2x + b_2y = k(a_1x + b_1y),$$

so that equation (1) appears in the form

$$(6) \qquad (a_1x + b_1y + c_1)\, dx + [k(a_1x + b_1y) + c_2]\, dy = 0.$$

The recurrence of the expression $(a_1x + b_1y)$ in (6) suggests the introduction of a new variable $w = a_1x + b_1y$. Then the new equation, in w and x or in w and y, is one with variables separable, since its coefficients contain only w and constants.

EXAMPLE (a): Solve the equation

$$(7) \qquad (x + 2y - 4)\, dx - (2x + y - 5)\, dy = 0.$$

The lines

$$\begin{aligned} x + 2y - 4 &= 0, \\ 2x + y - 5 &= 0 \end{aligned}$$

intersect at the point $(2, 1)$. Hence put

$$x = u + 2,$$
$$y = v + 1.$$

Then equation (7) becomes

(8) $$(u + 2v) \, du - (2u + v) \, dv = 0,$$

which has coefficients homogeneous and of degree one in u and v. Therefore let $u = vz$, which transforms (8) into

$$(z + 2)(z \, dv + v \, dz) - (2z + 1) \, dv = 0,$$

or

$$(z^2 - 1) \, dv + v(z + 2) \, dz = 0.$$

Separation of the variables v and z leads us to the equation

$$\frac{dv}{v} + \frac{(z + 2) \, dz}{z^2 - 1} = 0.$$

With the aid of partial fractions, we can write the above equation in the form

$$\frac{2 \, dv}{v} + \frac{3 \, dz}{z - 1} - \frac{dz}{z + 1} = 0.$$

Hence we get

$$2 \ln v + 3 \ln (z - 1) - \ln (z + 1) = \ln c$$

from which it follows that

$$v^2(z - 1)^3 = c(z + 1),$$

or

$$(vz - v)^3 = c(vz + v).$$

Now $vz = u$, so our solution appears as

$$(u - v)^3 = c(u + v).$$

But $u = x - 2$ and $v = y - 1$. Therefore the desired result in terms of x and y is

$$(x - y - 1)^3 = c(x + y - 3).$$

For other methods of solution of equation (7), see Exs. 23 and 30 below.

EXAMPLE (b): Solve the equation

(9) $$(2x + 3y - 1) \, dx + (2x + 3y + 2) \, dy = 0,$$

with the condition that $y = 3$ when $x = 1$.

The lines

$$2x + 3y - 1 = 0$$

and

$$2x + 3y + 2 = 0$$

are parallel. Therefore we proceed, as we should have upon first glancing at the equation, to put

$$2x + 3y = v.$$

Then $2\,dx = dv - 3\,dy$, and equation (9) is transformed into

$$(v - 1)(dv - 3\,dy) + 2(v + 2)\,dy = 0,$$

or

(10) $$\qquad\qquad (v - 1)\,dv - (v - 7)\,dy = 0.$$

Equation (10) is easily solved, thus leading us to the relation

$$v - y + c + 6\ln (v - 7) = 0.$$

Therefore the general solution of (9) is

$$2x + 2y + c = -6\ln (2x + 3y - 7).$$

But $y = 3$ when $x = 1$, so $c = -8 - 6\ln 4$. Hence the particular solution required is

$$x + y - 4 = -3\ln [\tfrac{1}{4}(2x + 3y - 7)].$$

Exercises

In Exs. 1–18 find the general solution.

1. $(y - 2)\,dx - (x - y - 1)\,dy = 0.$

ANS. $\quad x - 3 = (2 - y)\ln [c(y - 2)].$

2. $(x - 4y - 9)\,dx + (4x + y - 2)\,dy = 0.$

ANS. $\quad \ln [(x - 1)^2 + (y + 2)^2] - 8\operatorname{Arctan}\dfrac{x - 1}{y + 2} = c.$

3. $(2x - y)\,dx + (4x + y - 6)\,dy = 0.$

ANS. $\quad (x + y - 3)^3 = c(2x + y - 4)^2.$

4. $(x - 4y - 3)\,dx - (x - 6y - 5)\,dy = 0.$

ANS. $\quad (x - 2y - 1)^2 = c(x - 3y - 2).$

5. $(2x + 3y - 5)\,dx + (3x - y - 2)\,dy = 0.$ Solve by two methods.

6. $2\,dx + (2x - y + 3)\,dy = 0.$ Use a change of variable.

ANS. $\quad y + c = ' - \ln (2x - y + 4).$

7. Solve the equation of Ex. 6 by using the fact that the equation is linear in x.

8. $(x - y + 2)\,dx + 3\,dy = 0.$ ANS. $x + c = 3 \ln (x - y + 5).$

9. Solve Ex. 8 by another method.

10. $(x + y - 1)\,dx + (2x + 2y + 1)\,dy = 0.$

ANS. $x + 2y + c = 3 \ln (x + y + 2).$

11. $(3x + 2y + 7)\,dx + (2x - y)\,dy = 0.$ Solve by two methods.

12. $(x - 2)\,dx + 4(x + y - 1)\,dy = 0.$

ANS. $2(y + 1) = -(x + 2y) \ln [c(x + 2y)].$

13. $(x - 3y + 2)\,dx + 3(x + 3y - 4)\,dy = 0.$

ANS. $\ln [(x - 1)^2 + 9(y - 1)^2] - 2 \operatorname{Arctan} \dfrac{x - 1}{3(y - 1)} = c.$

14. $(6x - 3y + 2)\,dx - (2x - y - 1)\,dy = 0.$

ANS. $3x - y + c = 5 \ln (2x - y + 4).$

15. $(9x - 4y + 4)\,dx - (2x - y + 1)\,dy = 0.$

ANS. $y - 1 = 3(y - 3x - 1) \ln [c(3x - y + 1)].$

16. $(x + 3y - 4)\,dx + (x + 4y - 5)\,dy = 0.$

ANS. $y - 1 = (x + 2y - 3) \ln [c(x + 2y - 3)].$

17. $(x + 2y - 1)\,dx - (2x + y - 5)\,dy = 0.$

ANS. $(x - y - 4)^3 = c(x + y - 2).$

18. $(x - 1)\,dx - (3x - 2y - 5)\,dy = 0.$

ANS. $(2y - x + 3)^2 = c(y - x + 2).$

In Exs. 19–22 obtain the particular solution indicated.

19. $(2x - 3y + 4)\,dx + 3(x - 1)\,dy = 0;$ when $x = 3, y = 2.$

ANS. $3(y - 2) = -2(x - 1) \ln \dfrac{x - 1}{2}.$

20. The equation of Ex. 19 but with the condition: when $x = -1, y = 2.$

ANS. $3(y - 2) = -2(x - 1) \ln \dfrac{1 - x}{2}.$

21. $(x + y - 4)\,dx - (3x - y - 4)\,dy = 0;$ when $x = 4, y = 1.$

ANS. $2(x + 2y - 6) = 3(x - y) \ln \dfrac{x - y}{3}.$

22. The equation of Ex. 21 but with the condition: when $x = 3, y = 7.$

ANS. $y - 5x + 8 = 2(y - x) \ln \dfrac{y - x}{4}.$

23. Prove that the change of variables

$$x = \alpha_1 u + \alpha_2 v, \qquad y = u + v$$

will transform the equation

(A) $(a_1 x + b_1 y + c_1)\,dx + (a_2 x + b_2 y + c_2)\,dy = 0$

into an equation in which the variables u and v are separable, if α_1 and

α_2 are roots of the equation

(B) $\qquad\qquad a_1\alpha^2 + (a_2 + b_1)\alpha + b_2 = 0,$

and if $\alpha_2 \neq \alpha_1$.

Note that this method of solution of (A) is not practical for us unless the roots of equation (B) are real and distinct.

Solve Exs. 24–29 by the method indicated in Ex. 23.

24. Ex. 4 above. As a check, the equation (B) for this case is

$$\alpha^2 - 5\alpha + 6 = 0,$$

so we may choose $\alpha_1 = 2$ and $\alpha_2 = 3$.

The equation in u and v turns out to be

$$(v - 1)\,du - 2(u + 2)\,dv = 0.$$

25. Ex. 3 above.   **26.** Ex. 10 above.

27. Ex. 17 above.   **28.** Ex. 18 above.

29. Example (a) in the text of this section.

30. Prove that the change of variables

$$x = \alpha_1 u + \beta v, \qquad y = u + v$$

will transform the equation

(A) $\qquad (a_1 x + b_1 y + c_1)\,dx + (a_2 x + b_2 y + c_2)\,dy = 0$

into an equation that is linear in the variable u, if α_1 is a root of the equation

(B) $\qquad\qquad a_1\alpha^2 + (a_2 + b_1)\alpha + b_2 = 0,$

and if β is any number such that $\beta \neq \alpha_1$.

Note that this method is not practical for us unless the roots of equation (B) are real. But they need not be distinct as they had to be in the theorem of Ex. 23. The method of this exercise is particularly useful when the roots of (B) are equal.

Solve Exs. 31–35 by the method indicated in Ex. 30.

31. Ex. 16 above. The only possible α_1 is (-2). Then β may be chosen to be anything else.

32. Ex. 12 above.   **33.** Ex. 15 above.   **34.** Ex. 18 above.

35. Ex. 4 above. As seen in Ex. 24, the roots of the "α-equation" are 2 and 3. If you choose $\alpha_1 = 2$, for example, then you may make β anything except 2. Of course, if you choose $\alpha_1 = 2$ and $\beta = 3$, then you are reverting to the method of Ex. 23.

22. Solutions involving nonelementary integrals

In solving differential equations we frequently are confronted with the need for integrating an expression that is not the differential of any elementary* function. Following is a short list of nonelementary integrals:

$$\int \exp\left(-x^2\right) dx \qquad \int \frac{e^{-x}}{x}\, dx \qquad \int x \tan x \, dx$$

$$\int \sin x^2 \, dx \qquad \int \frac{\sin x}{x}\, dx \qquad \int \frac{dx}{\ln x}$$

$$\int \cos x^2 \, dx \qquad \int \frac{\cos x}{x}\, dx \qquad \int \frac{dx}{\sqrt{1 - x^3}}.$$

Integrals involving the square root of a polynomial of degree greater than two are, in general, nonelementary. In special instances they may degenerate into elementary integrals.

The following example presents two ways of dealing with problems in which nonelementary integrals arise.

EXAMPLE: Solve the equation

$$y' - 2xy = 1$$

with the boundary condition that when $x = 0$, $y = 1$.

The equation being linear in y, we write

$$dy - 2xy \, dx = dx,$$

obtain the integrating factor $\exp\left(-x^2\right)$, and prepare to solve

(1) $$\exp\left(-x^2\right) dy - 2xy \exp\left(-x^2\right) dx = \exp\left(-x^2\right) dx.$$

The left member is, of course, the differential of $y \exp\left(-x^2\right)$. But the right member is not the differential of any elementary function; that is, $\int \exp\left(-x^2\right) dx$ is a nonelementary integral.

---

* By an elementary function we mean a function studied in the ordinary beginning calculus course. For example, polynomials, exponentials, logarithms, trigonometric, and inverse trigonometric functions are elementary. All functions obtained from them by a finite number of applications of the elementary operations of addition, subtraction, multiplication, division, extraction of roots, and raising to powers are elementary. Finally, we include such functions as sin (sin x), in which the argument in a function previously classed as elementary is replaced by an elementary function.

There are various ways to proceed. We could write a "solution" in the form

$$y \exp(-x^2) = \int \exp(-x^2)\, dx,$$

but that is evidently incomplete. We cannot satisfy the boundary condition with the above form of solution because putting $x = 0$ in the indefinite integral is meaningless.

Let us turn to power series for help. From the series

$$\exp(-x^2) = \sum_{n=0}^{\infty} \frac{(-1)^n x^{2n}}{n!},$$

obtained in calculus, it follows that

$$\int \exp(-x^2)\, dx = c + \sum_{n=0}^{\infty} \frac{(-1)^n x^{2n+1}}{n!(2n+1)}.$$

Thus the differential equation (1) has the solution

$$y \exp(-x^2) = c + \sum_{n=0}^{\infty} \frac{(-1)^n x^{2n+1}}{n!(2n+1)}.$$

Since $y = 1$ when $x = 0$, c may be found from

$$1 = c + 0.$$

Therefore, the particular solution desired is

$$(2) \qquad y \exp(-x^2) = 1 + \sum_{n=0}^{\infty} \frac{(-1)^n x^{2n+1}}{n!(2n+1)}.$$

An alternative procedure is the introduction of a definite integral. In calculus, the error function defined by

$$(3) \qquad \operatorname{erf} x = \frac{2}{\sqrt{\pi}} \int_0^x \exp(-\beta^2)\, d\beta$$

is sometimes* studied. Since, from (3),

$$\frac{d}{dx} \operatorname{erf} x = \frac{2}{\sqrt{\pi}} \exp(-x^2),$$

we may integrate the exact equation (1) as follows:

* See E. D. Rainville, *Unified Calculus and Analytic Geometry* (New York: The Macmillan Co., 1961), pp. 605–607.

(4) $$y \exp(-x^2) = \tfrac{1}{2} \sqrt{\pi} \operatorname{erf} x + c.$$

Since erf $0 = 0$, the condition that $y = 1$ when $x = 0$ yields $c = 1$. Hence, as an alternative to (2) we obtain

(5) $$y \exp(-x^2) = 1 + \tfrac{1}{2} \sqrt{\pi} \operatorname{erf} x.$$

Equation (5) means the same as

(6) $$y \exp(-x^2) = 1 + \int_0^x \exp(-\beta^2) \, d\beta.$$

Writing a solution in the form of (6) implies that the definite integral is to be evaluated by power series, approximate integration such as Simpson's rule, mechanical quadrature, or any other available tool. If it happens, as in this case, that the definite integral is itself a tabulated function, that is a great convenience, but it is not vital. The essential thing is to reduce the solution to a computable form.

Exercises

In each exercise, express the solution with the aid of power series or definite integrals.

1. $y' = y[1 - \exp(-x^2)]$.   ANS. $\ln(cy) = x - \tfrac{1}{2} \sqrt{\pi} \operatorname{erf} x$.

2. $(xy - \sin x) \, dx + x^2 \, dy = 0$.   ANS. $xy = c + \displaystyle\int_0^x \dfrac{\sin w}{w} \, dw,$

$$\text{or } y = cx^{-1} + \sum_{n=0}^{\infty} (-1)^n \frac{x^{2n}}{(2n+1)(2n+1)!}.$$

3. $y' = 1 - 4x^3 y$.   ANS. $y = \exp(-x^4) \left[c + \displaystyle\int_0^x \exp(\beta^4) \, d\beta \right].$

4. $(y \cos^2 x - x \sin x) \, dx + \sin x \cos x \, dy = 0$.

ANS. $y \sin x = c + \displaystyle\int_0^x \beta \tan \beta \, d\beta.$

5. $(1 + xy) \, dx - x \, dy = 0$; when $x = 1, y = 0$.

ANS. $y = e^x \displaystyle\int_1^x \dfrac{e^{-\beta}}{\beta} \, d\beta.$

6. $\left[x \exp\left(\dfrac{y^2}{x^2} \right) - y \right] dx + x \, dy = 0$; when $x = 1, y = 2$.

ANS. $\ln x = \displaystyle\int_{y/x}^2 \exp(-\beta^2) \, d\beta.$

7. $x(2y + x) \, dx - dy = 0$; when $x = 0, y = 1$.

ANS. $2y = 2 \exp(x^2) - x + \tfrac{1}{2} \sqrt{\pi} \exp(x^2) \operatorname{erf} x.$

Miscellaneous Exercises

In each exercise, find the general solution unless the statement of the exercise stipulates otherwise.

1. $(y^2 - 3y - x)\,dx + (2y - 3)\,dy = 0.$
ANS. $y^2 - 3y - x + 1 = ce^{-x}.$

2. $(y^3 + y + 1)\,dx + x(x - 3y^2 - 1)\,dy = 0.$
ANS. $y^3 - xy + y + 1 = cx.$

3. $(x + 3y - 5)\,dx - (x - y - 1)\,dy = 0.$
ANS. $2(y - 1) = (x + y - 3)\ln[c(x + y - 3)].$

4. $(x^5 - y^2)\,dx + 2xy\,dy = 0.$ ANS. $x^5 + 4y^2 = cx.$

5. $(2x + y - 4)\,dx + (x - 3y + 12)\,dy = 0.$
ANS. $2x^2 + 2xy - 3y^2 - 8x + 24y = c.$

6. Solve in two ways the equation $y' = ax + by + c$ with $b \neq 0.$
ANS. $b^2 y = c_1 e^{bx} - abx - a - cb.$

7. $y^3 \sec^2 x\,dx - (1 - 2y^2 \tan x)\,dy = 0.$ ANS. $y^2 \tan x = \ln(cy).$

8. $x^3 y\,dx + (3x^4 - y^3)\,dy = 0.$ ANS. $15x^4 y^{12} = 4y^{15} + c.$

9. $(a_1 x + ky + c_1)\,dx + (kx + b_2 y + c_2)\,dy = 0.$
ANS. $a_1 x^2 + 2kxy + b_2 y^2 + 2c_1 x + 2c_2 y = c.$

10. $(x - 4y + 7)\,dx + (x + 2y + 1)\,dy = 0.$
ANS. $(x - y + 4)^3 = c(x - 2y + 5)^2.$

11. $xy\,dx + (y^4 - 3x^2)\,dy = 0.$ ANS. $x^2 = y^4(1 + cy^2).$

12. $(x + 2y - 1)\,dx - (2x + y - 5)\,dy = 0.$

13. $(5x + 3e^y)\,dx + 2xe^y\,dy = 0.$ ANS. $x^3(x + e^y)^2 = c.$

14. $(3x + y - 2)\,dx + (3x + y + 4)\,dy = 0.$
ANS. $x + y + c = 3\ln(3x + y + 7).$

15. $(x - 3y + 4)\,dx + 2(x - y - 2)\,dy = 0.$
ANS. $(x + y - 8)^4 = c(x - 2y + 1).$

16. $(x - 2)\,dx + 4(x + y - 1)\,dy = 0.$
ANS. $2(y + 1) = -(x + 2y)\ln[c(x + 2y)].$

17. $y\,dx = x(1 + xy^4)\,dy.$ ANS. $y(5 + xy^4) = cx.$

18. $2x\,dv + v(2 + v^2 x)\,dx = 0;$ when $x = 1, v = \frac{1}{2}.$
ANS. $xv^2(5x - 1) = 1.$

19. $2(x - y)\,dx + (3x - y - 1)\,dy = 0.$
ANS. $(x + y - 1)^4 = c(4x - 2y - 1).$

20. $(2x - 5y + 12)\,dx + (7x - 4y + 15)\,dy = 0.$
ANS. $(x + 2y - 3)^3 = c(x - y + 3).$

21. $y\,dx + x(x^2 y - 1)\,dy = 0.$ ANS. $y^2(2x^2 y - 3) = cx^2.$

22. $\dfrac{dy}{dx} = \tan y \cot x - \sec y \cos x.$ ANS. $\sin y + \sin x \ln(c \sin x) = 0.$

23. $[1 + (x + y)^2] \, dx + [1 + x(x + y)] \, dy = 0.$

ANS. $y^2 = (x + y)^2 + 2 \ln (x + y) + c.$

24. $(x - 2y - 1) \, dx - (x - 3) \, dy = 0.$ Solve by two methods.

ANS. $(x - 3)^2(x - 3y) = c.$

25. $(2x - 3y + 1) \, dx - (3x + 2y - 4) \, dy = 0.$ Solve by two methods.

ANS. $x^2 + x - 3xy - y^2 + 4y = c.$

26. $(4x + 3y - 7) \, dx + (4x + 3y + 1) \, dy = 0.$

ANS. $x + y + c = 8 \ln (4x + 3y + 25).$

27. Find a change of variables that will reduce any equation of the form

$$xy' = yf(xy)$$

to an equation in which the variables are separable.

28. $(x + 4y + 3) \, dx - (2x - y - 3) \, dy = 0.$

ANS. $3(y + 1) = (x + y) \ln [c(x + y)].$

29. $(3x - 3y - 2) \, dx - (x - y + 1) \, dy = 0.$

ANS. $2(y - 3x + c) = 5 \ln (2x - 2y - 3).$

30. $(x - 6y + 2) \, dx + 2(x + 2y + 2) \, dy = 0.$

ANS. $4y = -(x - 2y + 2) \ln [c(x - 2y + 2)].$

31. $(x^4 - 4x^2y^2 - y^4) \, dx + 4x^3y \, dy = 0;$ when $x = 1, y = 2.$

ANS. $y^2(5 - 3x) = x^2(5 + 3x).$

32. $(x - y - 1) \, dx - 2(y - 2) \, dy = 0.$

ANS. $(x + y - 5)^2(x - 2y + 1) = c.$

33. $(x - 3y + 3) \, dx + (3x + y + 9) \, dy = 0.$

ANS. $\ln [(x + 3)^2 + y^2] = c + 6 \operatorname{Arctan} [(x + 3)/y].$

34. $(2x + 4y - 1) \, dx - (x + 2y - 3) \, dy = 0.$

ANS. $\ln (x + 2y - 1) = y - 2x + c.$

35. $4y \, dx + 3(2x - 1)(dy + y^4 \, dx) = 0;$ when $x = 1, y = 1.$

ANS. $y^3(2x - 1)(5x - 4) = 1.$

36. $y(x - 1) \, dx - (x^2 - 2x - 2y) \, dy = 0.$ ANS. $x^2 - 2x - 4y = cy^2.$

37. $(6xy - 3y^2 + 2y) \, dx + 2(x - y) \, dy = 0.$ ANS. $y(2x - y) = ce^{-3x}.$

38. $y' = x - y + 2.$ Solve by two methods.

ANS. $\ln (x - y + 1) = c - x.$

39. $(x + y - 2) \, dx - (x - 4y - 2) \, dy = 0.$

ANS. $\ln [(x - 2)^2 + 4y^2] + \operatorname{Arctan} \dfrac{x - 2}{2y} = c.$

40. $4 \, dx + (x - y + 2)^2 \, dy = 0.$ ANS. $y + 2 \operatorname{Arctan} \dfrac{x - y + 2}{2} = c.$

CHAPTER 5

Orthogonal Trajectories

23. Orthogonal trajectories; rectangular coordinates

Suppose that we have a family of curves

(1) $$f(x, y, c) = 0,$$

one curve corresponding to each c in some range of values of the parameter c. In certain applications, as illustrated in Section 25 below, it is found desirable to know what curves have the property that wherever any one of them intersects a curve of the family (1) it does so at right angles.

That is, we wish to determine a family of curves

(2) $$g(x, y, k) = 0$$

such that at any intersection of a curve of the family (2) with a curve of the family (1) the tangents to the two curves are perpendicular. The families (1) and (2) are then said to be *orthogonal trajectories** of each other.

---

* The word orthogonal comes from the Greek $o\rho\theta\eta$ (right) and $\gamma\omega\nu\iota\alpha$ (angle); the word trajectory comes from the Latin *trajectus* (cut across). Hence a curve that cuts across certain others at right angles is called an orthogonal trajectory of those others.

If two curves are to be orthogonal, then at each point of inter-section the slopes of the curves must be negative reciprocals of each other. That fact leads us to a method for finding orthogonal trajec-tories of a given family of curves. First we find the differential equation of the given family. Then replacing $\frac{dy}{dx}$ by $-\frac{dx}{dy}$ in that equation yields the differential equation of the orthogonal trajectories to the given curves. It remains only to solve the latter differential equation.

So far we have solved differential equations of only one form,

$$M \, dx + N \, dy = 0.$$

For such an equation

$$\frac{dy}{dx} = -\frac{M}{N},$$

so the differential equation of the orthogonal trajectories is

$$\frac{dy}{dx} = \frac{N}{M}$$

or

$$N \, dx - M \, dy = 0.$$

EXAMPLE: Find the orthogonal trajectories of all parabolas with vertices at the origin and foci on the x-axis.

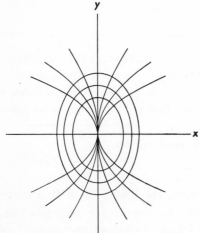

FIGURE 9

The algebraic equation of such parabolas is

(3) $y^2 = 4ax.$

Hence, from

$$\frac{y^2}{x} = 4a,$$

we find the differential equation of the family (3) to be

(4) $2x \, dy - y \, dx = 0.$

Therefore the orthogonal trajec-tories of the family (3) must satisfy the equation

(5) $2x \, dx + y \, dy = 0.$

From (5) it follows that

(6) $$2x^2 + y^2 = b^2,$$

where b is the arbitrary constant. Thus the orthogonal trajectories of (3) are certain ellipses (6) with centers at the origin. See Figure 9.

Exercises

In each exercise, find the orthogonal trajectories of the given family of curves. Draw a few representative curves of each family whenever a figure is requested.

1. $x - 4y = c$. Draw the figure.   ANS. $4x + y = k$.

2. $x^2 + y^2 = c^2$. Draw the figure.   ANS. $y = kx$.

3. $x^2 - y^2 = c_1$. Draw the figure.   ANS. $xy = c_2$.

4. Circles through the origin with centers on the x-axis. Draw the figure.
        ANS.   Circles through the origin with centers on the y-axis.

5. Straight lines with slope and y-intercept equal. Draw the figure.
        ANS. $(x + 1)^2 + y^2 = a^2$.

6. $y^2 = cx^3$. Draw the figure.   ANS. $2x^2 + 3y^2 = k^2$.

7. $e^x + e^{-y} = c_1$.   ANS. $e^y - e^{-x} = c_2$.

8. $y = c_1(\sec x + \tan x)$.   ANS. $y^2 = 2(c_2 - \sin x)$.

9. $x^3 = 3(y - c)$. Draw the figure.   ANS. $x(y - k) = 1$.

10. $x = c \exp(y^2)$.   ANS. $y = c_1 \exp(-x^2)$.

11. $y = ce^{-mx}$, with m held fixed. Draw the figure.
        ANS. $my^2 = 2(x - c_1)$.

12. Ellipses with centers at $(0, 0)$ and two vertices at $(1, 0)$ and $(-1, 0)$.
        ANS. $x^2 + y^2 = 2 \ln(cx)$.

13. $x^2 - y^2 = cx$.   ANS. $y(y^2 + 3x^2) = c_1$.

14. The cissoids, $y^2 = x^3/(a - x)$. See also Ex. 14 of Section 24 below.
        ANS. $(x^2 + y^2)^2 = b(2x^2 + y^2)$.

15. The trisectrices of Maclaurin, $(a + x)y^2 = x^2(3a - x)$. See also Ex. 15 of Section 24 below.   ANS. $(x^2 + y^2)^5 = cy^3(5x^2 + y^2)$.

16. $ax^2 + by^2 = c$, with a and b held fixed.   ANS. $y^a = kx^b$.

17. $ax^2 + y^2 = 2acx$, with a held fixed.
        ANS.   If $a \neq 2$, $(2 - a)x^2 + y^2 = c_1y^a$.
        If $a = 2$, $x^2 = -y^2 \ln(c_2y)$.

18. $y(x^2 + c) + 2 = 0$.   ANS. $y^3 = -3 \ln(kx)$.

19. $x^n + y^n = a^n$, with n held fixed and $n \neq 2$.   ANS. $x^{2-n} - y^{2-n} = c$.

20. $y^2 = x^2(1 - cx)$.   ANS. $x^2 + 3y^2 = c_1y$.

21. $y^2 = 4x^2(1 - cx)$.   ANS. $2x^2 = 3y^2(1 - c_1y^2)$.

22. $y^2 = ax^2(1 - cx)$, with a held fixed.

ANS. If $a \neq 2$, $(a - 2)x^2 = 3y^2(1 - c_1y^{a-2})$.

If $a = 2$, $x^2 = -3y^2 \ln (c_2y)$.

23. $y(x^2 + 1) = cx$.   ANS. $y^2 = x^2 + 2 \ln [k(x^2 - 1)]$.

24. $y = 3x - 1 + ce^{-3x}$.   ANS. $27x = 9y - 1 + ke^{-9y}$.

25. $y^2(2x^2 + y^2) = c^2$.   ANS. $y^2 = 2x^2 \ln (kx)$.

26. $y^4 = c^2(x^2 + 4y^2)$.   ANS. $x^8(2x^2 + 5y^2) = k^2$.

27. $x^4(4x^2 + 3y^2) = c^2$.   ANS. $y^8 = k^2(3x^2 + 2y^2)$.

28. For the family $x^2 + 3y^2 = cy$, find that member of the orthogonal trajectories which passes through $(1, 2)$.   ANS. $y^2 = x^2(3x + 1)$.

24. Orthogonal trajectories; polar coordinates

Consider a curve whose equation is expressed in polar coordinates. In calculus it is shown that the angle ψ (Figure 10), measured positive in the counterclockwise direction from the radius vector to the tangent line at a point, is given by

$$\tan \psi = r\frac{d\theta}{dr}.$$

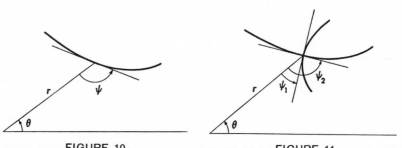

FIGURE 10   FIGURE 11

If two curves are orthogonal, as they are shown in Figure 11, then $\psi_2 = \psi_1 + \pi/2$ and thus $\tan \psi_2 = - \cot \psi_1 = -1/\tan \psi_1$. Therefore, if two curves are to cut one another at right angles, then at the point of intersection the value of the product

$$r\frac{d\theta}{dr}$$

for one curve must be the negative reciprocal of the value of that product for the other curve.

When polar coordinates are used, suppose a family of curves has the differential equation

(1) $P \, dr + Q \, d\theta = 0.$

Then
$$\frac{d\theta}{dr} = -\frac{P}{Q}$$

so

(2) $r \frac{d\theta}{dr} = -\frac{Pr}{Q}.$

Hence the family of the orthogonal trajectories of the solutions of (1) must be solutions of the equation

$$r \frac{d\theta}{dr} = +\frac{Q}{Pr},$$

or

(3) $Q \, dr - r^2 P \, d\theta = 0.$

EXAMPLE: Find the orthogonal trajectories of the family of cardioids $r = a(1 + \cos \theta)$. A few curves of each family are shown in Figure 12.

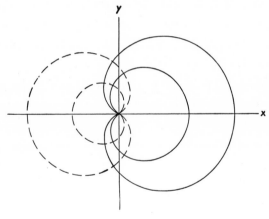

FIGURE 12

From

$$\frac{r}{1 + \cos \theta} = a$$

the differential equation

$$(1 + \cos \theta) \, dr + r \sin \theta \, d\theta = 0$$

follows at once. Then the differential equation of the orthogonal trajectories is

$$r \sin \theta \, dr - r^2(1 + \cos \theta) \, d\theta = 0$$

or

$$\sin \theta \, dr - r(1 + \cos \theta) \, d\theta = 0.$$

Separating the variables, we use the form

$$\frac{dr}{r} - \frac{(1 + \cos \theta) \, d\theta}{\sin \theta} = 0,$$

or

$$\frac{dr}{r} - \csc \theta \, d\theta - \frac{\cos \theta}{\sin \theta} \, d\theta = 0.$$

Hence

$$\ln r - \ln (\csc \theta - \cot \theta) - \ln \sin \theta = \ln b,$$

so the orthogonal trajectories of the original family of cardioids are seen to be

$$r = b \sin \theta (\csc \theta - \cot \theta),$$

or

$$r = b(1 - \cos \theta).$$

The student should show that this is the same family as the one we started with; that is, the family of cardioids is self-orthogonal.

Exercises

In each exercise, find the orthogonal trajectories of the given family of curves. Draw the figures in Exs. 1–8.

1. $r = a \cos^2 \theta$.   ANS. $r^2 = b \sin \theta$.

2. $r = a \cos 2\theta$.   ANS. $r^4 = b \sin 2\theta$.

3. $r = 2a \sin \theta$.   ANS. $r = 2b \cos \theta$.

4. $r = 2a(\sin \theta + \cos \theta)$.   ANS. $r = 2b(\sin \theta - \cos \theta)$.

5. $r = a(1 + \sin \theta)$.   ANS. $r = b(1 - \sin \theta)$.

6. $r^2 = a \sin 2\theta$.   ANS. $r^2 = b \cos 2\theta$.

7. $r = 4a \sec \theta \tan \theta$.   ANS. $r^2(1 + \sin^2 \theta) = b^2$.

8. $r^2 \cos 2\theta = c_1$.   ANS. $r^2 \sin 2\theta = c_2$.

9. $r = k/(1 + 2 \cos \theta)$.   ANS. $r^2 \sin^3 \theta = b(1 + \cos \theta)$.

10. $r = k/(2 + \cos \theta)$.   ANS. $r \sin^3 \theta = b(1 + \cos \theta)^2$.

11. $r = k/(1 + \epsilon \cos \theta)$ with ϵ fixed. What are k and ϵ geometrically?

                            ANS. $r^\epsilon \sin^{\epsilon+1} \theta = b(1 + \cos \theta)$.

12. $r = a(1 - 2 \sin \theta)$.   ANS. $r^2 = b \cos \theta (1 + \sin \theta)$.

13. The strophoids, $r = a(\sec \theta + \tan \theta)$.   ANS. $r = be^{-\sin \theta}$.

14. The cissoids, $r = a \sin \theta \tan \theta$.   ANS. $r^2 = b(1 + \cos^2 \theta)$.

15. The trisectrices of Maclaurin, $r = a(4 \cos \theta - \sec \theta)$.

ANS. $r^5 = b \sin^3 \theta(4 \cos^2 \theta + 1)$.

16. $r = a(1 + \sin^2 \theta)$.   ANS. $r^2 = b \cos \theta \cot \theta$.

25. Electric potential

The electric force between two particles charged with electricity is proportional to the magnitude of the two charges and inversely proportional to the square of the distance between them. An electric field is a portion of space the electrical properties of which we wish to consider. Those properties are determined by the distribution of electric* charges in the field. Very often interest is centered not upon the whole field but upon some portion which may itself not contain any electric charges.

The resultant electric force at a point P in an electric field is the force that would be exerted on a unit positive charge of electricity placed at P without disturbing the previous distribution of electric charges in the field. That resultant force has direction as well as magnitude at each point; it is a vector.

A curve whose tangent at each point on the curve is in the direction of the resultant electric force at that point is called a line of force or a flux line.

The difference in electric potential between two points in an electric field is the amount of work necessary for the electric force to perform to move a unit positive charge from one point to the other. Thus, electric potential is defined except for algebraic sign and an additive constant. If some fixed position in the electric field is used as a place of zero potential and if a convention of signs is introduced, then the electric potential is completely defined. Since our interest will be concentrated upon the family of curves on which the potential is constant, the concept of difference in potential† suffices.

Laplace showed that in any region in space not occupied by an electric charge, the potential function V satisfies the partial differential equation

---

* Electrostatic charges are the only ones being considered in this discussion.

† For the student who has had advanced calculus it may help to know that electric potential is a function of the coordinates such that at each point the directional derivative of the potential is the negative of the component of electric force in that direction.

(1)
$$\frac{\partial^2 V}{\partial x^2} + \frac{\partial^2 V}{\partial y^2} + \frac{\partial^2 V}{\partial z^2} = 0$$

where x, y, z are the rectangular space coordinates in the electric field. If the distribution of charges in the field is such that the potential function is independent of the z coordinate, then the problem is two-dimensional and the potential function must satisfy the equation

(2)
$$\frac{\partial^2 V}{\partial x^2} + \frac{\partial^2 V}{\partial y^2} = 0.$$

We shall restrict our study to two-dimensional situations, but we are not yet prepared to attack the relatively difficult problem of determining appropriate solutions of (2).

Curves along which the potential is constant,

(3) $V = c,$

are called equipotential curves. An important theorem in electricity states that:

The flux lines are the orthogonal trajectories of the equipotential curves.

Given the potential function, or the family of equipotential curves, for an electric field, we shall determine the corresponding flux lines. This is simply a problem of finding the orthogonal trajectories of a given family of curves. The material of this and the next two sections is in the nature of physical interpretations of problems in orthogonal trajectories rather than actual applications. For example, in practice, it is not necessary to resort to the methods we are studying here to determine the flux lines when the equipotential curves are known.

EXAMPLE: Suppose two wires perpendicular to the xy-plane and piercing it at the points $(1, 0)$ and $(-1, 0)$ carry static electric charges of equal intensity but opposite sign. Then it can be shown that the equipotential lines are the circles

(4) $x^2 + y^2 - 2cx + 1 = 0.$

Obtain the flux lines and draw the figure.

From (4) it follows by elimination of c that the family of equipotential curves has the differential equation

(5) $(x^2 - y^2 - 1)\, dx + 2xy\, dy = 0.$

Since the flux lines must be orthogonal to the solutions of (5), the differential equation of the family of flux lines is

$$(6) \qquad\qquad 2xy \, dx - (x^2 - y^2 - 1) \, dy = 0.$$

Equation (6) is linear in x^2. It can also be solved by finding the integrating factor y^{-2} by inspection. By one or the other of these methods, the general solution of equation (6) is found to be

$$(7) \qquad\qquad x^2 + y^2 - 1 = 2ky.$$

Equation (7) is the desired equation of the family of flux lines. From (7) we get

$$(8) \qquad\qquad x^2 + (y - k)^2 = 1 + k^2,$$

so the flux lines are seen to be circles with centers on the y-axis and passing through both the points $(1, 0)$ and $(-1, 0)$. See Figure 13.

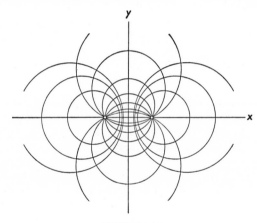

FIGURE 13

26. Steady-state temperatures

Consider the situation in which some physical object has been subjected to unvarying temperature conditions for a time sufficiently long that the temperatures within the object have stopped changing. In such an instance the temperatures in the object are said to have reached the steady-state condition.

If x, y, z are rectangular space coordinates and T denotes steady-state temperature, then it can be shown that in the interior of the object the function T must satisfy Laplace's equation

(1)
$$\frac{\partial^2 T}{\partial x^2} + \frac{\partial^2 T}{\partial y^2} + \frac{\partial^2 T}{\partial z^2} = 0.$$

If the temperature conditions are such that there is no variation of temperature (no flow of heat) in some one direction, taken as the direction of the z-axis, then the problem is two-dimensional and equation (1) may be replaced by

(2)
$$\frac{\partial^2 T}{\partial x^2} + \frac{\partial^2 T}{\partial y^2} = 0.$$

Again we make no attempt to solve the partial differential equation (2) with its associated boundary conditions.

The curves along which the temperature is constant,

$$T = c,$$

are called isotherms. The orthogonal trajectories of the isotherms are the curves whose tangents give the direction of heat flow at any point. They are called the lines of flow. Being given the isotherms we shall determine the corresponding lines of flow.

EXAMPLE: A very long concrete wedge whose right section is a circular sector of angle α and radius R has one of its plane faces kept at temperature T_1 and the other at temperature T_2, while the curved surface is insulated against heat transfer. Except near the ends of the wedge the steady-state temperature variation is essentially two-dimensional and T is known to be given by

$$T = T_1 + \frac{T_2 - T_1}{\alpha} \operatorname{Arctan} \frac{y}{x}.$$

where the coordinates x and y are defined in Figure 14. Draw the isotherms and the lines of flow.

In this problem when T is constant, y/x is also constant, so the isotherms have the form

$$y = cx.$$

Hence the differential equation of the isotherms is

$$y \, dx - x \, dy = 0$$

and that of the lines of flow is

$$x \, dx + y \, dy = 0.$$

Therefore the lines of flow are

$$x^2 + y^2 = k^2.$$

Both families of curves are shown in Figure 14.

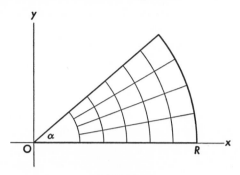

FIGURE 14

27. Two-dimensional steady-state fluid flow

If certain problems in the flow of a fluid are sufficiently idealized, they become two-dimensional steady-state problems in which orthogonal trajectories play an important part. In such problems the members of one family of curves

(1) $$\psi(x, y) = c$$

are called streamlines and the members of the family orthogonal to the family (1),

(2) $$\varphi(x, y) = k,$$

are called equipotential curves. Also, the function ψ is known as the stream function and φ is the velocity potential. Both the functions ψ and φ are solutions of the same partial differential equation that is satisfied by steady-state temperature and by electrostatic potential. The directional derivative of the velocity potential represents the component of the fluid velocity in that direction.

We are considering a two-dimensional fluid flow in which conditions are identical in all planes parallel to the xy-plane, and there is no flow in the direction perpendicular to the xy-plane. As an example we may visualize such a problem as that in which a large body of the fluid is flowing with uniform velocity parallel to the x-axis. An object is immersed in the fluid and allowed to remain for a long time. We are interested in the streamline pattern near the immersed object after the temporary disturbances due to the immersion of the object have disappeared so far as measurable effects are concerned.

Since streamlines are perhaps easy for us to visualize, and therefore make interesting answers, we shall assume that we are given either the equipotential curves or, what amounts to the same thing, the velocity potential function. Then we are to determine and draw the streamlines. Natural boundaries of the flow are streamlines.

EXAMPLE: Consider the effect of a long cylindrical object immersed in a fluid which is flowing with uniform velocity in a direction perpendicular to the axis of the cylinder. Away from the ends of the cylinder the pattern of streamlines will be identical in planes perpendicular to the axis of the cylinder. Let us choose as our unit of length the radius of the cylinder.

Given the equipotential curves

(3) $$(r^2 + 1) \cos \theta = cr$$

in polar coordinates with the origin $r = 0$ at the center of the circular cross section, determine and sketch the streamlines.

FIGURE 15

We are to find the orthogonal trajectories of the family (3). First we obtain the differential equation of the equipotentials (3) in the usual manner, by isolating c and differentiating both members of the equation to get

$$\left(1 - \frac{1}{r^2}\right) \cos \theta \, dr - \left(r + \frac{1}{r}\right) \sin \theta \, d\theta = 0,$$

or

(4) $$(r^2 - 1) \cos \theta \, dr - r(r^2 + 1) \sin \theta \, d\theta = 0.$$

Then the differential equation of the streamlines is

(5) $$(r^2 + 1) \sin \theta \, dr + r(r^2 - 1) \cos \theta \, d\theta = 0.$$

From (5) it follows that

$$\frac{r^2 + 1}{r(r^2 - 1)} \, dr + \frac{\cos \theta}{\sin \theta} \, d\theta = 0,$$

or

$$\frac{2r^2 - (r^2 - 1)}{r(r^2 - 1)} \, dr + \frac{\cos \theta}{\sin \theta} \, d\theta = 0,$$

so we need merely to solve the equation

(6) $$\frac{2r \, dr}{r^2 - 1} - \frac{dr}{r} + \frac{\cos \theta}{\sin \theta} \, d\theta = 0.$$

The solution of (6) is

$$\ln (r^2 - 1) - \ln r + \ln \sin \theta = \ln k,$$

which may be written as

(7) $$(r^2 - 1) \sin \theta = kr.$$

Equation (7) is the desired family of streamlines, of which several are shown in Figure 15.

CHAPTER 6

Hyperbolic Functions

28. Definition of the hyperbolic functions

Two particular combinations of exponential functions appear with such frequency in both pure and applied mathematics that it has been worth-while to use special symbols for those combinations. The hyperbolic sine of x, written $\sinh x$, is defined by

$$(1) \qquad \sinh x = \frac{e^x - e^{-x}}{2};$$

the hyperbolic cosine of x, written* $\cosh x$, is defined by

$$(2) \qquad \cosh x = \frac{e^x + e^{-x}}{2}.$$

The use of symbols and names so similar to those of trigonometry may seem unwise. Some justification will appear in the next section, where the basic formulas for these new functions are shown to bear a striking resemblance to those of ordinary trigonometry. It will be shown also that the hyperbolic sine and cosine are related to the equilateral hyperbola in much the same way that the ordinary (circular) sine and cosine are related to the circle.

---

* Another common notation is Sh x to replace our $\sinh x$, and with it Ch x to replace our $\cosh x$.

92

Four more hyperbolic functions are defined in a manner to be expected, namely,

$$\tanh x = \frac{\sinh x}{\cosh x}, \qquad \operatorname{sech} x = \frac{1}{\cosh x},$$

$$\operatorname{csch} x = \frac{1}{\sinh x}, \qquad \coth x = \frac{1}{\tanh x}.$$

In solving differential equations we use the functions $\sinh x$ and $\cosh x$ more often than the other four functions.

29. Basic formulas of hyperbolic trigonometry

From the definitions of $\sinh x$ and $\cosh x$ it follows that

$$\sinh^2 x = \tfrac{1}{4}(e^{2x} - 2 + e^{-2x})$$

and

$$\cosh^2 x = \tfrac{1}{4}(e^{2x} + 2 + e^{-2x}),$$

so

(1) $$\cosh^2 x - \sinh^2 x = 1,$$

an identity similar to the well-known identity $\cos^2 x + \sin^2 x = 1$ in circular trigonometry. See also Exs. 2 and 3 below.

Directly from the definition we find that

$$y = \sinh u$$

is equivalent to

$$y = \tfrac{1}{2}(e^u - e^{-u}).$$

Hence, if u is a function of x, then

$$\frac{dy}{dx} = \tfrac{1}{2}(e^u + e^{-u})\frac{du}{dx},$$

that is,

(2) $$\frac{d}{dx}\sinh u = \cosh u \frac{du}{dx}.$$

The same method yields the result

(3) $$\frac{d}{dx}\cosh u = \sinh u \frac{du}{dx}.$$

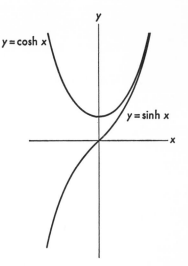

$y = \cosh x$

$y = \sinh x$

FIGURE 16

The derivations of the corresponding formulas for the derivatives of the other hyperbolic functions are left as exercises.

The curves $y = \cosh x$ and $y = \sinh x$ are exhibited in Figure 16, page 93. Note the important properties:

(a) $\cosh x \geqq 1$ for all real x;
(b) the only real value of x for which $\sinh x = 0$ is $x = 0$;
(c) $\cosh(-x) = \cosh x$; that is, $\cosh x$ is an even function of x;
(d) $\sinh(-x) = -\sinh x$; $\sinh x$ is an odd function of x.

The hyperbolic functions have no real period. Corresponding to the period 2π possessed by the circular functions, there is a period $2\pi i$ for the six hyperbolic functions.

The hyperbolic cosine curve is that in which a transmission line, cable, piece of string, watch chain, etc., hangs between two points at which it is suspended. This result is obtained in Chapter 19.

With regard to the word hyperbolic in the names of the functions being treated here, consider the equations

$$(4) \qquad\qquad x = a \cosh t, \quad y = a \sinh t.$$

In the equations (4), let t be a parameter and a a fixed constant. Then those equations are parametric equations of an equilateral hyperbola because from

$$\cosh^2 t - \sinh^2 t = 1$$

it follows that

$$\frac{x^2}{a^2} - \frac{y^2}{a^2} = 1$$

or

$$x^2 - y^2 = a^2.$$

This is analogous to the result that the two equations

$$x = a \cos t, \quad y = a \sin t,$$

are parametric equations of the circle $x^2 + y^2 = a^2$.

In elementary trigonometry texts there is usually given a line representation of the six trigonometric functions in a figure based upon a circle of radius unity. A similar line representation* of the six hyperbolic functions can be obtained.

The formulas used to define the hyperbolic sine and cosine also have analogs in the study of the trigonometric functions. The definition

---

* See C. A. Hutchinson, "Line Representation of the Hyperbolic Functions," *Amer. Math. Monthly*, **40** (1933), 413–414.

given on page 121 for the exponential function with pure imaginary exponent may be used to derive the pertinent formulas. The results are shown in Ex. 24, page 96.

Exercises

In Exs. 1–16, prove the stated property of the hyperbolic functions. Use the definitions, the results in the text, or the properties obtained in any previous exercises.

1. $\sinh(-x) = -\sinh x; \cosh(-x) = \cosh x; \tanh(-x) = -\tanh x.$

2. $\text{sech}^2 x = 1 - \tanh^2 x.$

3. $\text{csch}^2 x = \coth^2 x - 1.$

4. $e^x = \cosh x + \sinh x; e^{-x} = \cosh x - \sinh x.$

5. $\sinh^2 y = \frac{1}{2}(\cosh 2y - 1).$

6. $\cosh^2 y = \frac{1}{2}(\cosh 2y + 1).$

7. $\cosh 2y = \cosh^2 y + \sinh^2 y$
$$= 2\cosh^2 y - 1$$
$$= 2\sinh^2 y + 1.$$

8. $\sinh 2y = 2\sinh y \cosh y.$

9. $\sinh(x + y) = \sinh x \cosh y + \cosh x \sinh y;$
$\sinh(x - y) = \sinh x \cosh y - \cosh x \sinh y.$

10. $\cosh(x + y) = \cosh x \cosh y + \sinh x \sinh y;$
$\cosh(x - y) = \cosh x \cosh y - \sinh x \sinh y.$

11. $\tanh(x + y) = \dfrac{\tanh x + \tanh y}{1 + \tanh x \tanh y};$

$\tanh(x - y) = \dfrac{\tanh x - \tanh y}{1 - \tanh x \tanh y}.$

12. $\dfrac{d}{dx}\cosh u = \sinh u \dfrac{du}{dx}.$

13. $\dfrac{d}{dx}\tanh u = \text{sech}^2 u \dfrac{du}{dx}.$

14. $\dfrac{d}{dx}\text{csch}\, u = -\text{csch}\, u \coth u \dfrac{du}{dx}.$

15. $\dfrac{d}{dx}\text{sech}\, u = -\text{sech}\, u \tanh u \dfrac{du}{dx}.$

16. $\dfrac{d}{dx}\coth u = -\text{csch}^2 u \dfrac{du}{dx}.$

17. Obtain the differential equation formed by eliminating the constants c_1 and c_2 from $y = c_1 \sinh(kx) + c_2 \cosh(kx).$

$$\text{ANS.}\quad \frac{d^2y}{dx^2} - k^2 y = 0.$$

18. Solve the equation

$$(y \sinh x - y + 2x)\, dx + (\cosh x - x)\, dy = 0.$$

ANS. $y \cosh x - xy + x^2 = c.$

19. Solve the equation $xy\, dx + (x^2 + 1)(1 - y \tanh y)\, dy = 0.$

ANS. $y^2(x^2 + 1) = c \cosh^2 y.$

20. Solve the equation $y' \sinh x = 1 - 2y \cosh x.$

ANS. $y \sinh^2 x = c + \cosh x.$

21. Find the orthogonal trajectories of the curves $\sin x \cosh y = c.$

ANS. $\cos x \sinh y = k.$

22. Define the inverse hyperbolic sine of x, written $y = \sinh^{-1} x$, by the equation

$$x = \sinh y$$

or

(A) $$x = \tfrac{1}{2}(e^y - e^{-y}).$$

Put (A) in the form

$$e^{2y} - 2xe^y - 1 = 0$$

and thus conclude that

$$y = \sinh^{-1} x = \ln (x + \sqrt{x^2 + 1}),$$

pointing out why $y = \ln (x - \sqrt{x^2 + 1})$ is thrown out.

23. With the notation of Ex. 22, show that

$$d \sinh^{-1} x = \frac{dx}{\sqrt{1 + x^2}}.$$

24. For real x, define e^{ix} by

$$e^{ix} = \cos x + i \sin x.$$

Then prove that

$$\sin x = \frac{e^{ix} - e^{-ix}}{2i}, \quad \cos x = \frac{e^{ix} + e^{-ix}}{2}.$$

CHAPTER 7

Linear Differential Equations

30. The general linear equation

The general linear differential equation of order n may be written

$$(1) \quad b_0(x) \frac{d^n y}{dx^n} + b_1(x) \frac{d^{n-1}y}{dx^{n-1}} + \cdots + b_{n-1}(x) \frac{dy}{dx} + b_n(x)y = R(x).$$

The functions $R(x)$ and $b_i(x)$; $i = 0, 1, \cdots, n$, are to be independent of the variable y. If $R(x)$ is identically zero, equation (1) is said to be *homogeneous;* if $R(x)$ is not identically zero, equation (1) is called *non-homogeneous.* Here the word homogeneous is being used with reference to the quantities $y, y', y'', \cdots, y^{(n)}$; it has nothing to do with the way in which x enters the equation. In this chapter we shall obtain some fundamental and important properties of linear equations.

To simplify the wording of statements relating to solutions of linear differential equations, we shall adopt a common convention. When a relation $y = f(x)$ is a solution of a linear differential equation, we shall also call $f(x)$ itself a solution of the differential equation.

First we prove that if y_1 and y_2 are solutions of the homogeneous equation

(2) $b_0(x)y^{(n)} + b_1(x)y^{(n-1)} + \cdots + b_{n-1}(x)y' + b_n(x)y = 0,$

and if c_1 and c_2 are constants, then

$$y = c_1y_1 + c_2y_2$$

is a solution of equation (2).

The statement that y_1 and y_2 are solutions of (2) means that

(3) $b_0y_1^{(n)} + b_1y_1^{(n-1)} + \cdots + b_{n-1}y_1' + b_ny_1 = 0$

and

(4) $b_0y_2^{(n)} + b_1y_2^{(n-1)} + \cdots + b_{n-1}y_2' + b_ny_2 = 0.$

Now let us multiply each member of (3) by c_1, each member of (4) by c_2, and add the results. We get

(5) $b_0[c_1y_1^{(n)} + c_2y_2^{(n)}] + b_1[c_1y_1^{(n-1)} + c_2y_2^{(n-1)}] + \cdots$

$$+ b_{n-1}[c_1y_1' + c_2y_2'] + b_n[c_1y_1 + c_2y_2] = 0.$$

Since $c_1y_1' + c_2y_2' = (c_1y_1 + c_2y_2)'$, etc., equation (5) is neither more nor less than the statement that $c_1y_1 + c_2y_2$ is a solution of equation (2). The proof is completed. The special case $c_2 = 0$ is worth noting; that is, for a homogeneous linear equation any constant times a solution is also a solution.

In a similar manner, or by iteration of the above result, it can be seen that if y_i; $i = 1, 2, \cdots, k$, are solutions of equation (2), and if c_i; $i = 1, 2, \cdots, k$, are constants, then

$$y = c_1y_1 + c_2y_2 + \cdots + c_ky_k$$

is a solution of equation (2).

31. Linear independence

Given the functions $f_1(x), \cdots, f_n(x)$, if constants $c_1, c_2, \cdots, c_n$, not all zero, exist such that

(1) $c_1f_1(x) + c_2f_2(x) + \cdots + c_nf_n(x) = 0$

identically in some interval $a \leq x \leq b$, then the functions $f_1(x), f_2(x), \cdots, f_n(x)$ are said to be *linearly dependent*. If no such relation exists, the functions are said to be *linearly independent*. That is, the functions $f_1, f_2, \cdots, f_n$ are linearly independent when equation (1) implies that $c_1 = c_2 = \cdots = c_n = 0.$

If the functions of a set are linearly dependent, then at least one of them is a linear combination of the others; if they are linearly independent, then none of them is a linear combination of the others.

32. The Wronskian

With the definitions of Section 31 in mind, we shall now obtain a sufficient condition that n functions be linearly independent over an interval $a \leqq x \leqq b$.

Let us assume that each of the functions $f_1(x)$, $f_2(x)$, $\cdots$, $f_n(x)$ is differentiable at least $(n - 1)$ times in the interval $a \leqq x \leqq b$. Then from the equation

$$(1) \qquad c_1 f_1 + c_2 f_2 + \cdots + c_n f_n = 0,$$

it follows by successive differentiation that

$$c_1 f_1' + c_2 f_2' + \cdots + c_n f_n' = 0,$$
$$c_1 f_1'' + c_2 f_2'' + \cdots + c_n f_n'' = 0,$$
$$\cdots$$
$$c_1 f_1^{(n-1)} + c_2 f_2^{(n-1)} + \cdots + c_n f_n^{(n-1)} = 0.$$

Considered as a system of equations in $c_1, c_2, \cdots , c_n$, the n linear equations directly above will have no solution except the one with each of the c's equal to zero, if the determinant of the system does not vanish. That is, if

$$(2) \qquad \begin{vmatrix} f_1 & f_2 & \cdots & f_n \\ f_1' & f_2' & \cdots & f_n' \\ f_1'' & f_2'' & \cdots & f_n'' \\ \cdots & & & \\ f_1^{(n-1)} & f_2^{(n-1)} & \cdots & f_n^{(n-1)} \end{vmatrix} \neq 0,$$

then the functions $f_1, f_2, \cdots , f_n$ are linearly independent. The determinant in (2) is called the *Wronskian* of the n functions involved. We have shown that the nonvanishing of the Wronskian is a sufficient condition that the functions be linearly independent.

The nonvanishing of the Wronskian on an interval is not a necessary condition for linear independence. The Wronskian may vanish even when the functions are linearly independent, as exhibited in Ex. 9 below.

If the n functions involved are solutions of a homogeneous linear differential equation, the situation is simplified as is shown by the theorem below. Proof is omitted.

THEOREM 4: *If, on the interval* $a \leqq x \leqq b$, $b_0(x) \neq 0$, b_0, b_1, $\cdots$, b_n *are continuous, and* y_1, y_2, $\cdots$, y_n *are solutions of the equation*

(3) $$b_0 y^{(n)} + b_1 y^{(n-1)} + \cdots + b_{n-1} y' + b_n y = 0,$$

then a necessary and sufficient condition that y_1, $\cdots$, y_n *be linearly independent is the nonvanishing of the Wronskian of* y_1, $\cdots$, y_n *on the interval* $a \leqq x \leqq b$.

The functions $\cos \omega t$, $\sin \omega t$, $\sin (\omega t + \alpha)$, in which t is the variable and ω and α are constants, are linearly dependent because there exist constants c_1, c_2, c_3 such that

$$c_1 \cos \omega t + c_2 \sin \omega t + c_3 \sin (\omega t + \alpha) = 0$$

for all t. Indeed, one set of such constants is $c_1 = \sin \alpha$, $c_2 = \cos \alpha$, $c_3 = -1$.

One of the best-known sets of n linearly independent functions of x is the set 1, x, x^2, $\cdots$, x^{n-1}. The linear independence of the powers of x follows at once from the fact that if c_1, c_2, $\cdots$, c_n are not all zero, the equation

$$c_1 + c_2 x + \cdots + c_n x^{n-1} = 0$$

can have, at most, $(n - 1)$ distinct roots and so cannot vanish identically in any interval. See also Ex. 1 below.

Exercises

   1. Obtain the Wronskian of the functions

$$1, x, x^2, \cdots , x^{n-1} \text{ for } n > 1.$$
          ANS. $W = 0! 1! 2! \cdots (n - 1)!$.
   2. Show that the functions e^x, e^{2x}, e^{3x} are linearly independent.
          ANS. $W = 2e^{6x} \neq 0$.
   3. Show that the functions e^x, $\cos x$, $\sin x$ are linearly independent.
          ANS. $W = 2e^x \neq 0$.
   4. By determining constants c_1, c_2, c_3, c_4, not all zero and which are such that $c_1 f_1 + c_2 f_2 + c_3 f_3 + c_4 f_4 = 0$ identically, show that the functions

$$f_1 = x, f_2 = e^x, f_3 = xe^x, f_4 = (2 - 3x)e^x$$

are linearly dependent.
          ANS.   One such set of c's is: $c_1 = 0$, $c_2 = -2$, $c_3 = 3$, $c_4 = 1$.
   5. Show that $\cos (\omega t - \beta)$, $\cos \omega t$, $\sin \omega t$ are linearly dependent functions of t.

6. Show that 1, $\sin x$, $\cos x$ are linearly independent.

7. Show that 1, $\sin^2 x$, $\cos^2 x$ are linearly dependent.

8. Show that two nonvanishing differentiable functions of x are linearly dependent if, and only if, their Wronskian vanishes identically. This statement is not true for more than two functions.

9. Let $f_1(x) = 1 + x^3$ for $x \leqq 0$, $f_1(x) = 1$ for $x \geqq 0$;

$\quad f_2(x) = 1$ for $x \leqq 0$, $f_2(x) = 1 + x^3$ for $x \geqq 0$;

$\quad f_3(x) = 3 + x^3$ for all x.

Show that: (a) f, f', f'' are continuous for all x for each of f_1, f_2, f_3;

                (b) the Wronskian of f_1, f_2, f_3 is zero for all x;

                (c) f_1, f_2, f_3 are linearly independent over the interval $-1 \leqq x \leqq 1$.

In part (c) you must show that if $c_1 f_1(x) + c_2 f_2(x) + c_3 f_3(x) = 0$ for all x in $-1 \leqq x \leqq 1$, $c_1 = c_2 = c_3 = 0$. Use $x = -1, 0, 1$ successively to obtain three equations to solve for c_1, c_2, and c_3.

33. General solution of a homogeneous equation

Let y_1, y_2, $\cdots$, y_n be linearly independent solutions of the homogeneous equation

(1) $\qquad b_0(x)y^{(n)} + b_1(x)y^{(n-1)} + \cdots + b_{n-1}(x)y' + b_n(x)y = 0.$

Then the general solution of equation (1) is

(2) $\qquad\qquad y = c_1 y_1 + c_2 y_2 + \cdots + c_n y_n,$

where c_1, c_2, $\cdots$, c_n are arbitrary constants.

In a sense each particular solution of the linear differential equation (1) is a special case (some choice of the c's) of the general solution (2). The basic ideas needed for a proof of this important result are exhibited here for the equation of order two. No additional complications enter for equations of higher order.

Consider the equation

(3) $\qquad\qquad b_0(x)y'' + b_1(x)y' + b_2(x)y = 0.$

Let the relation

(4) $\qquad\qquad y = f(x)$

be any particular solution of equation (3), the solution being valid in some interval $a < x < b$ in which $b_0(x)$ does not vanish and in which the functions b_1/b_0 and b_2/b_0 possess derivatives of all orders.

We assume (it can be proved) that at $x = \alpha$, within the stipulated interval, $f(x)$ is sufficiently well behaved to insure that the Taylor series for $f(x)$,

$$(5) \qquad f(x) = \sum_{k=0}^{\infty} \frac{f^{(k)}(\alpha)(x - \alpha)^k}{k!},$$

converges to $f(x)$ in some interval about $x = \alpha$.

Then the solution $f(x)$ is completely determined by knowledge of $f(\alpha)$ and $f'(\alpha)$, the values of f and f' taken at some point α within the interval. For, since we can divide by $b_0(x)$, equation (3) yields y'' in terms of y, y', and the known coefficients in the equation. Then $y''(\alpha) = f''(\alpha)$ can be determined. Successive differentiation of the equation for y'' will yield the higher derivatives. Thus $f^{(k)}(\alpha)$ can be computed for $k = 2, 3, \cdots$, from the values of $f(\alpha)$ and $f'(\alpha)$. Then, using Taylor's series (5), we see that $f(x)$ is determined by the differential equation and the two values $f(\alpha)$ and $f'(\alpha)$.

Now let $y_1(x)$, $y_2(x)$ be any two linearly independent solutions of equation (3). Further, let α be chosen as some point in the interval, $a < \alpha < b$, where the Wronskian of y_1 and y_2 does not vanish,

$$(6) \qquad \begin{vmatrix} y_1(\alpha) & y_2(\alpha) \\ y_1'(\alpha) & y_2'(\alpha) \end{vmatrix} \neq 0.$$

Consider the solution

$$(7) \qquad y = c_1 y_1(x) + c_2 y_2(x),$$

from which

$$y' = c_1 y_1'(x) + c_2 y_2'(x).$$

We wish to choose c_1 and c_2 so that the y of equation (7) will become the solution $f(x)$. But we can surely force that y to be such that $y(\alpha) = f(\alpha)$ and $y'(\alpha) = f'(\alpha)$. That is, the equations

$$(8) \qquad c_1 y_1(\alpha) + c_2 y_2(\alpha) = f(\alpha),$$

$$c_1 y_1'(\alpha) + c_2 y_2'(\alpha) = f'(\alpha),$$

can be solved for c_1 and c_2 because of the inequality (6), the nonvanishing of the Wronskian. Then $f(x)$ and $y(x)$ have the same Taylor series (5), so they are identical.

It is necessary to keep in mind that the above discussion used the fact that $b_0(x) \neq 0$ in the interval $a < x < b$. It is easy to see that the linear equation

$$xy' - 2y = 0$$

has the general solution $y = cx^2$ and also such particular solutions as

$$y_1 = x^2, \qquad 0 \leqq x,$$
$$= -4x^2, \qquad x < 0.$$

The solution y_1 is not a special case of the general solution. But in any interval throughout which $b_0(x) = x \neq 0$, this particular solution is a special case of the general solution. It was, of course, made up by piecing together at $x = 0$ two parts, each drawn from the general solution.

34. General solution of a nonhomogeneous equation

Let y_p be any particular solution (not necessarily involving any arbitrary constants) of the equation

(1) $$b_0y^{(n)} + b_1y^{(n-1)} + \cdots + b_{n-1}y' + b_ny = R(x)$$

and let y_c be a solution of the corresponding homogeneous equation

(2) $$b_0y^{(n)} + b_1y^{(n-1)} + \cdots + b_{n-1}y' + b_ny = 0.$$

Then

(3) $$y = y_c + y_p$$

is a solution of equation (1). For, using the y of equation (3) we see that

$$b_0y^{(n)} + \cdots + b_ny = (b_0y_c^{(n)} + \cdots + b_ny_c)$$
$$+ (b_0y_p^{(n)} + \cdots + b_ny_p)$$
$$= 0 + R(x) = R(x).$$

If $y_1, y_2, \cdots, y_n$ are linearly independent solutions of equation (2), then

(4) $$y_c = c_1y_1 + c_2y_2 + \cdots + c_ny_n,$$

in which the c's are arbitrary constants, is the general solution of equation (2). The right member of equation (4) is called the *complementary function* for equation (1).

The general solution of the nonhomogeneous equation (1) is the sum of the complementary function and any particular solution.

For instance, consider the equation

(5) $$y'' - y = 4.$$

It is easily seen that $y = -4$ is a solution of equation (5). Therefore the y_p in equation (3) may be taken to be (-4). As we shall see later, the homogeneous equation

$$y'' - y = 0$$

has as its general solution

$$y_c = c_1 e^x + c_2 e^{-x}.$$

Thus the complementary function for equation (5) is $(c_1 e^x + c_2 e^{-x})$ and a particular solution of (5) is $y_p = -4$. Hence the general solution of equation (5) is

$$y = c_1 e^x + c_2 e^{-x} - 4,$$

in which c_1 and c_2 are arbitrary constants.

35. Differential operators

Let D denote differentiation with respect to x, D^2 differentiation twice with respect to x, and so on; that is, for integral k,

$$D^k y = \frac{d^k y}{dx^k}.$$

The expression

(1) $A = a_0 D^n + a_1 D^{n-1} + \cdots + a_{n-1} D + a_n$

is called a differential operator of order n. It may be defined as that operator which, when applied to any function* y, yields the result

(2) $Ay = a_0 \dfrac{d^n y}{dx^n} + a_1 \dfrac{d^{n-1} y}{dx^{n-1}} + \cdots + a_{n-1} \dfrac{dy}{dx} + a_n y.$

The coefficients $a_0, a_1, \cdots, a_n$ in the operator A may be functions of x, but in this book the only operators used will be those with constant coefficients.

Two operators A and B are said to be equal if, and only if, the same result is produced when each acts upon the function y. That is, $A = B$ if, and only if, $Ay = By$ for all functions y possessing the derivatives necessary for the operations involved.

The product AB of two operators A and B is defined as that operator which produces the same result as is obtained by using the operator B followed by the operator A. Thus $ABy = A(By)$. The product of two

---

* The function y is assumed to possess as many derivatives as may be encountered in whatever operations take place.

differential operators always exists and is a differential operator. For operators with *constant coefficients*, but not usually for those with variable coefficients, it is true that $AB = BA$.

EXAMPLE (a): Let $A = D + 2$ and $B = 3D - 1$.
    Then

$$By = (3D - 1)y = 3\frac{dy}{dx} - y$$

and

$$A(By) = (D + 2)\left(3\frac{dy}{dx} - y\right)$$

$$= 3\frac{d^2y}{dx^2} - \frac{dy}{dx} + 6\frac{dy}{dx} - 2y$$

$$= 3\frac{d^2y}{dx^2} + 5\frac{dy}{dx} - 2y$$

$$= (3D^2 + 5D - 2)y.$$

Hence $AB = (D + 2)(3D - 1) = 3D^2 + 5D - 2$.

Now consider BA. Acting upon y, the operator BA yields

$$B(Ay) = (3D - 1)\left(\frac{dy}{dx} + 2y\right)$$

$$= 3\frac{d^2y}{dx^2} + 6\frac{dy}{dx} - \frac{dy}{dx} - 2y$$

$$= 3\frac{d^2y}{dx^2} + 5\frac{dy}{dx} - 2y.$$

Hence

$$BA = 3D^2 + 5D - 2 = AB.$$

EXAMPLE (b): Let $G = xD + 2$, and $H = D - 1$. Then

$$G(Hy) = (xD + 2)\left(\frac{dy}{dx} - y\right)$$

$$= x\frac{d^2y}{dx^2} - x\frac{dy}{dx} + 2\frac{dy}{dx} - 2y$$

$$= x\frac{d^2y}{dx^2} + (2 - x)\frac{dy}{dx} - 2y,$$

so

$$GH = xD^2 + (2 - x)D - 2.$$

    On the other hand

$$H(Gy) = (D - 1)\left(x\frac{dy}{dx} + 2y\right)$$

$$= \frac{d}{dx}\left(x\frac{dy}{dx} + 2y\right) - \left(x\frac{dy}{dx} + 2y\right)$$

$$= x\frac{d^2y}{dx^2} + \frac{dy}{dx} + 2\frac{dy}{dx} - x\frac{dy}{dx} - 2y$$

$$= x\frac{d^2y}{dx^2} + (3 - x)\frac{dy}{dx} - 2y;$$

that is,

$$HG = xD^2 + (3 - x)D - 2.$$

It is worthy of notice that here we have two operators G and H (one of them with variable coefficients), the product of which is dependent on the order of the factors. On this topic see also Exs. 17–22 in the next section.

The sum of two differential operators is obtained by expressing each in the form

$$a_0D^n + a_1D^{n-1} + \cdots + a_{n-1}D + a_n$$

and adding corresponding coefficients. For instance, if

$$A = 3D^2 - D + x - 2$$

and

$$B = x^2D^2 + 4D + 7,$$

then

$$A + B = (3 + x^2)D^2 + 3D + x + 5.$$

Differential operators are linear operators; that is, if A is any differential operator, if c_1 and c_2 are constants, and if f_1 and f_2 are any functions of x each possessing the required number of derivatives, then

$$A(c_1f_1 + c_2f_2) = c_1Af_1 + c_2Af_2.$$

36. The fundamental laws of operation

Let A, B, and C be any differential operators as defined in Section 35. With the above definitions of addition and multiplication, it follows that differential operators satisfy the following:

(1) The commutative law of addition:

$$A + B = B + A.$$

(2) The associative law of addition:

$$(A + B) + C = A + (B + C).$$

(3) The associative law of multiplication:

$$(AB)C = A(BC).$$

(4) The distributive law of multiplication with respect to addition:

$$A(B + C) = AB + AC.$$

If A, B, and C are operators with *constant coefficients*, then they also satisfy

(5) The commutative law of multiplication:

$$AB = BA.$$

Therefore, differential operators with constant coefficients satisfy all the laws of ordinary algebra* with regard to addition and multiplication. In Chapter 10 we shall touch upon the question of division of operators.

If m and n are any two positive integers, then

$$D^m D^n = D^{m+n},$$

a useful result which follows immediately from the definitions.

Since for purposes of addition and multiplication the operators with constant coefficients behave just as algebraic polynomials behave, it is legitimate to use the tools of elementary algebra. In particular, synthetic division may be used to factor operators with constant coefficients.

Exercises

Perform the indicated multiplications in Exs. 1–4.

1. $(4D + 1)(D - 2)$.   ANS. $4D^2 - 7D - 2$.
2. $(2D - 3)(2D + 3)$.   ANS. $4D^2 - 9$.
3. $(D + 2)(D^2 - 2D + 5)$.   ANS. $D^3 + D + 10$.
4. $(D - 2)(D + 1)^2$.   ANS. $D^3 - 3D - 2$.

In Exs. 5–16, factor each of the operators.

5. $2D^2 + 3D - 2$.   ANS. $(D + 2)(2D - 1)$.
6. $2D^2 - 5D - 12$.
7. $D^3 - 2D^2 - 5D + 6$.   ANS. $(D - 1)(D + 2)(D - 3)$.

* See any college algebra—for example, J. R. Britton and L. C. Snively, *Algebra for College Students* (New York: Rinehart and Co., 1954), pp. 31–32.

8. $4D^3 - 4D^2 - 11D + 6$.

9. $D^4 - 4D^2$.   ANS. $D^2(D - 2)(D + 2)$.

10. $D^3 - 3D^2 + 4$.

11. $D^3 - 21D + 20$.   ANS. $(D - 1)(D - 4)(D + 5)$.

12. $2D^3 - D^2 - 13D - 6$.

13. $2D^4 + 11D^3 + 18D^2 + 4D - 8$.   ANS. $(D + 2)^3(2D - 1)$.

14. $8D^4 + 36D^3 - 66D^2 + 35D - 6$.

15. $D^4 + D^3 - 2D^2 + 4D - 24$.   ANS. $(D - 2)(D + 3)(D^2 + 4)$.

16. $D^3 - 11D - 20$.   ANS. $(D - 4)(D^2 + 4D + 5)$.

Perform the indicated multiplications in Exs. 17–22.

17. $(D - x)(D + x)$.   ANS. $D^2 + 1 - x^2$.

18. $(D + x)(D - x)$.   ANS. $D^2 - 1 - x^2$.

19. $D(xD - 1)$.   ANS. xD^2.

20. $(xD - 1)D$.   ANS. $xD^2 - D$.

21. $(xD + 2)(xD - 1)$.   ANS. $x^2D^2 + 2xD - 2$.

22. $(xD - 1)(xD + 2)$.   ANS. $x^2D^2 + 2xD - 2$.

37. Some properties of differential operators

Since for constant m and positive integral k,

(1) $$D^k e^{mx} = m^k e^{mx},$$

it is easy to find the effect an operator has upon e^{mx}. Let $f(D)$ be a polynomial in D,

(2) $$f(D) = a_0 D^n + a_1 D^{n-1} + \cdots + a_{n-1} D + a_n.$$

Then

$$f(D)e^{mx} = a_0 m^n e^{mx} + a_1 m^{n-1} e^{mx} + \cdots + a_{n-1} m e^{mx} + a_n e^{mx},$$

so

(3) $$f(D)e^{mx} = e^{mx} f(m).$$

If m is a root of the equation $f(m) = 0$, then in view of equation (3),

$$f(D)e^{mx} = 0.$$

EXAMPLE: Let $f(D) = 2D^2 + 5D - 12$. Then the equation $f(m) = 0$ is

$$2m^2 + 5m - 12 = 0,$$

or

$$(m + 4)(2m - 3) = 0,$$

of which the roots are $m_1 = -4$ and $m_2 = \frac{3}{2}$.

With the aid of equation (3) above it can be seen that

$$(2D^2 + 5D - 12)e^{-4x} = 0$$

and that

$$(2D^2 + 5D - 12) \exp (\tfrac{3}{2}x) = 0.$$

In other words, $y_1 = e^{-4x}$ and $y_2 = \exp (\tfrac{3}{2}x)$ are solutions of

$$(2D^2 + 5D - 12)y = 0.$$

Next consider the effect of the operator $(D - m)$ on the product of e^{mx} and a power of x. Since

$$(D - m)(x^k e^{mx}) = kx^{k-1}e^{mx} + mx^k e^{mx} - mx^k e^{mx},$$

we get

$$(D - m)(x^k e^{mx}) = kx^{k-1}e^{mx}.$$

Then

$$(D - m)^2(x^k e^{mx}) = k(D - m)(x^{k-1}e^{mx})$$
$$= k(k - 1)x^{k-2}e^{mx}.$$

Repeating the operation, we are led to

$$(D - m)^k(x^k e^{mx}) = k(k - 1) \cdots 2 \cdot 1 x^0 e^{mx}$$
$$= k!e^{mx}.$$

But $(D - m)e^{mx} = 0$. Therefore, for all $n > k$,

(4) $$(D - m)^n(x^k e^{mx}) = 0.$$

It will be convenient to think of the exponent of x in (4) as varying rather than the exponent of the operator $(D - m)$. Hence we rewrite (4) as

(5) $(D - m)^n(x^k e^{mx}) = 0$ for $k = 0, 1, 2, \cdots, (n - 1).$

Equation (5) forms the basis for all the solutions obtained in the next chapter.

38. The *n*th derivative of a product

It is often convenient to be able to write down for a product of functions a derivative of fairly high order without first obtaining the derivatives of lower order. For instance, we may wish to form the fourth derivative of the function

$$y = x^2 e^{3x},$$

but may have no need for the first, second, or third derivatives.

A formula for the nth derivative of the product of two functions was discovered by Leibnitz. Since that formula is not always included in a first course in calculus, it will be stated here.

Consider the product

(1) $y = uv$

in which u and v are functions of the independent variable x. Let us use the notation

$$u^{(n)} = \frac{d^n u}{dx^n},$$

including $u^{(0)} = u$ and $u^{(1)} = u'$, together with similar notations for derivatives of v and y. From equation (1) we obtain, by the usual rule for the derivative of a product, the result

$$y' = u'v + uv',$$

or

(2) $y^{(1)} = u^{(1)}v^{(0)} + u^{(0)}v^{(1)}.$

Let us now differentiate both members of equation (2) with respect to x, keeping in mind that each term on the right side of equation (2) is itself a product of functions. We thus get

$$y^{(2)} = u^{(2)}v^{(0)} + u^{(1)}v^{(1)} + u^{(1)}v^{(1)} + u^{(0)}v^{(2)},$$

or

(3) $y^{(2)} = u^{(2)}v^{(0)} + 2u^{(1)}v^{(1)} + u^{(0)}v^{(2)}.$

Another such step brings us to the result

(4) $y^{(3)} = u^{(3)}v^{(0)} + 3u^{(2)}v^{(1)} + 3u^{(1)}v^{(2)} + u^{(0)}v^{(3)},$

for the third derivative of a product. The resemblance of equations (3) and (4) to the binomial expansions

$$(a + b)^2 = a^2 + 2ab + b^2$$

and

$$(a + b)^3 = a^3 + 3a^2b + 3ab^2 + b^3$$

is striking. It encourages one to go on to the general formula.

Leibnitz' rule for the nth derivative of a product is: If $y = uv$, then

$$(5) \qquad y^{(n)} = \sum_{k=0}^{n} C_{n,k} u^{(n-k)} v^{(k)},$$

in which $C_{n,k}$ is the binomial coefficient,

$$C_{n,k} = \frac{n!}{k!(n-k)!} = \frac{n(n-1) \cdots (n-k+1)}{k!}.$$

Equation (5) may be validated quite easily by induction with the aid of the relation

$$(6) \qquad C_{n,k} + C_{n,k+1} = C_{n+1,k+1},$$

the latter being a fundamental property of the Pascal triangle.*

Leibnitz' rule is particularly simple to use when the factors involved are simple exponentials, powers of x, or sines or cosines.

EXAMPLE (a): Find the fourth derivative of the product

$$y = x^2 e^{3x}.$$

First we have in mind the coefficients in the binomial expansion $(a + b)^4$—or we build the Pascal triangle far enough to obtain them. The required coefficients are 1, 4, 6, 4, 1. As we write down the product we form the successive derivatives from each end, first writing

$$y^{(4)} = 1 \cdot (x^2)(\quad) + 4(\quad)(\quad) + 6(\quad)(\quad) + 4(\quad)(\quad) + 1(\quad)(e^{3x})$$

and then filling in the empty spaces with the proper derivatives in succession. Thus we arrive, in one step after a bit of practice, at the result

$$y^{(4)} = (x^2)(81e^{3x}) + 4(2x)(27e^{3x}) + 6(2)(9e^{3x}) + 4(0)(3e^{3x}) + (0)(e^{3x}),$$

or

$$y^{(4)} = 9e^{3x}(9x^2 + 24x + 12).$$

EXAMPLE (b): Find the third derivative of $w = e^{2x} \cos 3x$.
We form

$$w^{(3)} = (e^{2x})(\quad) + 3(\quad)(\quad) \\ + 3(\quad)(\quad) + (\quad)(\cos 3x),$$

and fill in the spaces to obtain

---

* See J. R. Britton and L. C. Snively, *Algebra for College Students* (New York: Rinehart and Co., 1954), pp. 277–279.

$$w^{(3)} = (e^{2x})(27 \sin 3x) + 3(2e^{2x})(-9 \cos 3x)$$
$$+ 3(4e^{2x})(-3 \sin 3x) + (8e^{2x})(\cos 3x),$$

or

$$w^{(3)} = e^{2x}[(27 - 36) \sin 3x + (8 - 54) \cos 3x].$$

Finally, we have

$$w^{(3)} = -e^{2x}(9 \sin 3x + 46 \cos 3x).$$

The method is particularly pleasant, of course, when some of the terms drop out as happened in Example (a).

EXAMPLE (c): Find the fourth derivative of $v = x \sin 3x$.

At once, since $3^4 = 81$ and $3^3 \cdot 4 = 108$, we write

$$v^{(4)} = 81x \sin 3x - 108 \cos 3x.$$

Exercises

Answers to these exercises can be verified, and the efficacy of the method investigated, by also obtaining the desired derivative by successive differentiation.

1. Find $y^{(2)}$ from $y = x^3 e^x$.   ANS. $y^{(2)} = e^x(x^3 + 6x^2 + 6x)$.

2. Find $y^{(2)}$ from $y = x^4 e^{-x}$.

3. Find $y^{(2)}$ from $y = x \sin 2x$.   ANS. $y^{(2)} = -4x \sin 2x + 4 \cos 2x$.

4. Find $y^{(2)}$ from $y = x \cos 2x$.

5. Find $y^{(3)}$ from $y = x^2 \cos 4x$.

ANS. $y^{(3)} = 64x^2 \sin 4x - 96x \cos 4x - 24 \sin 4x$.

6. Find $y^{(3)}$ from $y = x^2 \sin 3x$.

7. Find $v^{(3)}$ from $v = xe^{3x}$.   ANS. $v^{(3)} = 27e^{3x}(x + 1)$.

8. Find $v^{(3)}$ from $v = x \sin 4x$.   ANS. $v^{(3)} = -64x \cos 4x - 48 \sin 4x$.

9. Find $y^{(4)}$ from $y = xe^{-2x}$.   ANS. $y^{(4)} = 16e^{-2x}(x - 2)$.

10. Find $y^{(4)}$ from $y = xe^{-3x}$.

11. Find $y^{(4)}$ from $y = x \sin 2x$.   ANS. $y^{(4)} = 16x \sin 2x - 32 \cos 2x$.

12. Find $y^{(4)}$ from $y = x \cos 2x$.

13. Find $y^{(4)}$ from $y = x^2 e^x$.

14. Find $y^{(4)}$ from $y = x^2 e^{-x}$.

15. Find $y^{(4)}$ from $y = x^2 \sin x$.

ANS. $y^{(4)} = x^2 \sin x - 8x \cos x - 12 \sin x$.

16. Find $y^{(4)}$ from $y = x^2 \cos x$.

CHAPTER 8

Linear Equations with Constant Coefficients

39. Introduction

Two methods for solving linear differential equations with constant coefficients are presented in this book. A classical technique is treated in this and the next chapter. Chapters 11 and 12 contain a development of the Laplace transform and its use in solving differential equations. Each method has its advantages and its disadvantages. Each is theoretically sufficient; both are necessary for maximum efficiency.

40. The auxiliary equation; distinct roots

Any linear homogeneous differential equation with constant coefficients,

(1) $$a_0 \frac{d^n y}{dx^n} + a_1 \frac{d^{n-1}y}{dx^{n-1}} + \cdots + a_{n-1} \frac{dy}{dx} + a_n y = 0,$$

may be written in the form

(2) $$f(D)y = 0,$$

where $f(D)$ is a linear differential operator. As we saw in the preceding chapter, if m is any root of the algebraic equation $f(m) = 0$, then

$$f(D)e^{mx} = 0,$$

which means simply that $y = e^{mx}$ is a solution of equation (2). The equation

$$(3) \qquad\qquad f(m) = 0$$

is called the *auxiliary equation* associated with (1) or (2).

The auxiliary equation for (1) is of degree n. Let its roots be m_1, $m_2, \cdots , m_n$. If these roots are all real and distinct, then the n solutions

$$y_1 = \exp(m_1 x), \; y_2 = \exp(m_2 x), \; \cdots , \; y_n = \exp(m_n x)$$

are linearly independent and the general solution of (1) can be written at once. It is

$$y = c_1 \exp(m_1 x) + c_2 \exp(m_2 x) + \cdots + c_n \exp(m_n x),$$

in which $c_1, c_2, \cdots , c_n$ are arbitrary constants.

Repeated roots of the auxiliary equation will be treated in the next section. Imaginary roots will be avoided until Section 43, where the corresponding solutions will be put into a desirable form.

EXAMPLE (a): Solve the equation

$$\frac{d^3 y}{dx^3} - 4\frac{d^2 y}{dx^2} + \frac{dy}{dx} + 6y = 0.$$

First write the auxiliary equation

$$m^3 - 4m^2 + m + 6 = 0,$$

whose roots $m = -1, 2, 3$ may be obtained by synthetic division. Then the general solution is seen to be

$$y = c_1 e^{-x} + c_2 e^{2x} + c_3 e^{3x}.$$

EXAMPLE (b): Solve the equation

$$(3D^3 + 5D^2 - 2D)y = 0.$$

The auxiliary equation is

$$3m^3 + 5m^2 - 2m = 0$$

and its roots are $m = 0, -2, \frac{1}{3}$. Using the fact that $e^{0x} = 1$, the desired solution may be written

$$y = c_1 + c_2 e^{-2x} + c_3 \exp(\tfrac{1}{3}x).$$

EXAMPLE (c): Solve the equation

$$\frac{d^2x}{dt^2} - 4x = 0$$

with the conditions that when $t = 0$, $x = 0$ and $\frac{dx}{dt} = 3$.

The auxiliary equation is

$$m^2 - 4 = 0,$$

with roots $m = 2, -2$. Hence the general solution of the differential equation is

$$x = c_1e^{2t} + c_2e^{-2t}.$$

It remains to enforce the conditions at $t = 0$. Now

$$\frac{dx}{dt} = 2c_1e^{2t} - 2c_2e^{-2t}.$$

Thus the condition that $x = 0$ when $t = 0$ requires that

$$0 = c_1 + c_2,$$

and the condition that $\frac{dx}{dt} = 3$ when $t = 0$ requires that

$$3 = 2c_1 - 2c_2.$$

From the simultaneous equations for c_1 and c_2 we conclude that $c_1 = \frac{3}{4}$ and $c_2 = -\frac{3}{4}$. Therefore

$$x = \tfrac{3}{4}(e^{2t} - e^{-2t}),$$

which can also be put in the form

$$x = \tfrac{3}{2}\sinh(2t).$$

Exercises

In Exs. 1–22, find the general solution. When the operator D is used, it is implied that the independent variable is x.

1. $(D^2 + 2D - 3)y = 0$.   ANS. $y = c_1e^x + c_2e^{-3x}$.
2. $(D^2 + 2D)y = 0$.
3. $(D^2 + D - 6)y = 0$.   ANS. $y = c_1e^{2x} + c_2e^{-3x}$.
4. $(D^2 - 5D + 6)y = 0$.
5. $(D^3 + 3D^2 - 4D)y = 0$.   ANS. $y = c_1 + c_2e^x + c_3e^{-4x}$.
6. $(D^3 - 3D^2 - 10D)y = 0$.

7. $(D^3 + 6D^2 + 11D + 6)y = 0.$ ANS. $y = c_1e^{-x} + c_2e^{-2x} + c_3e^{-3x}.$

8. $(D^3 + 3D^2 - 4D - 12)y = 0.$

9. $(4D^3 - 7D + 3)y = 0.$

                 ANS. $y = c_1e^x + c_2 \exp\left(\tfrac{1}{2}x\right) + c_3 \exp\left(-\tfrac{3}{2}x\right).$

10. $(4D^3 - 13D - 6)y = 0.$

11. $\dfrac{d^3x}{dt^3} + \dfrac{d^2x}{dt^2} - 2\dfrac{dx}{dt} = 0.$ ANS. $x = c_1 + c_2e^t + c_3e^{-2t}.$

12. $\dfrac{d^3x}{dt^3} - 19\dfrac{dx}{dt} + 30x = 0.$

13. $(9D^3 - 7D + 2)y = 0.$

                 ANS. $y = c_1e^{-x} + c_2 \exp\left(\tfrac{1}{3}x\right) + c_3 \exp\left(\tfrac{2}{3}x\right).$

14. $(4D^3 - 21D - 10)y = 0.$

15. $(D^3 - 14D + 8)y = 0.$

     ANS. $y = c_1e^{-4x} + c_2 \exp\left[(2 + \sqrt{2})x\right] + c_3 \exp\left[(2 - \sqrt{2})x\right].$

16. $(D^3 - D^2 - 4D - 2)y = 0.$

17. $(4D^4 - 8D^3 - 7D^2 + 11D + 6)y = 0.$

         ANS. $y = c_1e^{-x} + c_2e^{2x} + c_3 \exp\left(-\tfrac{1}{2}x\right) + c_4 \exp\left(\tfrac{3}{2}x\right).$

18. $(4D^4 - 16D^3 + 7D^2 + 4D - 2)y = 0.$

19. $(4D^4 + 4D^3 - 13D^2 - 7D + 6)y = 0.$

20. $(4D^5 - 8D^4 - 17D^3 + 12D^2 + 9D)y = 0.$

21. $(D^2 - 4aD + 3a^2)y = 0,$ a real $\neq 0.$

22. $[D^2 - (a + b)D + ab]y = 0,$ a and b real and unequal.

In Exs. 23–24, find the particular solution indicated.

23. $(D^2 - 2D - 3)y = 0;$ when $x = 0,$ $y = 0,$ and $y' = -4.$

                 ANS. $y = e^{-x} - e^{3x}.$

24. $(D^2 - D - 6)y = 0;$ when $x = 0,$ $y = 0,$ and when $x = 1,$ $y = e^3.$

           ANS. $y = (e^{3x} - e^{-2x})/(1 - e^{-5}).$

In Exs. 25–29, find for $x = 1$ the y value for the particular solution required.

25. $(D^2 - 2D - 3)y = 0;$ when $x = 0,$ $y = 4$ and $y' = 0.$

        ANS.   When $x = 1,$ $y = e^3 + 3e^{-1} = 21.2.$

26. $(D^3 - 4D)y = 0;$ when $x = 0,$ $y = 0,$ $y' = 0,$ and $y'' = 2.$

        ANS.   When $x = 1,$ $y = \sinh^2 1.$

27. $(D^2 - D - 6)y = 0;$ when $x = 0,$ $y = 3$ and $y' = -1.$

        ANS.   When $x = 1,$ $y = 20.4.$

28. $(D^2 + 3D - 10)y = 0;$ when $x = 0,$ $y = 0,$ and when $x = 2,$ $y = 1.$

        ANS.   When $x = 1,$ $y = 0.135.$

29. $(D^3 - 2D^2 - 5D + 6)y = 0;$ when $x = 0,$ $y = 1,$ $y' = -7,$ and $y'' = -1.$ ANS.   When $x = 1,$ $y = -19.8.$

41. The auxiliary equation; repeated roots

Suppose that in the equation

(1) $$f(D)y = 0$$

the operator $f(D)$ has repeated factors; that is, the auxiliary equation $f(m) = 0$ has repeated roots. Then the method of the previous section does not yield the general solution. Let the auxiliary equation have three equal roots $m_1 = b$, $m_2 = b$, $m_3 = b$. The corresponding part of the solution yielded by the method of Section 40 is

(2)
$$y = c_1 e^{bx} + c_2 e^{bx} + c_3 e^{bx},$$
$$y = (c_1 + c_2 + c_3)e^{bx}.$$

Now (2) can be replaced by

(3) $$y = c_4 e^{bx}$$

with $c_4 = c_1 + c_2 + c_3$. Thus, corresponding to the three roots under consideration, this method has yielded only the solution (3). The difficulty is present, of course, because the three solutions corresponding to the roots $m_1 = m_2 = m_3 = b$ are not linearly independent.

What is needed is a method for obtaining n linearly independent solutions corresponding to n equal roots of the auxiliary equation. Suppose the auxiliary equation $f(m) = 0$ has the n equal roots

$$m_1 = m_2 = \cdots = m_n = b.$$

Then the operator $f(D)$ must have a factor $(D - b)^n$. We wish to find n linearly independent y's for which

(4) $$(D - b)^n y = 0.$$

Turning to the result (5) near the end of Section 37 and writing $m = b$, we find that

(5) $$(D - b)^n(x^k e^{bx}) = 0 \text{ for } k = 0, 1, 2, \cdots, (n - 1).$$

The functions $y_k = x^k e^{bx}$; $k = 0, 1, 2, \cdots, (n - 1)$ are linearly independent because aside from the common factor e^{bx} they contain only the respective powers $x^0, x^1, x^2, \cdots, x^{n-1}$.

The general solution of equation (4) is

(6) $$y = c_1 e^{bx} + c_2 x e^{bx} + \cdots + c_n x^{n-1} e^{bx}.$$

Furthermore, if $f(D)$ contains the factor $(D - b)^n$, then the equation

(1) $f(D)y = 0$

can be written

(7) $g(D)(D - b)^n y = 0$

where $g(D)$ contains all the factors of $f(D)$ except $(D - b)^n$. Then any solution of

(4) $(D - b)^n y = 0$

is also a solution of (7) and therefore of (1).

Now we are in a position to write the solution of equation (1) whenever the auxiliary equation has only real roots. Each root of the auxiliary equation is either distinct from all the other roots or it is one of a set of equal roots. Corresponding to a root m_i distinct from all others, there is the solution

(8) $y_i = c_i \exp{(m_i x)}$,

and corresponding to n equal roots $m_1, m_2, \cdots, m_n$, each equal to b, there is the solution

(9) $y = c_1 e^{bx} + c_2 x e^{bx} + \cdots + c_n x^{n-1} e^{bx}$.

The sum of such solutions (8) and (9) yields the proper number of solutions, a number equal to the order of the differential equation, because there is one solution corresponding to each root of the auxiliary equation. The solutions thus obtained can be proved to be linearly independent.

EXAMPLE (a): Solve the equation

(10) $(D^4 - 7D^3 + 18D^2 - 20D + 8)y = 0$.

With the aid of synthetic division, it is easily seen that the auxiliary equation

$$m^4 - 7m^3 + 18m^2 - 20m + 8 = 0$$

has the roots $m = 1, 2, 2, 2$. Then the general solution of equation (10) is

$$y = c_1 e^x + c_2 e^{2x} + c_3 x e^{2x} + c_4 x^2 e^{2x},$$

or

$$y = c_1 e^x + (c_2 + c_3 x + c_4 x^2)e^{2x}.$$

EXAMPLE (b): Solve the equation

$$\frac{d^4 y}{dx^4} + 2\frac{d^3 y}{dx^3} + \frac{d^2 y}{dx^2} = 0.$$

The auxiliary equation is

$$m^4 + 2m^3 + m^2 = 0,$$

with roots $m = 0, 0, -1, -1$. Hence the desired solution is

$$y = c_1 + c_2x + c_3e^{-x} + c_4xe^{-x}.$$

Exercises

In Exs. 1–20 find the general solution.

1. $(D^2 - 6D + 9)y = 0.$ ANS. $y = (c_1 + c_2x)e^{3x}.$

2. $(D^2 + 4D + 4)y = 0.$

3. $(4D^3 + 4D^2 + D)y = 0.$ ANS. $y = c_1 + (c_2 + c_3x) \exp\left(-\tfrac{1}{2}x\right).$

4. $(D^3 - 8D^2 + 16D)y = 0.$

5. $(D^4 + 6D^3 + 9D^2)y = 0.$

  ANS. $y = c_1 + c_2x + (c_3 + c_4x)e^{-3x}.$

6. $(D^3 - 3D^2 + 4)y = 0.$

7. $(4D^3 - 3D + 1)y = 0.$ ANS. $y = c_1e^{-x} + (c_2 + c_3x) \exp\left(\tfrac{1}{2}x\right).$

8. $(D^4 - 3D^3 - 6D^2 + 28D - 24)y = 0.$

9. $(4D^4 - 4D^3 - 23D^2 + 12D + 36)y = 0.$

  ANS. $y = (c_1 + c_2x)e^{2x} + (c_3 + c_4x) \exp\left(-\tfrac{3}{2}x\right).$

10. $(D^3 + 6D^2 + 12D + 8)y = 0.$

11. $(D^5 - D^3)y = 0.$ ANS. $y = c_1 + c_2x + c_3x^2 + c_4e^x + c_5e^{-x};$

  or $y = c_1 + c_2x + c_3x^2 + c_6 \cosh x + c_7 \sinh x.$

12. $(D^5 - 16D^3)y = 0.$

13. $(4D^4 + 4D^3 - 3D^2 - 2D + 1)y = 0.$

14. $(54D^4 - 27D^3 - 9D^2 + 7D - 1)y = 0.$

15. $(D^4 - 2D^3 - 3D^2 + 4D + 4)y = 0.$

  ANS. $y = (c_1 + c_2x)e^{-x} + (c_3 + c_4x)e^{2x}.$

16. $(4D^4 + 4D^3 - 3D^2 - 2D + 1)y = 0.$

17. $(4D^5 + 4D^4 - 9D^3 - 11D^2 + D + 3)y = 0.$

18. $(D^5 - 15D^3 + 10D^2 + 60D - 72)y = 0.$

19. $(D^4 + 2D^3 - 6D^2 - 16D - 8)y = 0.$

  ANS. $y = (c_1 + c_2x)e^{-2x} + c_3 \exp[(1 + \sqrt{3})x] + c_4 \exp[(1 - \sqrt{3})x].$

20. $(D^4 - 2D^3 - 5D^2 + 2)y = 0.$

In Exs. 21–26, find the particular solution indicated.

21. $(D^2 + 4D + 4)y = 0$; when $x = 0$, $y = 1$ and $y' = -1$.

  ANS. $y = (1 + x)e^{-2x}.$

22. The equation of Ex. 21 with the condition that the graph of the solution pass through the points $(0, 2)$ and $(2, 0)$.

  ANS. $y = (2 - x)e^{-2x}.$

23. $(D^3 - 3D - 2)y = 0$; when $x = 0$, $y = 0$, $y' = 9$, $y'' = 0$.

ANS. $y = 2e^{2x} + (3x - 2)e^{-x}$.

24. $(D^4 + 3D^3 + 2D^2)y = 0$; when $x = 0$, $y = 0$, $y' = 4$, $y'' = -6$, $y''' = 14$.

ANS. $y = 2(x + e^{-x} - e^{-2x})$.

25. The equation of Ex. 24 with the conditions: when $x = 0$, $y = 0$, $y' = 3$, $y'' = -5$, $y''' = 9$.

ANS. $y = 2 - e^{-x} - e^{-2x}$.

26. $(D^3 + D^2 - D - 1)y = 0$; when $x = 0$, $y = 1$, when $x = 2$, $y = 0$, and also as $x \to \infty$, $y \to 0$.

ANS. $y = \frac{1}{2}(2 - x)e^{-x}$.

In Exs. 27–29, find for $x = 2$ the y value for the particular solution required.

27. $(4D^2 - 4D + 1)y = 0$; when $x = 0$, $y = -2$, $y' = 2$.

ANS. When $x = 2$, $y = 4e$.

28. $(D^3 + 2D^2)y = 0$; when $x = 0$, $y = -3$, $y' = 0$, $y'' = 12$.

ANS. When $x = 2$, $y = 3e^{-4} + 6$.

29. $(D^3 + 5D^2 + 3D - 9)y = 0$; when $x = 0$, $y = -1$, when $x = 1$, $y = 0$, and also as $x \to \infty$, $y \to 0$.   ANS. When $x = 2$, $y = e^{-6}$.

42. A definition of exp z for imaginary z

Since the auxiliary equation may have imaginary roots, we need now to lay down a definition of exp z for imaginary z.

Let $z = \alpha + i\beta$ with α and β real. Since it is desirable to have the ordinary laws of exponents remain valid, it is wise to require that

$$(1) \qquad \exp(\alpha + i\beta) = e^\alpha \cdot e^{i\beta}.$$

To e^α with α real, we attach the usual meaning.

Now consider $e^{i\beta}$, β real. In calculus it is shown that for all real x

$$(2) \qquad e^x = 1 + \frac{x}{1!} + \frac{x^2}{2!} + \frac{x^3}{3!} + \cdots + \frac{x^n}{n!} + \cdots,$$

or

$$(2) \qquad e^x = \sum_{n=0}^{\infty} \frac{x^n}{n!}.$$

If we now tentatively put $x = i\beta$ in (2) as a definition of $e^{i\beta}$, we get

$$(3) \quad e^{i\beta} = 1 + \frac{i\beta}{1!} + \frac{i^2\beta^2}{2!} + \frac{i^3\beta^3}{3!} + \frac{i^4\beta^4}{4!} + \cdots + \frac{i^n\beta^n}{n!} + \cdots.$$

Separating the even powers of β from the odd powers of β in (3) yields

(4)
$$e^{i\beta} = 1 + \frac{i^2\beta^2}{2!} + \frac{i^4\beta^4}{4!} + \cdots + \frac{i^{2k}\beta^{2k}}{(2k)!} + \cdots$$
$$+ \frac{i\beta}{1!} + \frac{i^3\beta^3}{3!} + \cdots + \frac{i^{2k+1}\beta^{2k+1}}{(2k+1)!} + \cdots ,$$

or

(4)
$$e^{i\beta} = \sum_{k=0}^{\infty} \frac{i^{2k}\beta^{2k}}{(2k)!} + \sum_{k=0}^{\infty} \frac{i^{2k+1}\beta^{2k+1}}{(2k+1)!}.$$

Now $i^{2k} = (-1)^k$, so we may write

(5)
$$e^{i\beta} = 1 - \frac{\beta^2}{2!} + \frac{\beta^4}{4!} + \cdots + \frac{(-1)^k\beta^{2k}}{(2k)!} + \cdots$$
$$+ i\left[\frac{\beta}{1!} - \frac{\beta^3}{3!} + \cdots + \frac{(-1)^k\beta^{2k+1}}{(2k+1)!} + \cdots\right],$$

or

(5)
$$e^{i\beta} = \sum_{k=0}^{\infty} \frac{(-1)^k\beta^{2k}}{(2k)!} + i\sum_{k=0}^{\infty} \frac{(-1)^k\beta^{2k+1}}{(2k+1)!}.$$

But the series on the right in (5) are precisely those for $\cos \beta$ and $\sin \beta$ as developed in calculus. Hence we are led to the tentative result

(6)
$$e^{i\beta} = \cos \beta + i \sin \beta.$$

The student should realize that the manipulations above have no meaning in themselves at this stage (assuming that infinite series with complex terms are not a part of the content of elementary mathematics). What has been accomplished is this: the formal manipulations above have suggested the meaningful definition (6). Combining (6) with (1) we now put forward a reasonable *definition* of exp $(\alpha + i\beta)$, namely,

(7)
$$\exp (\alpha + i\beta) = e^{\alpha}(\cos \beta + i \sin \beta), \quad \alpha \text{ and } \beta \text{ real.}$$

Replacing β by $(-\beta)$ in (7) yields a result which is of value to us in the next section,

$$\exp (\alpha - i\beta) = e^{\alpha}(\cos \beta - i \sin \beta).$$

It is interesting and important that with the definition (7), the function e^z for complex z retains many of the properties possessed by the function e^x for real x. Such matters are often studied in detail in books on complex variables.* Here we need in particular to know that if

* For example, R. V. Churchill, *Complex Variables and Applications* (2nd edition; New York: McGraw-Hill Book Co., 1960), pp. 46–50.

$$y = \exp{(a + ib)x},$$

with a, b, and x real, then

$$(D - a - ib)y = 0.$$

The result desired follows at once by differentiation, with respect to x, of the function

$$y = e^{ax}(\cos bx + i \sin bx).$$

43. The auxiliary equation; imaginary roots

Consider a differential equation $f(D)y = 0$ for which the auxiliary equation $f(m) = 0$ has real coefficients. From elementary algebra we know that if the auxiliary equation has any imaginary roots, those roots must occur in conjugate pairs. Thus if

$$m_1 = a + ib$$

is a root of the equation $f(m) = 0$, with a and b real and $b \neq 0$, then

$$m_2 = a - ib$$

is also a root of $f(m) = 0$. It must be kept in mind that this result is a consequence of the reality of the coefficients in the equation $f(m) = 0$. Imaginary roots do not necessarily appear in pairs in an algebraic equation whose coefficients involve imaginaries.

We can now construct in usable form solutions of

(1) $$f(D)y = 0$$

corresponding to imaginary roots of $f(m) = 0$. For, since $f(m)$ is assumed to have real coefficients, any imaginary roots appear in conjugate pairs $m_1 = a + ib$ and $m_2 = a - ib$. Then, according to the preceding section, equation (1) is satisfied by

(2) $$y = c_1 \exp{[(a + ib)x]} + c_2 \exp{[(a - ib)x]}.$$

Taking x to be real along with a and b, we get from (2) the result

(3) $$y = c_1 e^{ax}(\cos bx + i \sin bx) + c_2 e^{ax}(\cos bx - i \sin bx).$$

Now (3) may be written

$$y = (c_1 + c_2)e^{ax} \cos bx + i(c_1 - c_2)e^{ax} \sin bx.$$

Finally, let $c_1 + c_2 = c_3$, and $i(c_1 - c_2) = c_4$, where c_3 and c_4 are new arbitrary constants. Then equation (1) is seen to have the solutions

(4) $$y = c_3 e^{ax} \cos bx + c_4 e^{ax} \sin bx,$$

corresponding to the two roots $m_1 = a + ib$ and $m_2 = a - ib$, $(b \neq 0)$ of the auxiliary equation.

Taking a, b, x, and y to be real, it follows readily from equation (4) that c_3 and c_4 are real. But $c_1 + c_2 = c_3$, and $i(c_1 - c_2) = c_4$, so

$$c_1 = \tfrac{1}{2}(c_3 - ic_4)$$

and

$$c_2 = \tfrac{1}{2}(c_3 + ic_4).$$

Hence, if $c_4 \neq 0$, c_1 and c_2 are conjugate complex numbers.

The reduction of the solution (2) above to the desirable form (4) has been done once and that is enough. Whenever a pair of conjugate imaginary roots of the auxiliary equation appears, we write down at once in the form given on the right in equation (4) the particular solution corresponding to those two roots.

EXAMPLE (a): Solve the equation

$$(D^3 - 3D^2 + 9D + 13)y = 0.$$

For the auxiliary equation

$$m^3 - 3m^2 + 9m + 13 = 0,$$

one root, $m_1 = -1$, is easily found. When the factor $(m + 1)$ is removed by synthetic division, it is seen that the other two roots are solutions of the quadratic

$$m^2 - 4m + 13 = 0.$$

Those roots are found to be $m_2 = 2 + 3i$ and $m_3 = 2 - 3i$. The auxiliary equation has the roots $m = -1$, $2 \pm 3i$. Hence the general solution of the differential equation is

$$y = c_1 e^{-x} + c_2 e^{2x} \cos 3x + c_3 e^{2x} \sin 3x.$$

Repeated imaginary roots lead to solutions analogous to those brought in by repeated real roots. For instance, if the roots $m = a \pm ib$ occur three times, then the corresponding six linearly independent solutions of the differential equation are those appearing in the expression

$$(c_1 + c_2 x + c_3 x^2)e^{ax} \cos bx + (c_4 + c_5 x + c_6 x^2)e^{ax} \sin bx.$$

EXAMPLE (b): Solve the equation

$$(D^4 + 8D^2 + 16)y = 0.$$

The auxiliary equation $m^4 + 8m^2 + 16 = 0$ may be written

$$(m^2 + 4)^2 = 0,$$

so its roots are seen to be $m = \pm 2i, \pm 2i$. The roots $m_1 = 2i$ and $m_2 = -2i$ occur twice each. Thinking of $2i$ as $0 + 2i$ and recalling that $e^{0x} = 1$, we write the solution of the differential equation as

$$y = (c_1 + c_2x) \cos 2x + (c_3 + c_4x) \sin 2x.$$

In such exercises as those below a fine check can be obtained by direct substitution of the result and its appropriate derivatives into the differential equation. The verification is particularly effective because the operations performed in the check are so different from those performed in obtaining the solution.

Exercises

Find the general solution except when the exercise stipulates otherwise.

1. Verify directly that the relation

(4) $$y = c_3e^{ax} \cos bx + c_4e^{ax} \sin bx$$

satisfies the equation

$$[(D - a)^2 + b^2]y = 0.$$

2. $(D^2 - 2D + 5)y = 0$. Verify your answer.
    ANS. $y = c_1e^x \cos 2x + c_2e^x \sin 2x.$
3. $(D^2 - 2D + 2)y = 0.$
4. $(D^2 + 9)y = 0$. Verify your answer. ANS. $y = c_1 \cos 3x + c_2 \sin 3x.$
5. $(D^2 - 9)y = 0.$ ANS. $y = c_1 \cosh 3x + c_2 \sinh 3x.$
6. $(D^2 + 4D + 5)y = 0$. Verify your answer.
7. $(D^2 - 6D + 25)y = 0.$ ANS. $y = e^{3x}(c_1 \cos 4x + c_2 \sin 4x).$
8. $(D^3 + D^2 + 4D + 4)y = 0$. Verify your answer.
9. $(D^2 - 1)y = 0$; when $x = 0$, $y = y_0$ and $y' = 0.$
    ANS. $y = y_0 \cosh x.$
10. $(D^2 + 1)y = 0$; when $x = 0$, $y = y_0$ and $y' = 0$. ANS. $y = y_0 \cos x.$
11. $(D^4 + 2D^3 - 11D^2 - 52D)y = 0.$
12. $(D^3 + 5D^2 + 17D + 13)y = 0$; when $x = 0$, $y = 0$, $y' = 1$, and $y'' = 6.$ ANS. $y = e^{-x} - e^{-2x} \cos 3x.$

13. $(D^5 - 2D^3 - 2D^2 - 3D - 2)y = 0.$

14. $(D^4 - 2D^3 + 2D^2 - 2D + 1)y = 0.$ Verify your answer.

15. $(D^4 + 18D^2 + 81)y = 0.$

ANS. $y = (c_1 + c_2 x) \cos 3x + (c_3 + c_4 x) \sin 3x.$

16. $(2D^4 + 11D^3 - 4D^2 - 69D + 34)y = 0.$ Verify your answer.

17. $(D^6 + 6D^4 + 9D^2 + 4)y = 0.$

18. $(16D^3 - 11D - 5)y = 0.$

19. $\dfrac{d^2x}{dt^2} + k^2x = 0,$ k real; when $t = 0,$ $x = 0$ and $\dfrac{dx}{dt} = v_0.$ Verify your result completely.

ANS. $x = (v_0/k) \sin kt.$

20. $(D^3 + D^2 + 4D + 4)y = 0;$ when $x = 0,$ $y = 0,$ $y' = -1,$ and $y'' = 5.$

ANS. $y = e^{-x} - \cos 2x.$

21. $\dfrac{d^2x}{dt^2} + 2b\dfrac{dx}{dt} + k^2x = 0,$ $k > b > 0;$ when $t = 0,$ $x = 0$ and $\dfrac{dx}{dt} = v_0.$

ANS. $x = (v_0/a)e^{-bt} \sin at,$ where $a = \sqrt{k^2 - b^2}.$

Miscellaneous Exercises

Obtain the general solution unless otherwise instructed. Your answer can be checked by direct substitution.

1. $(9D^4 + 6D^3 + D^2)y = 0.$

2. $(4D^3 - 13D + 6)y = 0.$

3. $(D^3 + 2D^2 - 15D)y = 0.$

4. $(D^3 + 2D^2 + D + 2)y = 0.$

5. $(D^3 - 2D^2 - 3D)y = 0.$

6. $(D^3 + 3D^2 - 4)y = 0.$

7. $(4D^3 - 27D + 27)y = 0.$

8. $(10D^3 + D^2 - 7D + 2)y = 0.$

9. $(D^3 + 7D^2 + 19D + 13)y = 0;$ when $x = 0,$ $y = 0,$ $y' = 2,$ and $y'' = -12.$

10. $(D^2 - D - 6)y = 0;$ when $x = 0,$ $y = 2$ and $y' = 1.$

11. $(D^4 + 6D^3 + 9D^2)y = 0;$ when $x = 0,$ $y = 0,$ $y' = 0,$ and $y'' = 6,$ and as $x \to \infty,$ $y' \to 1.$ For this particular solution, find the value of y when $x = 1.$

ANS. $y = 1 - e^{-3}.$

12. $(D^3 + 6D^2 + 12D + 8)y = 0;$ when $x = 0,$ $y = 1,$ $y' = -2,$ and $y'' = 2.$

13. $(D^3 + 3D^2 + 3D + 1)y = 0.$

14. $(D^4 - 2D^3 - 13D^2 + 38D - 24)y = 0.$

15. $(D^6 + 9D^4 + 24D^2 + 16)y = 0.$

16. $(8D^3 - 4D^2 - 2D + 1)y = 0.$

17. $(D^4 + D^3 - 4D^2 - 4D)y = 0.$

18. $(D^4 - 2D^3 + 5D^2 - 8D + 4)y = 0.$

19. $(D^4 + 2D^2 + 1)y = 0.$

20. $(D^4 + 5D^2 + 4)y = 0.$

21. $(D^4 + 3D^3 - 4D)y = 0.$

22. $(D^5 + D^4 - 9D^3 - 13D^2 + 8D + 12)y = 0.$

23. $(D^4 - 11D^3 + 36D^2 - 16D - 64)y = 0.$

24. $(D^2 + 2D + 5)y = 0.$

25. $(D^4 + 4D^3 + 2D^2 - 8D - 8)y = 0.$

26. $(4D^4 - 24D^3 + 35D^2 + 6D - 9)y = 0.$

27. $(4D^4 + 20D^3 + 35D^2 + 25D + 6)y = 0.$

28. $(D^4 - 7D^3 + 11D^2 + 5D - 14)y = 0.$

29. $(D^3 + 5D^2 + 7D + 3)y = 0.$

30. $(D^3 - 2D^2 + D - 2)y = 0.$

31. $(D^3 - D^2 + D - 1)y = 0.$

32. $(D^3 + 4D^2 + 5D)y = 0.$

33. $(D^4 - 13D^2 + 36)y = 0.$

34. $(D^4 - 5D^3 + 5D^2 + 5D - 6)y = 0.$

35. $(4D^3 + 8D^2 - 11D + 3)y = 0.$

36. $(D^3 + D^2 - 16D - 16)y = 0.$

37. $(D^4 - D^3 - 3D^2 + D + 2)y = 0.$

38. $(D^3 - 2D^2 - 3D + 10)y = 0.$

39. $(D^5 + D^4 - 6D^3)y = 0.$

40. $(4D^3 + 28D^2 + 61D + 37)y = 0.$

41. $(4D^3 + 12D^2 + 13D + 10)y = 0.$

42. $(18D^3 - 33D^2 + 20D - 4)y = 0.$

43. $(4D^4 - 15D^2 + 5D + 6)y = 0.$

44. $(D^5 + D^4 - 7D^3 - 11D^2 - 8D - 12)y = 0.$

45. $(D^4 + 3D^3 - 6D^2 - 28D - 24)y = 0.$

46. $(4D^4 - 4D^3 - 23D^2 + 12D + 36)y = 0.$

47. $(4D^5 - 23D^3 - 33D^2 - 17D - 3)y = 0.$

CHAPTER 9

Nonhomogeneous Equations:

Undetermined Coefficients

44. Construction of a homogeneous equation from a specified solution

In Section 34 we saw that the general solution of the equation

(1) $$(b_0D^n + b_1D^{n-1} + \cdots + b_{n-1}D + b_n)y = R(x)$$

is

$$y = y_c + y_p,$$

where y_c, the complementary function, is the general solution of the homogeneous equation

(2) $$(b_0D^n + b_1D^{n-1} + \cdots + b_{n-1}D + b_n)y = 0$$

and y_p is any particular solution of the original equation (1).

Various methods for getting a particular solution of (1) when the $b_0, b_1, \cdots, b_n$ are constants will be presented. In preparation for the method of undetermined coefficients it is wise to obtain proficiency in writing a homogeneous differential equation of which a given relation of proper form is a solution.

127

Recall that in solutions of homogeneous equations with constant coefficients, a term such as c_1e^{ax} occurred only when the auxiliary equation $f(m) = 0$ had a root $m = a$, and then the operator $f(D)$ had a factor $(D - a)$. In like manner, c_2xe^{ax} appeared only when $f(D)$ contained the factor $(D - a)^2$, $c_3x^2e^{ax}$ only when $f(D)$ contained $(D - a)^3$, etc. Such terms as $ce^{ax} \cos bx$ or $ce^{ax} \sin bx$ correspond to roots $m = a \pm ib$, or to a factor $[(D - a)^2 + b^2]$.

EXAMPLE (a): Find a homogeneous linear equation, with constant coefficients, which has as a particular solution

$$y = 7e^{3x} + 2x.$$

First note that the coefficients (7 and 2) are quite irrelevant for the present problem, so long as they are not zero. We shall obtain an equation satisfied by $y = c_1e^{3x} + c_2x$, no matter what the constants c_1 and c_2 may be.

A term c_1e^{3x} occurs along with a root $m = 3$ of the auxiliary equation. The term c_2x will appear if the auxiliary equation has $m = 0, 0$; that is, a double root $m = 0$. We have recognized that the equation

$$D^2(D - 3)y = 0,$$

or

$$(D^3 - 3D^2)y = 0,$$

has $y = c_1e^{3x} + c_2x + c_3$ as its general solution, and therefore that it also has $y = 7e^{3x} + 2x$ as a particular solution.

EXAMPLE (b): Find a homogeneous linear equation with real, constant coefficients that is satisfied by

$$(3) \qquad\qquad y = 6 + 3xe^x - \cos x.$$

The term 6 is associated with $m = 0$, the term $3xe^x$ with a double root $m = 1, 1$, and the term $(- \cos x)$ with the pair of imaginary roots $m = 0 \pm i$. Hence the auxiliary equation is

$$m(m - 1)^2(m^2 + 1) = 0,$$

or

$$m^5 - 2m^4 + 2m^3 - 2m^2 + m = 0.$$

Therefore the relation (3) is a solution of the differential equation

$$(4) \qquad\qquad (D^5 - 2D^4 + 2D^3 - 2D^2 + D)y = 0.$$

That is, from the general solution

$$y = c_1 + (c_2 + c_3 x)e^x + c_4 \cos x + c_5 \sin x$$

of equation (4), the relation (3) follows by an appropriate choice of the constants: $c_1 = 6$, $c_2 = 0$, $c_3 = 3$, $c_4 = -1$, $c_5 = 0$.

EXAMPLE (c): Find a homogeneous linear equation with real, constant coefficients which is satisfied by

$$y = 4xe^x \sin 2x.$$

The desired equation must have its auxiliary equation with roots $m = 1 \pm 2i$, $1 \pm 2i$. The roots $m = 1 \pm 2i$ correspond to factors $(m - 1)^2 + 4$, so the auxiliary equation must be

$$[(m - 1)^2 + 4]^2 = 0,$$

or

$$m^4 - 4m^3 + 14m^2 - 20m + 25 = 0.$$

Hence the desired equation is

$$(D^4 - 4D^3 + 14D^2 - 20D + 25)y = 0.$$

Note that in all such problems, a correct (but undesirable) solution may be obtained by inserting additional roots of the auxiliary equation.

Oral Exercises

In Exs. 1–14, obtain in factored form a linear differential equation, with real, constant coefficients and which is satisfied by the given relation.

1. $y = 4e^{2x} + 3e^{-x}$.   ANS. $(D - 2)(D + 1)y = 0$.
2. $y = 7 - 2x + \frac{1}{2}e^{4x}$.   ANS. $D^2(D - 4)y = 0$.
3. $y = -2x + \frac{1}{2}e^{4x}$.   ANS. $D^2(D - 4)y = 0$.
4. $y = x^2 - 5 \sin 3x$.   ANS. $D^3(D^2 + 9)y = 0$.
5. $y = 2e^x \cos 3x$.
   ANS. $(D - 1 - 3i)(D - 1 + 3i)y = 0$; or $[(D - 1)^2 + 9]y = 0$; or $(D^2 - 2D + 10)y = 0$.
6. $y = x^2 + 4e^x$.
7. $y = 3xe^x - 2e^{-x}$.
8. $y = 6 + 2e^{3x}$.
9. $y = 2x^2 + 1$.
10. $y = \sin 2x$.
11. $y = \sin 2x + 3 \cos 2x$.
12. $y = \cos kx$.

13. $y = x \sin 2x.$

14. $y = 2 \sinh x.$

In Exs. 15–36, state the roots of the auxiliary equation for a homogeneous linear equation with real, constant coefficients and having the given relation as a particular solution.

15. $y = 3xe^{2x}.$ ANS. $m = 2, 2.$

16. $y = x^2 e^{-x} + 4e^x.$ ANS. $m = -1, -1, -1, 1.$

17. $y = e^{-x} \cos 4x.$ ANS. $m = -1 \pm 4i.$

18. $y = 3e^{-x} \cos 4x + 15e^{-x} \sin 4x.$ ANS. $m = -1 \pm 4i.$

19. $y = x(e^{2x} + 4).$ ANS. $m = 0, 0, 2, 2.$

20. $y = 3 + 8e^{-2x}.$

21. $y = 2x^2 - e^{-3x}.$

22. $y = 4 + 2x^2 - e^{-3x}.$

23. $y = xe^x.$

24. $y = xe^x + 5e^x.$

25. $y = 4 \cos 2x.$

26. $y = 4 \cos 2x - 3 \sin 2x.$

27. $y = x \cos 2x - 3 \sin 2x.$

28. $y = x \cos 2x.$

29. $y = e^{-2x} \cos 3x.$

30. $y = e^{-2x}(\cos 3x + \sin 3x).$

31. $y = x^2 - x + e^{-x}(x + \cos x).$

32. $y = x^2 \sin x.$

33. $y = x^2 \sin x + x \cos x.$

34. $y = 8 \cos 4x + \sin 3x.$

35. $y = \sin^3 x.$ Use the fact that $\sin^3 x = \frac{1}{4}(3 \sin x - \sin 3x).$

36. $y = \cos^2 x.$

45. Solution of a nonhomogeneous equation

Before proceeding to the theoretical basis and the actual working technique of the useful method of undetermined coefficients, let us examine the underlying ideas as applied to a simple numerical example.

Consider the equation

(1) $$D^2(D - 1)y = 3e^x + \sin x.$$

The complementary function may be determined at once from the roots

(2) $$m = 0, 0, 1$$

of the auxiliary equation. The complementary function is

(3) $$y_c = c_1 + c_2 x + c_3 e^x.$$

Since the general solution of (1) is

$$y = y_c + y_p$$

where y_c is as given in (3) and y_p is any particular solution of (1), all that remains for us to do is to find a particular solution of (1).

The right-hand member of (1),

(4) $$R(x) = 3e^x + \sin x,$$

is a particular solution of a homogeneous linear differential equation whose auxiliary equation has the roots

(5) $$m' = 1, \pm i.$$

Therefore the relation (4) is a particular solution of the equation

(6) $$(D - 1)(D^2 + 1)R = 0.$$

We wish to convert (1) into a homogeneous linear differential equation with constant coefficients, because we know how to solve any such equation. But, by (6), the operator $(D - 1)(D^2 + 1)$ will annihilate the right member of (1). Therefore, we apply that operator to both sides of equation (1) and get

(7) $$(D - 1)(D^2 + 1)D^2(D - 1)y = 0.$$

Any solution of (1) must be a particular solution of (7). The general solution of (7) can be written at once from the roots of its auxiliary equation, those roots being the values $m = 0, 0, 1$ from (2) and the values $m' = 1, \pm i$ from (5). Thus the general solution of (7) is

(8) $$y = c_1 + c_2 x + c_3 e^x + c_4 x e^x + c_5 \cos x + c_6 \sin x.$$

But the desired general solution of (1) is

(9) $$y = y_c + y_p,$$

where

$$y_c = c_1 + c_2 x + c_3 e^x,$$

the c_1, c_2, c_3 being arbitrary constants as in (8). Thus there must exist a particular solution of (1) containing at most the remaining terms in (8). Using different letters as coefficients to emphasize that they are not arbitrary, we conclude that (1) has a particular solution

(10) $y_p = A x e^x + B \cos x + C \sin x.$

We now have only to determine the numerical coefficients A, B, C by direct use of the original equation

(1) $D^2(D - 1)y = 3e^x + \sin x.$

From (10) it follows that

$$Dy_p = A(xe^x + e^x) - B \sin x + C \cos x,$$

$$D^2y_p = A(xe^x + 2e^x) - B \cos x - C \sin x,$$

$$D^3y_p = A(xe^x + 3e^x) + B \sin x - C \cos x.$$

Substitution of y_p into (1) then yields

(11) $A e^x + (B + C) \sin x + (B - C) \cos x = 3e^x + \sin x.$

Since (11) is to be an identity and since e^x, $\sin x$, and $\cos x$ are linearly independent, the corresponding coefficients in the two members of (11) must be equal; that is,

$$A = 3$$
$$B + C = 1$$
$$B - C = 0.$$

Therefore $A = 3$, $B = \frac{1}{2}$, $C = \frac{1}{2}$. Returning to (10), we find that a particular solution of equation (1) is

$$y_p = 3xe^x + \tfrac{1}{2} \cos x + \tfrac{1}{2} \sin x.$$

The general solution of the original equation

(1) $D^2(D - 1)y = 3e^x + \sin x$

is therefore obtained by adding to the complementary function the y_p found above:

(12) $y = c_1 + c_2x + c_3e^x + 3xe^x + \tfrac{1}{2} \cos x + \tfrac{1}{2} \sin x.$

A careful analysis of the ideas behind the process used shows that to arrive at the solution (12), we need perform only the following steps:

(a) From (1) find the values of m and m' as exhibited in (2) and (5);
(b) From the values of m and m' write y_c and y_p as in (3) and (10);
(c) Substitute y_p into (1), equate corresponding coefficients, and obtain the numerical values of the coefficients in y_p;
(d) Write the general solution of (1).

46. The method of undetermined coefficients

Let us examine the general problem of the type treated in the preceding section. Let $f(D)$ be a polynomial in the operator D. Consider the equation

(1) $$f(D)y = R(x).$$

Let the roots of the auxiliary equation $f(m) = 0$ be

(2) $$m = m_1, m_2, \cdots, m_n.$$

The general solution of (1) is

(3) $$y = y_c + y_p$$

where y_c can be obtained at once from the values of m in (2) and where $y = y_p$ is any particular solution (yet to be obtained) of (1).

Now suppose that the right member $R(x)$ of (1) is itself a particular solution of some homogeneous linear differential equation with constant coefficients,

(4) $$g(D)R = 0,$$

whose auxiliary equation has the roots

(5) $$m' = m'_1, m'_2, \cdots, m'_k.$$

Recall that the values of m' in (5) can be obtained by inspection from $R(x)$.

The differential equation

(6) $$g(D)f(D)y = 0$$

has as the roots of its auxiliary equation the values of m from (2) and m' from (5). Hence the general solution of (6) contains the y_c of (3) and so is of the form

$$y = y_c + y_q.$$

But also any particular solution of (1) must satisfy (6). Now, if

$$f(D)(y_c + y_q) = R(x),$$

then $f(D)y_q = R(x)$ because $f(D)y_c = 0$. Then deleting the y_c from the general solution of (6) leaves a function y_q which for some numerical values of its coefficients must satisfy (1); that is, the coefficients in y_q can be determined so that $y_q = y_p$. The determination of those numerical coefficients may be accomplished as in the examples below.

It must be kept in mind that the method of this section is applicable when, and only when, the right member of the equation is itself a particular solution of some homogeneous linear differential equation with constant coefficients. Methods which apply to equations with less restricted right-hand members will be studied in Chapter 16.

EXAMPLE (a): Solve the equation

$$(7) \qquad (D^2 + D - 2)y = 2x - 40 \cos 2x.$$

Here we have

$$m = 1, -2$$

and

$$m' = 0, 0, \pm 2i.$$

Therefore we may write

$$y_c = c_1 e^x + c_2 e^{-2x},$$

$$y_p = A + Bx + C \cos 2x + E \sin 2x,$$

in which c_1 and c_2 are arbitrary constants, while A, B, C, and E are to be determined numerically so y_p will satisfy the equation (7).

Since

$$Dy_p = B - 2C \sin 2x + 2E \cos 2x$$

and

$$D^2 y_p = -4C \cos 2x - 4E \sin 2x,$$

direct substitution of y_p into (7) yields

$$(8) \quad -4C \cos 2x - 4E \sin 2x + B - 2C \sin 2x + 2E \cos 2x - 2A$$

$$-2Bx - 2C \cos 2x - 2E \sin 2x = 2x - 40 \cos 2x.$$

But (8) is to be an identity in x, so we must equate coefficients of each of the set of linearly independent functions $\cos 2x$, $\sin 2x$, x, 1 appearing in the identity. Thus it follows that

$$-6C + 2E = -40,$$
$$-6E - 2C = 0,$$
$$-2B = 2,$$
$$B - 2A = 0.$$

The above equations determine A, B, C, and E. Indeed, they lead to

$$A = -\tfrac{1}{2}, \qquad C = 6,$$
$$B = -1, \qquad E = -2.$$

Since the general solution of (7) is $y = y_c + y_p$, we can now write the desired result,

$$y = c_1 e^x + c_2 e^{-2x} - \tfrac{1}{2} - x + 6 \cos 2x - 2 \sin 2x.$$

EXAMPLE (b): Solve the equation

$$(9) \qquad (D^2 + 1)y = \sin x.$$

At once $m = \pm i$ and $m' = \pm i$. Therefore

$$y_c = c_1 \cos x + c_2 \sin x,$$
$$y_p = Ax \cos x + Bx \sin x.$$

Now

$$y_p'' = A(-x \cos x - 2 \sin x) + B(-x \sin x + 2 \cos x),$$

so the requirement that y_p satisfy equation (9) yields

$$-2A \sin x + 2B \cos x = \sin x,$$

from which $A = -\tfrac{1}{2}$ and $B = 0$.

The general solution of (9) is

$$y = c_1 \cos x + c_2 \sin x - \tfrac{1}{2}x \cos x.$$

EXAMPLE (c): Determine y so that it will satisfy the equation

$$(10) \qquad y''' - y' = 4e^{-x} + 3e^{2x}$$

with the conditions that when $x = 0$, $y = 0$, $y' = -1$, and $y'' = 2$.

First we note that $m = 0, 1, -1$, and $m' = -1, 2$. Thus

$$y_c = c_1 + c_2 e^x + c_3 e^{-x},$$
$$y_p = Axe^{-x} + Be^{2x}.$$

Now

$$y_p' = A(-xe^{-x} + e^{-x}) + 2Be^{2x},$$
$$y_p'' = A(xe^{-x} - 2e^{-x}) + 4Be^{2x},$$
$$y_p''' = A(-xe^{-x} + 3e^{-x}) + 8Be^{2x}.$$

Then

$$y_p''' - y_p' = 2Ae^{-x} + 6Be^{2x},$$

so that from (10) we may conclude that $A = 2$ and $B = \tfrac{1}{2}$.

The general solution of (10) is therefore

$$(11) \qquad y = c_1 + c_2 e^x + c_3 e^{-x} + 2xe^{-x} + \tfrac{1}{2}e^{2x}.$$

..e must determine c_1, c_2, c_3 so (11) will satisfy the conditions that when $x = 0$, $y = 0$, $y' = -1$, and $y'' = 2$.

From (11) it follows that

(12) $$y' = c_2 e^x - c_3 e^{-x} - 2xe^{-x} + 2e^{-x} + e^{2x}$$

and

(13) $$y'' = c_2 e^x + c_3 e^{-x} + 2xe^{-x} - 4e^{-x} + 2e^{2x}.$$

We put $x = 0$ in each of (11), (12), and (13) to get the equations for the determination of c_1, c_2, and c_3. These are

$$0 = c_1 + c_2 + c_3 + \tfrac{1}{2},$$
$$-1 = c_2 - c_3 + 3,$$
$$2 = c_2 + c_3 - 2,$$

from which $c_1 = -\tfrac{9}{2}$, $c_2 = 0$, $c_3 = 4$. Therefore, the final result is

$$y = -\tfrac{9}{2} + 4e^{-x} + 2xe^{-x} + \tfrac{1}{2}e^{2x}.$$

An important point, sometimes overlooked by students, is that it is the general solution, the y of (11), that must be made to satisfy the boundary conditions.

Exercises

In Exs. 1–35, obtain the general solution.

1. $(D^2 + D)y = -\cos x.$ ANS. $y = c_1 + c_2 e^{-x} + \tfrac{1}{2}\cos x - \tfrac{1}{2}\sin x.$

2. $(D^2 - 6D + 9)y = e^x.$ ANS. $y = (c_1 + c_2 x)e^{3x} + \tfrac{1}{4}e^x.$

3. $(D^2 + 3D + 2)y = 12x^2.$
ANS. $y = c_1 e^{-x} + c_2 e^{-2x} + 6x^2 - 18x + 21.$

4. $(D^2 + 3D + 2)y = 1 + 3x + x^2.$ ANS. $y = c_1 e^{-x} + c_2 e^{-2x} + \tfrac{1}{2}x^2.$

5. $(D^2 + 9)y = 5e^x - 162x.$
ANS. $y = c_1 \cos 3x + c_2 \sin 3x + \tfrac{1}{2}e^x - 18x.$

6. $(D^2 + 9)y = 5e^x - 162x^2.$
ANS. $y = c_1 \cos 3x + c_2 \sin 3x + \tfrac{1}{2}e^x - 18x^2 + 4.$

7. $y'' - 3y' - 4y = 30e^x.$ ANS. $y = c_1 e^{4x} + c_2 e^{-x} - 5e^x.$

8. $y'' - 3y' - 4y = 30e^{4x}.$ ANS. $y = (c_1 + 6x)e^{4x} + c_2 e^{-x}.$

9. $(D^2 - 4)y = e^{2x} + 2.$ ANS. $y = c_1 e^{-2x} + (c_2 + \tfrac{1}{4}x)e^{2x} - \tfrac{1}{2}.$

10. $(D^2 - D - 2)y = 6x + 6e^{-x}.$
ANS. $y = c_1 e^{-x} + c_2 e^{2x} - 3x + 3/2 - 2xe^{-x}.$

11. $y'' - 4y' + 3y = 20 \cos x.$
ANS. $y = c_1 e^x + c_2 e^{3x} + 2 \cos x - 4 \sin x.$

12. $y'' - 4y' + 3y = 2\cos x + 4\sin x$.   ANS. $y = c_1e^x + c_2e^{3x} + \cos x$.

13. $y'' + 2y' + y = 7 + 75\sin 2x$.

ANS. $y = e^{-x}(c_1 + c_2x) + 7 - 12\cos 2x - 9\sin 2x$.

14. $(D^2 + 4D + 5)y = 50x + 13e^{3x}$.

ANS. $y = e^{-2x}(c_1\cos x + c_2\sin x) + 10x - 8 + \frac{1}{2}e^{3x}$.

15. $(D^2 + 1)y = \cos x$.   ANS. $y = c_1\cos x + c_2\sin x + \frac{1}{2}x\sin x$.

16. $(D^2 - 4D + 4)y = e^{2x}$.   ANS. $y = e^{2x}(c_1 + c_2x + \frac{1}{2}x^2)$.

17. $(D^2 - 1)y = e^{-x}(2\sin x + 4\cos x)$.

18. $(D^2 - 1)y = 8xe^x$.   ANS. $y = c_1e^{-x} + e^x(c_2 - 2x + 2x^2)$.

19. $(D^3 - D)y = x$.   ANS. $y = c_1 + c_2e^x + c_3e^{-x} - \frac{1}{2}x^2$.

20. $(D^3 - D^2 + D - 1)y = 4\sin x$.

ANS. $y = c_1e^x + (c_2 + x)\cos x + (c_3 - x)\sin x$.

21. $(D^3 + D^2 - 4D - 4)y = 3e^{-x} - 4x - 6$.

ANS. $y = c_1e^{2x} + c_2e^{-2x} + (c_3 - x)e^{-x} + x + \frac{1}{2}$.

22. $(D^4 - 1)y = 7x^2$.

23. $(D^4 - 1)y = e^{-x}$.

ANS. $y = c_1e^x + (c_2 - \frac{1}{4}x)e^{-x} + c_3\cos x + c_4\sin x$.

24. $(D^2 - 1)y = 10\sin^2 x$. Use the identity $\sin^2 x = \frac{1}{2}(1 - \cos 2x)$.

ANS. $y = c_1e^x + c_2e^{-x} - 5 + \cos 2x$.

25. $(D^2 + 1)y = 12\cos^2 x$.

ANS. $y = c_1\cos x + c_2\sin x + 6 - 2\cos 2x$.

26. $(D^2 + 4)y = 4\sin^2 x$.

ANS. $y = c_1\cos 2x + c_2\sin 2x + \frac{1}{2}(1 - x\sin 2x)$.

27. $y'' - 3y' - 4y = 16x - 50\cos 2x$.

28. $(D^3 - 3D - 2)y = 100\sin 2x$.

29. $y'' + 4y' + 3y = 15e^{2x} + e^{-x}$.

30. $y'' - y = e^x - 4$.

31. $y'' - y' - 2y = 6x + 6e^{-x}$.

32. $y'' + 6y' + 13y = 60\cos x + 26$.

33. $(D^3 - 3D^2 + 4)y = 6 + 80\cos 2x$.

34. $(D^3 + D - 10)y = 29e^{4x}$.

35. $(D^3 + D^2 - 4D - 4)y = 8x + 8 + 6e^{-x}$.

In Exs. 36–44, find the particular solution indicated.

36. $(D^2 + 1)y = 10e^{2x}$; when $x = 0$, $y = 0$ and $y' = 0$.

ANS. $y = 2(e^{2x} - \cos x - 2\sin x)$.

37. $(D^2 - 4)y = 2 - 8x$; when $x = 0$, $y = 0$ and $y' = 5$.

ANS. $y = e^{2x} - \frac{1}{2}e^{-2x} + 2x - \frac{1}{2}$.

38. $(D^2 + 3D)y = -18x$; when $x = 0$, $y = 0$ and $y' = 5$.

ANS. $y = 1 + 2x - 3x^2 - e^{-3x}$.

39. $(D^2 + 4D + 5)y = 10e^{-3x}$; when $x = 0$, $y = 4$ and $y' = 0$.

40. $\dfrac{d^2x}{dt^2} + 4\dfrac{dx}{dt} + 5x = 10$; when $t = 0$, $x = 0$ and $\dfrac{dx}{dt} = 0$.

ANS. $x = 2(1 - e^{-2t}\cos t - 2e^{-2t}\sin t)$.

41. $\ddot{x} + 4\dot{x} + 5x = 8\sin t$; when $t = 0$, $x = 0$ and $\dot{x} = 0$. Note that $\dot{x} = \dfrac{dx}{dt}$, $\ddot{x} = \dfrac{d^2x}{dt^2}$ is a common notation when the independent variable is time.*   ANS. $x = (1 + e^{-2t})\sin t - (1 - e^{-2t})\cos t$.

42. $y'' + 9y = 81x^2 + 14\cos 4x$; when $x = 0$, $y = 0$ and $y' = 3$.

43. $(D^3 + 4D^2 + 9D + 10)y = -24e^x$; when $x = 0$, $y = 0$, $y' = -4$ and $y'' = 10$.

44. $y'' + 2y' + 5y = 8e^{-x}$; when $x = 0$, $y = 0$ and $y' = 8$.

In Exs. 45–48, obtain from the particular solution indicated the value of y and the value of y' at $x = 2$.

45. $y'' + 2y' + y = x$; at $x = 0$, $y = -3$, and at $x = 1$, $y = -1$.

ANS.   At $x = 2$, $y = e^{-2}$ and $y' = 1$.

46. $y'' + 2y' + y = x$; at $x = 0$, $y = -2$ and $y' = 2$.

ANS.   At $x = 2$, $y = 2e^{-2}$ and $y' = 1 - e^{-2}$.

47. $4y'' + y = 2$; at $x = \pi$, $y = 0$ and $y' = 1$.

ANS.   At $x = 2$, $y = -0.7635$ and $y' = +0.3012$.

48. $2y'' - 5y' - 3y = -9x^2 - 1$; at $x = 0$, $y = 1$ and $y' = 0$.

ANS.   At $x = 2$, $y = 5.64$ and $y' = 5.68$.

49. $(D^2 + D)y = x + 1$; when $x = 0$, $y = 1$, and when $x = 1$, $y = \frac{1}{2}$. Compute the value of y at $x = 4$.

ANS.   At $x = 4$, $y = 8 - e^{-1} - e^{-2} - e^{-3}$.

50. $(D^2 + 1)y = x^3$; when $x = 0$, $y = 0$, and when $x = \pi$, $y = 0$. Show that this boundary value problem has no solution.

51. $(D^2 + 1)y = 2\cos x$; when $x = 0$, $y = 0$, and when $x = \pi$, $y = 0$. Show that this boundary value problem has an unlimited number of solutions and obtain them.   ANS. $y = (c + x)\sin x$.

52. For the equation $(D^3 + D^2)y = 4$, find the solution whose graph has at the origin a point of inflection with a horizontal tangent line.

ANS. $y = 4 - 4x + 2x^2 - 4e^{-x}$.

53. For the equation $(D^2 - D)y = 2 - 2x$, find a particular solution which has at some point (to be determined) on the x-axis an inflection point with a horizontal tangent line.

ANS.   The point is $(1, 0)$; the solution is $y = x^2 + 1 - 2\exp(x - 1)$.

---

* The disadvantage of such a notation when derivatives of high order appear must be evident. Other objections can be raised; flies have been known to perform undesired differentiations.

47. Solution by inspection

It is frequently easy to obtain a particular solution of a non-homogeneous equation

$$(1) \qquad (b_0 D^n + b_1 D^{n-1} + \cdots + b_{n-1} D + b_n)y = R(x)$$

by inspection.

For example, if $R(x)$ is a constant R_0 and if $b_n \neq 0$,

$$(2) \qquad\qquad y_p = \frac{R_0}{b_n}$$

is a solution of

$$(3) \quad (b_0 D^n + b_1 D^{n-1} + \cdots + b_n)y = R_0; \, b_n \neq 0, \, R_0 \text{ constant},$$

because all derivatives of y_p are zero, so

$$(b_0 D^n + b_1 D^{n-1} + \cdots + b_n)y_p = b_n R_0 / b_n = R_0.$$

Suppose that $b_n = 0$ in equation (3). Let $D^k y$ be the lowest-ordered derivative that actually appears in the differential equation. Then the equation may be written

$$(4) \qquad (b_0 D^n + \cdots + b_{n-k} D^k)y = R_0; \, b_{n-k} \neq 0, \, R_0 \text{ constant}.$$

Now $D^k x^k = k!$, a constant, so that all higher derivatives of x^k are zero. Thus it becomes evident that (4) has a solution

$$(5) \qquad\qquad y_p = \frac{R_0 x^k}{k! b_{n-k}},$$

for then $(b_0 D^n + \cdots + b_{n-k} D^k)y_p = b_{n-k} R_0 k! / (k! b_{n-k}) = R_0.$

EXAMPLE (a): Solve the equation

$$(6) \qquad\qquad (D^2 - 3D + 2)y = 16.$$

By the methods of Chapter 8 we obtain the complementary function,

$$y_c = c_1 e^x + c_2 e^{2x}.$$

By inspection a particular solution of the original equation is

$$y_p = \tfrac{16}{2} = 8.$$

Hence the general solution of (6) is

$$y = c_1 e^x + c_2 e^{2x} + 8.$$

EXAMPLE (b): Solve the equation

(7) $$\frac{d^5y}{dx^5} + 4\frac{d^3y}{dx^3} = 7.$$

From the auxiliary equation $m^5 + 4m^3 = 0$ we get $m = 0, 0, 0, \pm 2i$. Hence

$$y_c = c_1 + c_2x + c_3x^2 + c_4 \cos 2x + c_5 \sin 2x.$$

A particular solution of (7) is

$$y_p = \frac{7x^3}{3! \cdot 4} = \frac{7x^3}{24}.$$

As a check, note that

$$(D^5 + 4D^3)\frac{7x^3}{24} = 0 + 4 \cdot \frac{7 \cdot 6}{24} = 7.$$

The general solution of equation (7) is

$$y = c_1 + c_2x + c_3x^2 + \tfrac{7}{24}x^3 + c_4 \cos 2x + c_5 \sin 2x,$$

in which the $c_1, \cdots, c_5$ are arbitrary constants.

Examination of

(8) $$(D^2 + 4)y = \sin 3x$$

leads us to search for a solution proportional to $\sin 3x$, because if y is proportional to $\sin 3x$, so is D^2y. Indeed, from

(9) $$y = A \sin 3x$$

we get

$$D^2y = -9A \sin 3x,$$

so (9) is a solution of (8) if

$$(-9 + 4)A = 1; A = -\tfrac{1}{5}.$$

Thus (8) has the general solution

$$y = c_1 \cos 2x + c_2 \sin 2x - \tfrac{1}{5} \sin 3x,$$

a result easily obtained mentally.

For equation (8), the general method of undetermined coefficients leads us to write

$$m = \pm 2i, m' = \pm 3i,$$

and so to write

(10) $$y_p = A \sin 3x + B \cos 3x.$$

When the y_p of (10) is substituted into (8), it is found, of course, that

$$A = -1/5, B = 0.$$

In contrast, consider the equation

(11) $(D^2 + 4D + 4)y = \sin 3x.$

Here any attempt to find a solution proportional to $\sin 3x$ is doomed to failure because, although D^2y will also be proportional to $\sin 3x$, the term Dy will involve $\cos 3x$. There is no other term on either side of (11) to compensate for this cosine term, so no solution of the form $y = A \sin 3x$ is possible. For this equation, $m = -2, -2, m' = \pm 3i$, and in the particular solution

$$y_p = A \sin 3x + B \cos 3x,$$

it must turn out that $B \neq 0$. No labor has been saved by the inspection.

In more complicated situations such as

$$(D^2 + 4)y = x \sin 3x - 2 \cos 3x,$$

the method of inspection will save no work.

For the equation

(12) $(D^2 + 4)y = e^{5x},$

we see, since $(D^2 + 4)e^{5x} = 29e^{5x}$, that

$$y_p = \tfrac{1}{29}e^{5x}$$

is a solution.

Finally, note that if y_1 is a solution of

$$f(D)y = R_1(x)$$

and y_2 is a solution of

$$f(D)y = R_2(x),$$

then

$$y_p = y_1 + y_2$$

is a solution of

$$f(D)y = R_1(x) + R_2(x).$$

It follows readily that the task of obtaining a particular solution of

$$f(D)y = R(x)$$

may be split into parts by treating separate terms of $R(x)$ independently, if convenient. See the examples below. This is the basis of the "method of superposition" which plays a useful role in applied mathematics.

EXAMPLE (c): Find a particular solution of

$$(13) \qquad (D^2 - 9)y = 3e^x + x - \sin 4x.$$

Since $(D^2 - 9)e^x = -8e^x$, we see by inspection that

$$y_1 = -\tfrac{3}{8}e^x$$

is a particular solution of

$$(D^2 - 9)y_1 = 3e^x.$$

In a similar manner, we see that $y_2 = -\tfrac{1}{9}x$ satisfies

$$(D^2 - 9)y_2 = x$$

and that

$$y_3 = \tfrac{1}{25} \sin 4x$$

satisfies

$$(D^2 - 9)y_3 = -\sin 4x.$$

Hence

$$y_p = -\tfrac{3}{8}e^x - \tfrac{1}{9}x + \tfrac{1}{25} \sin 4x$$

is a solution of equation (13).

EXAMPLE (d): Find a particular solution of

$$(14) \qquad (D^2 + 4)y = \sin x + \sin 2x.$$

At once we see that $y_1 = \tfrac{1}{3} \sin x$ is a solution of

$$(D^2 + 4)y_1 = \sin x.$$

Then we seek a solution of

$$(15) \qquad (D^2 + 4)y_2 = \sin 2x$$

by the method of undetermined coefficients. Since $m = \pm 2i$ and

$$m' = \pm 2i,$$

we put

$$y_2 = Ax \sin 2x + Bx \cos 2x$$

into (15) and easily determine that

$$4A \cos 2x - 4B \sin 2x = \sin 2x,$$

from which $A = 0, B = -\tfrac{1}{4}$.

Thus a particular solution of (14) is

$$y_p = \tfrac{1}{3} \sin x - \tfrac{1}{4}x \cos 2x.$$

Exercises

1. Show that if $b \neq a$, then

$$(D^2 + a^2)y = \sin bx$$

has the particular solution $y = (a^2 - b^2)^{-1} \sin bx$.

2. Show that the equation

$$(D^2 + a^2)y = \sin ax$$

has no solution of the form $y = A \sin ax$, with A constant. Find a particular solution of the equation. ANS. $y = -\dfrac{x}{2a} \cos ax$.

In Exs. 3–50, find a particular solution by inspection. Verify your solution.

3. $(D^2 + 4)y = 12$.
4. $(D^2 + 9)y = 18$.
5. $(D^2 + 4D + 4)y = 8$.
6. $(D^2 + 2D - 3)y = 6$.
7. $(D^3 - 3D + 2)y = -7$.
8. $(D^4 + 4D^2 + 4)y = -20$.
9. $(D^2 + 4D)y = 12$.
10. $(D^3 - 9D)y = 27$.
11. $(D^3 + D)y = 15$.
12. $(D^3 + D)y = -8$.
13. $(D^4 - 4D^2)y = 24$.
14. $(D^4 + D^2)y = -12$.
15. $(D^5 - D^3)y = 24$.
16. $(D^5 - 9D^3)y = 27$.
17. $(D^2 + 4)y = 6 \sin x$. ANS. $y = 2 \sin x$.
18. $(D^2 + 4)y = 10 \cos 3x$. ANS. $y = -2 \cos 3x$.
19. $(D^2 + 4)y = 8x + 1 - 15e^x$. ANS. $y = 2x + \frac{1}{4} - 3e^x$.
20. $(D^2 + D)y = 6 + 3e^{2x}$. ANS. $y = 6x + \frac{1}{2}e^{2x}$.
21. $(D^2 + 3D - 4)y = 18e^{2x}$. ANS. $y = 3e^{2x}$.
22. $(D^2 + 2D + 5)y = 4e^x - 10$. ANS. $y = \frac{1}{2}e^x - 2$.
23. $(D^2 - 1)y = 2e^{3x}$.
24. $(D^2 - 1)y = 2x + 3$.
25. $(D^2 - 1)y = \cos 2x$.
26. $(D^2 - 1)y = \sin 2x$.
27. $(D^2 + 1)y = e^x + 3x$.
28. $(D^2 + 1)y = 5e^{-3x}$.
29. $(D^2 + 1)y = -2x + \cos 2x$.
30. $(D^2 + 1)y = 4e^{-2x}$.
31. $(D^2 + 1)y = 10 \sin 4x$.
32. $(D^2 + 1)y = -6e^{-3x}$.
33. $(D^2 + 2D + 1)y = 12e^x$.
34. $(D^2 + 2D + 1)y = 7e^{-2x}$.
35. $(D^2 - 2D + 1)y = 12e^{-x}$.
36. $(D^2 - 2D + 1)y = 6e^{-2x}$.
37. $(D^2 - 2D - 3)y = e^x$.
38. $(D^2 - 2D - 3)y = e^{2x}$.
39. $(4D^2 + 1)y = 12 \sin x$.
40. $(4D^2 + 1)y = -12 \cos x$.
41. $(4D^2 + 4D + 1)y = 18e^x - 5$.
42. $(4D^2 + 4D + 1)y = 7e^{-x} + 2$.
43. $(D^3 - 1)y = e^{-x}$.
44. $(D^3 - 1)y = 4 - 3x^2$.
45. $(D^3 - D)y = e^{2x}$.
46. $(D^4 + 4)y = 5e^{2x}$.
47. $(D^4 + 4)y = 6 \sin 2x$.
48. $(D^4 + 4)y = \cos 2x$.
49. $(D^3 - D)y = 5 \sin 2x$.
50. $(D^3 - D)y = 5 \cos 2x$.

CHAPTER 10

Inverse Differential Operators

48. The exponential shift

Let $D \equiv d/dx$ as usual, and let $V(x)$ possess as many derivatives as may be encountered in the operations performed. Then

$$D[e^{-ax}V(x)] = e^{-ax}DV(x) - ae^{-ax}V(x)$$

$$= e^{-ax}(D - a)V(x).$$

Hence, operating with D again, we are led to

$$D^2[e^{-ax}V(x)] = D[e^{-ax}\{(D - a)V(x)\}]$$

$$= e^{-ax}(D - a)^2V(x).$$

Iteration of the process yields, for n any positive integer,

$$D^n[e^{-ax}V(x)] = e^{-ax}(D - a)^nV(x).$$

Using the linearity of differential operators, we conclude that when $f(D)$ is a polynomial in D with constant coefficients, then

(1) $$f(D)[e^{-ax}V(x)] = e^{-ax}f(D - a)V(x).$$

In equation (1), put $e^{-ax}V(x) = y$. Then (1) becomes

$$f(D)y = e^{-ax}f(D - a)[e^{ax}y],$$

or

144

(2) $$e^{ax}f(D)y = f(D - a)[e^{ax}y].$$

The relation (2) shows us how to shift an exponential factor from the left of a differential operator to the right of the operator. This relation has many uses, one of which is exhibited in the following examples.

EXAMPLE (a): Solve the equation

(3) $$(D^2 - 2D + 5)y = 16x^3e^{3x}.$$

Note that the complementary function is

(4) $$y_c = c_1e^x \cos 2x + c_2e^x \sin 2x.$$

We can conclude also that there is a particular solution,

(5) $$y_p = Ax^3e^{3x} + Bx^2e^{3x} + Cxe^{3x} + Ee^{3x},$$

which can be obtained by the method of Chapter 9. But the task of obtaining the derivatives of y_p and finding the numerical values of A, B, C, and E is a little tedious. It can be made easier by using the exponential shift (2).

Let us write (3) in the form

$$e^{-3x}(D^2 - 2D + 5)y = 16x^3,$$

and then apply the relation (2), with $a = -3$. In shifting the exponential e^{-3x} from the left to the right of the differential operator, we must replace D by $(D + 3)$ throughout, thus obtaining

$$[(D + 3)^2 - 2(D + 3) + 5](e^{-3x}y) = 16x^3,$$

or

(6) $$(D^2 + 4D + 8)(e^{-3x}y) = 16x^3.$$

In equation (6), the dependent variable is $(e^{-3x}y)$. We know at once that (6) has a particular solution of the form

(7) $$e^{-3x}y_p = Ax^3 + Bx^2 + Cx + E.$$

Successive differentiations of (7) are simple. Indeed,

$$D(e^{-3x}y_p) = 3Ax^2 + 2Bx + C,$$
$$D^2(e^{-3x}y_p) = 6Ax + 2B,$$

so from (6) we get

$$6Ax + 2B + 12Ax^2 + 8Bx + 4C + 8Ax^3 + 8Bx^2 + 8Cx + 8E = 16x^3.$$

Hence

$$8A = 16,$$
$$12A + 8B = 0,$$
$$6A + 8B + 8C = 0,$$
$$2B + 4C + 8E = 0,$$

from which $A = 2$, $B = -3$, $C = \frac{3}{2}$, $E = 0$.
Therefore

$$e^{-3x}y_p = 2x^3 - 3x^2 + \tfrac{3}{2}x,$$

or

$$y_p = (2x^3 - 3x^2 + \tfrac{3}{2}x)e^{3x},$$

and the general solution of the original equation (3) is

$$y = c_1 e^x \cos 2x + c_2 e^x \sin 2x + (2x^3 - 3x^2 + \tfrac{3}{2}x)e^{3x}.$$

The complementary function could also have been obtained from (6).

EXAMPLE (b): Solve the equation

(8) $$(D^2 - 2D + 1)y = xe^x + 7x - 2.$$

Here the immediate use of the exponential shift would do no good, because removing the e^x factor from the first term on the right would only insert a factor e^{-x} in the second and third terms on the right. The terms $7x - 2$ on the right give us no trouble as they stand. Therefore we break (8) into two problems, obtaining a particular solution for each of the equations

(9) $$(D^2 - 2D + 1)y_1 = xe^x$$

and

(10) $$(D^2 - 2D + 1)y_2 = 7x - 2.$$

On (9) we use the exponential shift, passing from

$$e^{-x}(D - 1)^2 y_1 = x$$

to

(11) $$D^2(e^{-x}y_1) = x.$$

A particular solution of (11) is easily obtained:

$$e^{-x}y_1 = \tfrac{1}{6}x^3,$$

so

(12) $$y_1 = \tfrac{1}{6}x^3 e^x.$$

Equation (10) is treated as in Chapter 9. Put

$$y_2 = Ax + B.$$

Then $Dy_2 = A$, and from (10) it is easily found that $A = 7$, $B = 12$. Thus a particular solution of (10) is

(13) $y_2 = 7x + 12.$

Using (12), (13), and the roots of the auxiliary equation for (8), the general solution of (8) can now be written. It is

$$y = (c_1 + c_2x)e^x + \tfrac{1}{6}x^3e^x + 7x + 12.$$

EXAMPLE (c): Solve the equation

(14) $D^2(D + 4)^2y = 96e^{-4x}.$

At once we have $m = 0, 0, -4, -4$ and $m' = -4$. We seek first a particular solution. Therefore we integrate each member of (14) twice before using the exponential shift. From (14) it follows that

(15) $(D + 4)^2y_p = 6e^{-4x},$

the constants of integration being disregarded because only a particular solution is sought. Equation (15) yields

$$e^{4x}(D + 4)^2y_p = 6,$$
$$D^2(y_pe^{4x}) = 6,$$
$$y_pe^{4x} = 3x^2,$$
$$y_p = 3x^2e^{-4x}.$$

Thus the general solution of (14) is seen to be

$$y = c_1 + c_2x + (c_3 + c_4x + 3x^2)e^{-4x}.$$

The exponential shift is particularly helpful when applied in connection with terms for which the values of m' (using the notations of Chapter 9) are repetitions of values of m.

Exercises

In Exs. 1–12, use the exponential shift to find a particular solution.

1. $(D - 3)^2y = e^{3x}.$ ANS. $y = \tfrac{1}{2}x^2e^{3x}.$
2. $(D - 1)^2y = e^x.$
3. $(D + 2)^2y = 12xe^{-2x}.$ ANS. $y = 2x^3e^{-2x}.$

4. $(D+1)^2 y = 3xe^{-x}$.

5. $(D-2)^3 y = 6xe^{2x}$.   ANS. $y = \frac{1}{4}x^4 e^{2x}$.

6. $(D+4)^3 y = 8xe^{-4x}$.

7. $(D+3)^3 y = 15x^2 e^{-3x}$.   ANS. $y = \frac{1}{4}x^5 e^{-3x}$.

8. $(D-4)^3 y = 15x^2 e^{4x}$.

9. $D^2(D-2)^2 y = 16e^{2x}$.   ANS. $y = 2x^2 e^{2x}$.

10. $D^2(D+3)^2 y = 9e^{-3x}$.

11. $(D^2 - D - 2)y = 18xe^{-x}$.   ANS. $y = -(3x^2 + 2x)e^{-x}$.

12. $(D^2 - D - 2)y = 36xe^{2x}$.

In Exs. 13–18, find a particular solution, using the exponential shift in part of your work, as in Example (b) above.

13. $(D-2)^2 y = 20 - 3xe^{2x}$.   ANS. $y = 5 - \frac{1}{2}x^3 e^{2x}$.

14. $(D-2)^2 y = 4 - 8x + 6xe^{2x}$.

15. $y'' - 9y = 9(2x - 3 + 4xe^{3x})$.   ANS. $y = 3 - 2x + (3x^2 - x)e^{3x}$.

16. $y'' + 4y' + 4y = 4x - 6e^{-2x} + 3e^x$.

17. $(D+1)^2 y = e^{-x} + 3x$.   ANS. $y = \frac{1}{2}x^2 e^{-x} + 3x - 6$.

18. $(D^2 - 4)y = 16xe^{-2x} + 8x + 4$.   ANS. $y = -(2x + 1)(xe^{-2x} + 1)$.

In Exs. 19–28, find the general solution.

19. $y'' - 4y = 8xe^{2x}$.   ANS. $y = c_1 e^{-2x} + (c_2 - \frac{1}{2}x + x^2)e^{2x}$.

20. $y'' - 9y = -72xe^{-3x}$.

21. $D(D+1)^2 y = e^{-x}$.   ANS. $y = c_1 + (c_2 + c_3 x - \frac{1}{2}x^2)e^{-x}$.

22. $D^2(D-2)^2 y = 2e^{2x}$.

23. $y'' + 2y' + y = 48e^{-x} \cos 4x$.   ANS. $y = (c_1 + c_2 x - 3 \cos 4x)e^{-x}$.

24. $y'' + 4y' + 4y = 18e^{-2x} \cos 3x$.

25. $(D-1)^2 y = e^x \sec^2 x \tan x$.   ANS. $y = e^x(c_1 + c_2 x + \frac{1}{2} \tan x)$.

26. $(D^2 + 4D + 4)y = -x^{-2}e^{-2x}$.   ANS. $y = e^{-2x}(c_1 + c_2 x + \ln x)$.

27. $(D-a)^2 y = e^{ax} f''(x)$.   ANS. $y = e^{ax}[c_1 + c_2 x + f(x)]$.

28. $(D^2 + 7D + 12)y = e^{-3x} \sec^2 x(1 + 2 \tan x)$.

ANS. $y = c_1 e^{-4x} + e^{-3x}(c_2 + \tan x)$.

49. The operator $1/f(D)$

In seeking a particular solution of

(1) $$f(D)y = R(x),$$

it is natural to write

(2) $$y = \frac{1}{f(D)} R(x)$$

and to try to define an operator $1/f(D)$ so that the function y of (2) will have meaning and will satisfy equation (1).

Instead of building a theory of such inverse differential operators, we shall adopt the following method of attack. Purely formal (unjustified) manipulations of the symbols will be performed, thus leading to a tentative evaluation of

$$\frac{1}{f(D)} R(x).$$

After all, the only thing which we require of our evaluation is that

(3) $$f(D) \cdot \frac{1}{f(D)} R(x) = R(x).$$

Hence the burden of proof will be placed on a direct verification of the condition (3) in each instance.

50. Evaluation of $[1/f(D)]e^{ax}$

We proved (pages 108–109) with slightly different notation that

(1) $$f(D)e^{ax} = e^{ax}f(a)$$

and

(2) $$(D - a)^n(x^n e^{ax}) = n!e^{ax}.$$

Equation (1) suggests

(3) $$\frac{1}{f(D)} e^{ax} = \frac{e^{ax}}{f(a)}, \quad f(a) \neq 0.$$

Now from (1) it follows that

$$f(D) \frac{e^{ax}}{f(a)} = \frac{f(a)e^{ax}}{f(a)} = e^{ax}.$$

Hence (3) is verified.

Now suppose that $f(a) = 0$. Then $f(D)$ contains the factor $(D - a)$. Suppose that the factor occurs precisely n times in $f(D)$; that is, let

$$f(D) = \varphi(D)(D - a)^n; \; \varphi(a) \neq 0.$$

With the aid of (2) we obtain

$$\varphi(D)(D - a)^n(x^n e^{ax}) = \varphi(D)n!e^{ax},$$

from which, by (1), it follows that

(4) $\varphi(D)(D - a)^n(x^n e^{ax}) = n!\varphi(a)e^{ax}.$

Therefore we write

(5) $$\frac{1}{\varphi(D)(D - a)^n} e^{ax} = \frac{x^n e^{ax}}{n!\varphi(a)}, \quad \varphi(a) \neq 0,$$

which is easily verified. Indeed,

$$\varphi(D)(D - a)^n \frac{x^n e^{ax}}{n!\varphi(a)} = \frac{n!\varphi(a)e^{ax}}{n!\varphi(a)} = e^{ax}.$$

Note that formula (3) is included in formula (5) as the special case, $n = 0$. See also Ex. 19, page 152.

EXAMPLE (a): Solve the equation

(6) $(D^2 + 1)y = e^{2x}.$

Here the roots of the auxiliary equation are $m = \pm i$. Further,

$$f(D) = (D^2 + 1)$$

and

$$f(2) \neq 0.$$

Hence, using (3),

$$y_p = \frac{1}{D^2 + 1} e^{2x} = \frac{e^{2x}}{2^2 + 1} = \frac{1}{5} e^{2x},$$

so the solution of (6) is

$$y = c_1 \cos x + c_2 \sin x + \frac{1}{5} e^{2x}.$$

EXAMPLE (b): Solve the equation

(7) $D^2(D - 1)^3(D + 1)y = e^x.$

Here $m = 0, 0, 1, 1, 1, -1$. To get a particular solution of (7), we use formula (5) with $a = 1$, $n = 3$, $\varphi(D) = D^2(D + 1)$. Then

$$\varphi(1) = 1^2 \cdot 2$$

and a particular solution of (7) is given by

$$y_p = \frac{1}{(D - 1)^3 D^2(D + 1)} e^x = \frac{x^3 e^x}{3!1^2 \cdot 2} = \frac{1}{12} x^3 e^x.$$

Then the general solution of (7) is

$$y = c_1 + c_2 x + c_3 e^{-x} + (c_4 + c_5 x + c_6 x^2 + \tfrac{1}{12}x^3)e^x.$$

51. Evaluation of $(D^2 + a^2)^{-1} \sin ax$ and $(D^2 + a^2)^{-1} \cos ax$

No special device is needed for the evaluation of

$$(D^2 + a^2)^{-1} \sin bx$$

when $b \neq a$. In fact

$$\frac{1}{D^2 + a^2} \sin bx = \frac{\sin bx}{a^2 - b^2}; b \neq a,$$

as indicated in Ex. 1, page 143, and a similar result holds for the expression $(D^2 + a^2)^{-1} \cos bx$, when $b \neq a$.

Consider next the evaluation of

(1) $$\frac{1}{D^2 + a^2} \sin ax.$$

The formulas of the preceding section can be put to good use here, since

$$\sin ax = \frac{e^{aix} - e^{-aix}}{2i}.$$

Then

$$\frac{1}{D^2 + a^2} \sin ax = \frac{1}{2i} \frac{1}{(D - ai)(D + ai)} (e^{aix} - e^{-aix})$$

$$= \frac{1}{2i} \left(\frac{xe^{aix}}{1!2ai} - \frac{xe^{-aix}}{1!(-2ai)} \right)$$

$$= -\frac{x}{2a} \frac{e^{aix} + e^{-aix}}{2},$$

so

(2) $$\frac{1}{D^2 + a^2} \sin ax = -\frac{x}{2a} \cos ax.$$

The verification of (2) is left as an exercise.

Another useful result,

(3) $$\frac{1}{D^2 + a^2} \cos ax = \frac{x}{2a} \sin ax,$$

can be obtained in the same way.

Oral Exercises

Give the general solution of each equation.

1. $(D^2 - 1)y = e^{2x}$.   ANS. $y = c_1e^x + c_2e^{-x} + \frac{1}{3}e^{2x}$.
2. $(D^2 - 1)y = e^x$.   ANS. $y = c_1e^x + c_2e^{-x} + \frac{1}{2}xe^x$.

3. $(D^2 + 1)y = \sin x.$ ANS. $y = c_1 \cos x + c_2 \sin x - \frac{1}{2}x \cos x.$

4. $(D^2 + 4)y = \cos 2x.$ ANS. $y = c_1 \cos 2x + c_2 \sin 2x + \frac{1}{4}x \sin 2x.$

5. $(D^2 + 9)y = e^{2x}.$ **6.** $(D^2 + 4)y = e^{3x}.$

7. $(4D^2 + 1)y = e^{-2x}.$ **8.** $D(D - 2)y = e^{-x}.$

9. $D(D - 2)^2 y = e^{2x}.$ **10.** $D(D + 3)^2 y = e^{-3x}.$

11. $(D^2 + 4)y = \cos 3x.$ **12.** $(D^2 + 9)y = \cos 3x.$

13. $(D^2 + 4)y = \sin 2x.$ **14.** $(D^2 + 36)y = \sin 6x.$

15. $(D^2 + 9)y = \sin 3x.$ **16.** $(D^2 + 36)y = \cos 6x.$

Exercises

1. Verify formula (2) of Section 51.

2. Obtain and verify formula (3) of Section 51.

In Exs. 3–18, find the general solution.

3. $(D^2 + 3D - 4)y = 12e^{2x}.$ ANS. $y = c_1 e^{-4x} + c_2 e^x + 2e^{2x}.$

4. $(D^2 + 3D - 4)y = 21e^{3x}.$

5. $(D^2 + 3D - 4)y = 15e^x.$ ANS. $y = c_1 e^{-4x} + (c_2 + 3x)e^x.$

6. $(D^2 + 3D - 4)y = 20e^{-4x}.$

7. $(D^2 - 3D + 2)y = e^x + e^{2x}.$ ANS. $y = (c_1 - x)e^x + (c_2 + x)e^{2x}.$

8. $(4D^2 - 1)y = e^{x/2} + 12e^x.$

9. $D^2(D - 2)^3 y = 48e^{2x}.$

         ANS. $y = c_1 + c_2 x + (c_3 + c_4 x + c_5 x^2 + 2x^3)e^{2x}.$

10. $(D^4 - 18D^2 + 81)y = 36e^{3x}.$

11. $(D^2 + 16)y = 14 \cos 3x.$ ANS. $y = c_1 \cos 4x + c_2 \sin 4x + 2 \cos 3x.$

12. $(4D^2 + 1)y = 33 \sin 3x.$

13. $y'' + 16y = 24 \sin 4x.$ ANS. $y = (c_1 - 3x) \cos 4x + c_2 \sin 4x.$

14. $y'' + 16y = 48 \cos 4x.$

15. $y'' + y = 12 \cos 2x - \sin x.$

         ANS. $y = (c_1 + \frac{1}{2}x) \cos x + c_2 \sin x - 4 \cos 2x.$

16. $y'' + y = \sin 3x + 4 \cos x.$

17. $(D^2 - 2D + 5)y = e^x \cos 2x.$ Hint: use the exponential shift followed by formula (3) of Section 51.

         ANS. $y = e^x(c_1 \cos 2x + c_2 \sin 2x) + \frac{1}{4}xe^x \sin 2x.$

18. $(D^2 + 2D + 5)y = e^{-x} \sin 2x.$

         ANS. $y = e^{-x}(c_1 \cos 2x + c_2 \sin 2x) - \frac{1}{4}xe^{-x} \cos 2x.$

19. Prove that if $f(x) = (x - a)^n \varphi(x)$, then $f^{(n)}(a) = n!\varphi(a)$. Then use equation (5) of Section 50 above to prove that

$$\frac{1}{f(D)} e^{ax} = \frac{x^n e^{ax}}{f^{(n)}(a)},$$

where n is the smallest non-negative integer for which $f^{(n)}(a) \neq 0$. See C. A. Hutchinson, "Another Note on Linear Operators," *Amer. Math. Monthly*, **46** (1939), 161.

In Exs. 20–23, use the formula of Ex. 19 above.

20. Ex. 5.   **21.** Ex. 6.
22. Ex. 9.   **23.** Ex. 10.

In Exs. 24–29, verify the formulas* stated.

24. $\dfrac{1}{f(D)}\,\sin ax = \dfrac{f(-D)\,\sin ax}{f(ai)f(-ai)}\,;\, f(ai)f(-ai) \neq 0.$

25. $\dfrac{1}{f(D)}\,\cos ax = \dfrac{f(-D)\,\cos ax}{f(ai)f(-ai)}\,;\, f(ai)f(-ai) \neq 0.$

26. $\dfrac{1}{f(D)}\,\sinh ax = \dfrac{f(-D)\,\sinh ax}{f(a)f(-a)}\,;\, f(a)f(-a) \neq 0.$

27. $\dfrac{1}{f(D)}\,\cosh ax = \dfrac{f(-D)\,\cosh ax}{f(a)f(-a)}\,;\, f(a)f(-a) \neq 0.$

28. $\dfrac{1}{(D^2 + a^2)^n}\,\sin ax = \dfrac{x^n}{(2a)^n n!}\,\sin (ax - \tfrac{1}{2}n\pi).$

29. $\dfrac{1}{(D^2 + a^2)^n}\,\cos ax = \dfrac{x^n}{(2a)^n n!}\,\cos (ax - \tfrac{1}{2}n\pi).$

In Exs. 30–33 use the formulas of Ex. 24–25 above.

30. Ex. 1, page 136.   **31.** Ex. 11, page 136.
32. Ex. 12, page 137.   **33.** Ex. 32, page 137.

52. Evaluation of $[1/f(D)]x^n$

It is proved in more advanced books† that

$$\frac{1}{f(D)}\,x^n$$

is correctly evaluated by replacing $1/f(D)$ by its formal series expansion in ascending powers of D and then carrying out the indicated operations.

---

* The formulas of Exs. 24–27 were obtained by C. A. Hutchinson, "An Operational Formula," *Amer. Math. Monthly*, **40** (1933), 482–483; those of Exs. 28–29 were given by C. A. Hutchinson, "Note on an Operational Formula," *Amer. Math. Monthly*, **44** (1937), 371–372.

† See E. L. Ince, *Ordinary Differential Equations* (London: Longmans, Green and Co., 1927), p. 140.

By correctly evaluated it is meant that if y_p be the result of the evaluation, then $f(D)y_p = x^n$.

The extension of this method to the evaluation of $[1/f(D)]p(x)$, where $p(x)$ is a polynomial in x, should be evident.

Two comments are in order here. First, if $f(D)$ has a factor D^k, $k > 0$, then negative powers of D will appear in the expansion. These are to be interpreted as iterated integrations, illustrated below:

$$D^{-1}x^3 = \frac{x^4}{4},$$

$$D^{-2}x^3 = D^{-1}\frac{x^4}{4} = \frac{x^5}{20}, \text{ etc.}$$

Note that in searching for a particular solution we disregard constants of integration. The presence of negative powers of D is easily avoided as is shown in Example (b) below.

Second, only a finite number of terms in the series expansion of $1/f(D)$ affect the result, since for $m > n$, $D^m x^n = 0$.

EXAMPLE (a): Find a particular solution of the equation

$$(D^2 + 1)y = x^2.$$

Now

$$\frac{1}{D^2 + 1} = 1 - D^2 + D^4 - \cdots,$$

so

$$y_p = \frac{1}{D^2 + 1} x^2 = (1 - D^2)x^2 = x^2 - 2,$$

in which all terms involving $D^m x^2$ for $m > 2$ have been dropped since each is zero.

EXAMPLE (b): Solve the equation

(1) $$D^3(D^2 - 1)y = x^2.$$

First let us integrate each member of equation (1) three times, disregarding constants of integration, thus obtaining

$$(D^2 - 1)y = \frac{x^5}{60}.$$

Then

$$y_p = \frac{1}{D^2 - 1} \cdot \frac{x^5}{60} = (-1 - D^2 - D^4 - D^6 - \cdots)\frac{x^5}{60},$$

from which

$$y_p = -\frac{x^5}{60} - \frac{x^3}{3} - 2x.$$

The general solution of (1) is

$$y = c_1 e^x + c_2 e^{-x} + c_3 + c_4 x + c_5 x^2 - \frac{x^3}{3} - \frac{x^5}{60},$$

where the term $(-2x)$ from y_p has been absorbed into the complementary function.

If we do not wish to avoid negative powers of D, we can, from (1), write at once

$$y_p = \frac{1}{D^3(D^2 - 1)} x^2 = D^{-3}(-1 - D^2 - D^4 - D^6 - \cdots)x^2$$

$$= (-D^{-3} - D^{-1} - D - D^3 - \cdots)x^2.$$

Now $D^{-1}x^2 = x^3/3$, $D^{-2}x^2 = x^4/12$, $D^{-3}x^2 = x^5/60$, $Dx^2 = 2x$, and $D^3 x^2 = 0$, so

$$y_p = -\frac{x^5}{60} - \frac{x^3}{3} - 2x$$

as before.

EXAMPLE (c): Find a particular solution of the equation

(2) $(D^2 + D - 2)y = 2x - x^3.$

Here

$$y_p = \frac{1}{D^2 + D - 2}(2x - x^3).$$

By dividing $(-2 + D + D^2)$ into 1 (long division), it is found that

(3) $y_p = (-\frac{1}{2} - \frac{1}{4}D - \frac{3}{8}D^2 - \frac{5}{16}D^3 - \cdots)(2x - x^3).$

From (3) we conclude with a little labor that

(4) $y_p = \frac{1}{2}x^3 + \frac{3}{4}x^2 + \frac{5}{4}x + \frac{11}{8}.$

The formal character of the process we have just used makes imperative the verification of our final result by direct substitution into the original differential equation. That verification is left for the student.

The brevity of the solution above is due to the omission of all the actual work, the long division, and the reduction of (3) to (4). Before getting too enthusiastic about this method, a student should solve equation (2) by the method of Chapter 9 and also supply the missing steps in the solution above. Then the two processes can be compared.

There does seem to be one type of equation for which the method of this section is a vast improvement over the previous attacks. See the next example.

EXAMPLE (d): Find a particular solution of the equation

$$(D^8 - 1)y = x^{15}.$$

Here

$$y_p = \frac{1}{D^8 - 1}\, x^{15} = (-1 - D^8 - \cdot \cdot \cdot)x^{15}.$$

But $D^8 x^{15} = 15!x^7/7!$. Hence*

$$y_p = -x^{15} - 15!x^7/7!.$$

53. Additional notes on the operational method

Since the equation

(1) $$(D - m)y = R(x)$$

is of the first order, an integrating factor e^{-mx} is available. It follows that a particular solution of (1) is

$$y_p = e^{mx} \int e^{-mx} R(x)\, dx,$$

where the constant of integration may be omitted. Thus it is seen that

(2) $$\frac{1}{D - m} R(x) = e^{mx} \int e^{-mx} R(x)\, dx.$$

Suppose $f(D) = (D - m_1)(D - m_2) \cdot \cdot \cdot (D - m_n)$, in which the factors are all distinct. Then there exists the partial fractions expansion

(3) $$\frac{1}{f(D)} = \frac{A_1}{D - m_1} + \frac{A_2}{D - m_2} + \cdot \cdot \cdot + \frac{A_n}{D - m_n},$$

the $A_1, A_2, \cdot \cdot \cdot, A_n$ being constants. It can be shown† that in

---

* For those who must live life the hard way, it is admitted that

$$15!/7! = 259\ 459\ 200.$$

† E. L. Ince, *Ordinary Differential Equations* (London: Longmans, Green and Co., 1927), pp. 140–141.

$[1/f(D)]R(x)$, the operator $1/f(D)$ may be replaced by the right member in (3). Then formula (2), or any other suitable tool, may be used to evaluate each term of the type $A_k(D - m_k)^{-1}R(x)$.

Even if $f(D)$ involves repeated factors, an evaluation similar to that above may be accomplished. The partial fractions expansion then requires the evaluation of terms of the kind $(D - m)^{-n}R(x)$ with $n > 1$. Put

$$y_p = (D - m)^{-n}R(x),$$

then

$$(D - m)^n y_p = R(x),$$

on which the exponential shift works neatly. Thus from

$$e^{-mx}(D - m)^n y_p = e^{-mx}R(x)$$

it follows that

$$D^n(e^{-mx}y_p) = e^{-mx}R(x),$$

so the value of y_p can be obtained with n integrations.

At one stage of the derivation of the exponential shift formula we showed (page 144) that for any y

$$f(D)y = e^{ax}f(D + a)(e^{-ax}y).$$

Let us choose

$$y = e^{ax} \frac{1}{f(D + a)} V(x).$$

Then

$$f(D)y = e^{ax}f(D + a)\left[\frac{1}{f(D + a)} V(x)\right]$$
$$= e^{ax}V(x).$$

Therefore

$$\frac{1}{f(D)} e^{ax}V(x) = y,$$

or

(4)
$$\frac{1}{f(D)} [e^{ax}V(x)] = e^{ax} \frac{1}{f(D + a)} V(x).$$

The relation (4) may be used to perform the exponential shift automatically in solving an equation such as

(5)
$$(D^2 - 2D + 5)y = e^x \cos 2x.$$

Here

$$y_p = \frac{1}{D^2 - 2D + 5} (e^x \cos 2x),$$

which, because of (4), can be written

$$y_p = e^x \frac{1}{(D+1)^2 - 2(D+1) + 5} \cos 2x$$

or

$$y_p = e^x \frac{1}{D^2 + 4} \cos 2x.$$

Then, using (3), page 151, we get

$$y_p = \tfrac{1}{4} x e^x \sin 2x.$$

Exercises

In each exercise, find a particular solution and verify your result.

1. $(D^2 - 1)y = x^3$.   ANS. $y = -x^3 - 6x$.
2. $(D^2 - 1)y = x^4$.   ANS. $y = -x^4 - 12x^2 - 24$.
3. $(4D^2 + 1)y = x^3$.   ANS. $y = x^3 - 24x$.
4. $(4D^2 + 1)y = x^4$.   ANS. $y = x^4 - 48x^2 + 384$.
5. $(D - 1)^2 y = x^2$.   ANS. $y = x^2 + 4x + 6$.
6. $(D + 1)^2 y = x^2 + 3x + 3$.   ANS. $y = x^2 - x + 3$.
7. $(D - 1)^2 y = x^3 - 4x^2$.   ANS. $y = x^3 + 2x^2 + 2x$.
8. $(D + 1)^2 y = x^3 + 6x^2$.   ANS. $y = x^3 - 6x + 12$.
9. $D(D^2 + 4)y = 4x^3 + 2x$.   ANS. $y = \tfrac{1}{4}x^4 - \tfrac{1}{2}x^2$.
10. $D^2(D^2 + 4)y = 12x$.   ANS. $y = \tfrac{1}{2}x^3$.
11. $D^2(D + 1)y = 12x - 2$.   ANS. $y = 2x^3 - 7x^2$.
12. $D^2(D - 1)y = 12x - 2$.   ANS. $y = -2x^3 - 5x^2$.
13. $(D^2 - 3D + 2)y = 6x^2 - 6x - 11$.   ANS. $y = 3x^2 + 6x + \tfrac{1}{2}$.
14. $(D^2 - 3D + 2)y = 2x^3 - 9x^2 + 2x - 16$. ANS. $y = x^3 - 2x - 11$.

15. $(D^6 - 1)y = x^{10}$.   ANS. $y = -x^{10} - \dfrac{10!}{4!} x^4$.

16. $(D^3 + 3D^2 - 4)y = 16x^3 + 20x^2$. ANS. $y = -4x^3 - 5x^2 - 18x - \tfrac{27}{2}$.

Miscellaneous Exercises

In Exs. 1–18, find a particular solution.

1. $(D^2 - 4D + 4)y = 6x^2 e^{2x}$.   ANS. $y = \tfrac{1}{2}x^4 e^{2x}$.
2. $(D - 3)^2 y = e^{3x}$.   ANS. $y = \tfrac{1}{2}x^2 e^{3x}$.
3. $D(D - 2)y = e^{2x}$.   ANS. $y = \tfrac{1}{2}x e^{2x}$.
4. $D^2(D + 1)y = e^{-x}$.   ANS. $y = x e^{-x}$.
5. $(D^2 + 4)y = 8x^5$.   ANS. $y = 2x^5 - 10x^3 + 15x$.
6. $(D^2 + 4)y = 16x e^{2x}$.   ANS. $y = (2x - 1)e^{2x}$.

7. $(D^2 + 4D + 5)y = 4e^{-2x} \cos x.$ ANS. $y = 2xe^{-2x} \sin x.$

8. $(D^2 - D - 2)y = 4x^2 - 3e^{-x}.$ ANS. $y = xe^{-x} - 2x^2 + 2x - 3.$

9. $(D^2 - 4D + 13)y = 24e^{2x} \sin 3x.$ ANS. $y = -4xe^{2x} \cos 3x.$

10. $(D^2 - 4D + 13)y = 24e^{2x} \sin x.$ ANS. $y = 3e^{2x} \sin x.$

11. $(D^2 - 3D + 2)y = (x - 2)e^x.$ ANS. $y = -\frac{1}{2}(x^2 - 2x)e^x.$

12. $(D^2 - 3D + 2)y = 72xe^{-x}.$ ANS. $y = 2(6x + 5)e^{-x}.$

13. $(D^2 + 4)y = 12(\sin x + \sin 2x).$ ANS. $y = 4 \sin x - 3x \cos 2x.$

14. $(D^2 + 4)y = 20(e^x - \cos 2x).$ ANS. $y = 4e^x - 5x \sin 2x.$

15. $(D^2 + 16)y = 8(x + \sin 4x).$ ANS. $y = x(\frac{1}{2} - \cos 4x).$

16. $(D^2 + 4)y = 8 \sin x \cos x.$ ANS. $y = -x \cos 2x.$

17. $(D^2 + 4)y = 8 \cos^2 x.$ ANS. $y = 1 + x \sin 2x.$

18. $(D^4 - 1)y = x^6.$ ANS. $y = -x^6 - 360x^2.$

In Exs. 19–28, find the general solution.

19. $(D^2 - 4D + 13)y = 24e^{2x} \cos x.$

ANS. $y = e^{2x}(c_1 \cos 3x + c_2 \sin 3x + 3 \cos x).$

20. $(D^2 - 4D + 13)y = 24e^{2x} \cos 3x.$

ANS. $y = e^{2x}(c_1 \cos 3x + c_2 \sin 3x + 4x \sin 3x).$

21. $(D^2 + 25)y = \sin 5x.$ ANS. $y = c_1 \cos 5x + c_2 \sin 5x - 0.1x \cos 5x.$

22. $D(D^2 + 1)y = \sin x.$ ANS. $y = c_1 + c_2 \cos x + (c_3 - \frac{1}{2}x) \sin x.$

23. $D^2(D^2 + 1)y = \sin x.$

ANS. $y = c_1 + c_2x + (c_3 + \frac{1}{2}x) \cos x + c_4 \sin x.$

24. $(D^2 - 3D + 2)y = x^2 - 2x.$

25. Ex. 8, page 136.

26. Ex. 10, page 136.

27. Ex. 18, page 137.

28. Ex. 19, page 137.

In Exs. 29–34, find the particular solution indicated.

29. $(D^2 + 1)y = 4e^x;$ when $x = 0,$ $y = 0$ and $y' = 0.$

ANS. $y = 2(e^x - \cos x - \sin x).$

30. $(D^2 + 4)y = 2x - 8;$ when $x = 0,$ $y = 1$ and $y' = 0.$

ANS. $4y = 12 \cos 2x - \sin 2x + 2x - 8.$

31. $(D^2 + 3D + 2)y = 4x^2;$ when $x = 0,$ $y = 0$ and $y' = 0.$

ANS. $y = 2x^2 - 6x + 7 - 8e^{-x} + e^{-2x}.$

32. $(D^2 - 1)y = \sin 2x;$ when $x = 0,$ $y = 0$ and $y' = 1.$

ANS. $10y = 7(e^x - e^{-x}) - 2 \sin 2x;$

or $5y = 7 \sinh x - \sin 2x.$

33. $(D^2 + 2D)y = 2x;$ when $x = 0,$ $y = 0,$ and when $x = 1,$ $y = 0.$

ANS. $2y = x^2 - x.$

34. The equation of Ex. 33 with the conditions that when $x = 0$, $y = 0$ and $y' = 0$.   ANS. $4y = 2x^2 - 2x + 1 - e^{-2x}$.

In Exs. 35–37, obtain from the particular solution indicated the value of y and the value of y' at $x = 1$.

35. $y'' + 2y' + y = x + 2$; when $x = 0$, $y = 1$ and $y' = 0$.

           ANS.   At $x = 1$, $y = (e + 1)/e$ and $y' = (e - 1)/e$.

36. $y'' + 2y' + y = x + 2$; when $x = 0$, $y = 0$ and $y' = 0$.

           ANS.   At $x = 1$, $y = (e - 1)/e$ and $y' = 1$.

37. $(D^2 + 1)y = 3$; when $x = \pi/2$, $y = 0$ and $y' = 0$.

           ANS.   At $x = 1$, $y = 0.4756$ and $y' = -1.6209$.

CHAPTER 11

The Laplace Transform

54. The transform concept

The reader is already familiar with some operators that transform functions into functions. An outstanding example is the differential operator D which transforms each function of a large class (those possessing a derivative) into another function.

We have already found that the operator D is useful in the treatment of linear differential equations with constant coefficients. In this chapter we study another transformation (a mapping of functions onto functions) which has played an increasingly important role in both pure and applied mathematics in the past few decades. The operator L, to be introduced in Section 55, is particularly effective in the study of boundary value problems involving linear differential equations with constant coefficients.

One class of transformations, which are called integral transforms, may be defined by

(1) $$ T\{F(t)\} = \int_{-\infty}^{\infty} K(s, t)\, F(t)\, dt = f(s). $$

Given a function $K(s, t)$, called the kernel of the transformation, equation (1) associates with each $F(t)$ of the class of functions for which the above integral exists a function $f(s)$ defined by (1). Generalizations and abstractions of (1), as well as studies of special cases, are to be found in profusion in mathematical literature.

Various particular choices of $K(s, t)$ in (1) have led to special transforms, each with its own properties to make it useful in specific circumstances. The transform defined by choosing

$$K(s, t) = 0, \qquad \text{for } t < 0,$$
$$= e^{-st}, \qquad \text{for } t \geqq 0,$$

is the one to which this chapter is devoted.

55. Definition of the Laplace transform

Let $F(t)$ be any function such that the integrations encountered may be legitimately performed on $F(t)$. The *Laplace transform* of $F(t)$ is denoted by $L\{F(t)\}$ and is defined by

$$(1) \qquad L\{F(t)\} = \int_0^\infty e^{-st}F(t)\, dt.$$

The integral in (1) is a function of the parameter s; call that function $f(s)$. We may write

$$(2) \qquad L\{F(t)\} = \int_0^\infty e^{-st}F(t)\, dt = f(s).$$

It is customary to refer to $f(s)$, as well as to the symbol $L\{F(t)\}$, as the transform, or the Laplace transform, of $F(t)$.

We may also look upon (2) as a definition of a Laplace operator L, which transforms each function $F(t)$ of a certain set of functions into some function $f(s)$.

It is easy to show that if the integral in (2) does converge, it will do so for all s greater than* some fixed value s_0. That is, equation (2) will define $f(s)$ for $s > s_0$. In extreme cases the integral may converge for all finite s.

It is important that the operator L, like the differential operator D, is a linear operator. If $F_1(t)$ and $F_2(t)$ have Laplace transforms and if c_1 and c_2 are any constants,

$$(3) \qquad L\{c_1 F_1(t) + c_2 F_2(t)\} = c_1 L\{F_1(t)\} + c_2 L\{F_2(t)\}.$$

Using elementary properties of definite integrals, the student can easily show the validity of equation (3).

We shall hereafter employ the relation (3) without restating the fact that the operator L is a linear one.

---

* If s is not to be restricted to real values, the convergence takes place for all s with real part greater than some fixed value.

56. Transforms of elementary functions

The transforms of certain exponential and trigonometric functions and of polynomials will now be obtained. These results enter our work frequently.

EXAMPLE (a):   Find $L\{e^{kt}\}$.

We proceed as follows:

$$L\{e^{kt}\} = \int_0^\infty e^{-st} \cdot e^{kt}\,dt = \int_0^\infty e^{-(s-k)t}\,dt.$$

For $s \leqq k$, the exponent on e is positive or zero and the integral diverges. For $s > k$, the integral converges.

Therefore, for $s > k$,

$$L\{e^{kt}\} = \int_0^\infty e^{-(s-k)t}\,dt$$

$$= \left[\frac{-e^{-(s-k)t}}{s-k} \right]_0^\infty$$

$$= 0 + \frac{1}{s-k}.$$

Thus we find that

(1) $$L\{e^{kt}\} = \frac{1}{s-k}, \qquad s > k.$$

Note the special case $k = 0$:

(2) $$L\{1\} = \frac{1}{s}, \qquad s > 0.$$

EXAMPLE (b): Obtain $L\{\sin kt\}$.

From any elementary calculus,* or by employing integration by parts twice, we obtain

$$\int e^{ax} \sin mx\,dx = \frac{e^{ax}(a \sin mx - m \cos mx)}{a^2 + m^2} + C.$$

Since

$$L\{\sin kt\} = \int_0^\infty e^{-st} \sin kt\,dt,$$

* For example, E. D. Rainville, *Unified Calculus and Analytic Geometry* (New York: The Macmillan Co., 1961), p. 345.

it follows that

(3) $$L\{\sin kt\} = \left[\frac{e^{-st}(-s \sin kt - k \cos kt)}{s^2 + k^2}\right]_0^\infty.$$

For positive s, $e^{-st} \to 0$ as $t \to \infty$. Furthermore, $\sin kt$ and $\cos kt$ are bounded as $t \to \infty$. Therefore (3) yields

$$L\{\sin kt\} = 0 - \frac{1(0 - k)}{s^2 + k^2},$$

or

(4) $$L\{\sin kt\} = \frac{k}{s^2 + k^2}, \qquad s > 0.$$

The result

(5) $$L\{\cos kt\} = \frac{s}{s^2 + k^2}, \qquad s > 0,$$

can be obtained in a similar manner from the elementary formula

(6) $$\int e^{ax} \cos mx \, dx = \frac{e^{ax}(a \cos mx + m \sin mx)}{a^2 + m^2} + C.$$

EXAMPLE (c): Obtain $L\{t^n\}$ for n a positive integer.
   By definition

$$L\{t^n\} = \int_0^\infty e^{-st} t^n \, dt.$$

Let us attack the integral using integration by parts with the choice exhibited in the table.

t^n	$e^{-st} \, dt$
$nt^{n-1} \, dt$	$-\dfrac{1}{s} e^{-st}$

We thus obtain

(7) $$\int_0^\infty e^{-st} t^n \, dt = \left[\frac{-t^n e^{-st}}{s}\right]_0^\infty + \frac{n}{s} \int_0^\infty e^{-st} t^{n-1} \, dt.$$

For $s > 0$ and $n > 0$, the first term on the right in (7) is zero, and we are left with

$$\int_0^\infty e^{-st} t^n \, dt = \frac{n}{s} \int_0^\infty e^{-st} t^{n-1} \, dt, \qquad s > 0,$$

or

(8) $$L\{t^n\} = \frac{n}{s} L\{t^{n-1}\}, \qquad s > 0.$$

From (8) we may conclude that, for $n > 1$,

$$L\{t^{n-1}\} = \frac{n-1}{s} L\{t^{n-2}\}$$

so

(9) $$L\{t^n\} = \frac{n(n-1)}{s^2} L\{t^{n-2}\}.$$

Iteration of this process yields

$$L\{t^n\} = \frac{n(n-1)(n-2) \cdots 2 \cdot 1}{s^n} L\{t^0\}.$$

From Example (a) above, we have

$$L\{t^0\} = L\{1\} = s^{-1}.$$

Hence, for n a positive integer,

(10) $$L\{t^n\} = \frac{n!}{s^{n+1}}, \qquad s > 0.$$

The Laplace transform of $F(t)$ will exist even if the object function $F(t)$ is discontinuous, provided the integral in the definition of $L\{F(t)\}$ exists. Little will be done at this time with specific discontinuous $F(t)$, because more efficient methods for obtaining such transforms are to be developed later.

EXAMPLE (d): Find the Laplace transform of $H(t)$ where

$$H(t) = t, \qquad 0 < t < 4,$$
$$= 5, \qquad t > 4.$$

Note that the fact that $H(t)$ is not defined at $t = 0$ and $t = 4$ has no bearing whatever on the existence, or the value, of $L\{H(t)\}$. We turn to the definition of $L\{H(t)\}$ to obtain

$$L\{H(t)\} = \int_0^\infty e^{-st} H(t)\, dt$$

$$= \int_0^4 e^{-st} t\, dt + \int_4^\infty e^{-st}\, 5\, dt.$$

Using integration by parts on the next-to-last integral above, we soon arrive, for $s > 0$, at

$$L\{H(t)\} = \left[-\frac{t}{s} e^{-st} - \frac{1}{s^2} e^{-st} \right]_0^4 + \left[-\frac{5}{s} e^{-st} \right]_4^\infty.$$

Thus

$$L\{H(t)\} = -\frac{4e^{-4s}}{s} - \frac{e^{-4s}}{s^2} + 0 + \frac{1}{s^2} - 0 + \frac{5e^{-4s}}{s}$$

$$= \frac{1}{s^2} + \frac{e^{-4s}}{s} - \frac{e^{-4s}}{s^2}.$$

Exercises

1. Using equation (6) above, show that

$$L\{\cos kt\} = \frac{s}{s^2 + k^2}, \quad s > 0.$$

2. Obtain $L\{t^2 - 3t + 5\}$. ANS. $\dfrac{2}{s^3} - \dfrac{3}{s^2} + \dfrac{5}{s}, \quad s > 0.$

3. Obtain $L\{\frac{1}{2}t^3 + t^2 - 1\}$. ANS. $\dfrac{3}{s^4} + \dfrac{2}{s^3} - \dfrac{1}{s}, \quad s > 0.$

4. Evaluate $L\{e^{-4t} + 3e^{-2t}\}$. ANS. $\dfrac{2(2s + 7)}{(s + 2)(s + 4)}, \quad s > -2.$

5. Evaluate $L\{2e^{3t} - e^{-3t}\}$. ANS. $\dfrac{s + 9}{s^2 - 9}, \quad s > 3.$

6. Show that $L\{\cosh kt\} = \dfrac{s}{s^2 - k^2}, \quad s > |k|.$

7. Show that $L\{\sinh kt\} = \dfrac{k}{s^2 - k^2}, \quad s > |k|.$

8. Use the trigonometric identity $\cos^2 A = \frac{1}{2}(1 + \cos 2A)$ and equation (5), Section 56, to evaluate $L\{\cos^2 kt\}$. ANS. $\dfrac{s^2 + 2k^2}{s(s^2 + 4k^2)}, \quad s > 0.$

9. Parallel the method suggested in Ex. 8 to obtain $L\{\sin^2 kt\}$.

ANS. $\dfrac{2k^2}{s(s^2 + 4k^2)}, \quad s > 0.$

10. Obtain $L\{\sin^2 kt\}$ directly from the answer to Ex. 8.

11. Evaluate $L\{\sin kt \cos kt\}$ with the aid of a trigonometric identity.

ANS. $\dfrac{k}{s^2 + 4k^2}, \quad s > 0.$

12. Evaluate $L\{e^{-at} - e^{-bt}\}$. ANS. $\dfrac{b - a}{(s + a)(s + b)}, \quad s > \text{Max}(-a, -b).$

13. Find $L\{\psi(t)\}$ where

$$\psi(t) = 4, \quad 0 < t < 1,$$
$$= 3, \quad t > 1.$$

ANS. $\dfrac{1}{s}(4 - e^{-s}), \quad s > 0.$

14. Find $L\{\varphi(t)\}$ where

$$\varphi(t) = 1, \quad 0 < t < 2,$$
$$= t, \quad t > 2.$$

ANS. $\dfrac{1}{s} + \dfrac{e^{-2s}}{s} + \dfrac{e^{-2s}}{s^2}, \quad s > 0.$

15. Find $L\{A(t)\}$ where

$$A(t) = 0, \quad 0 < t < 1,$$
$$= t, \quad 1 < t < 2,$$
$$= 0, \quad t > 2.$$

ANS. $\left(\dfrac{1}{s^2} + \dfrac{1}{s}\right)e^{-s} - \left(\dfrac{1}{s^2} + \dfrac{2}{s}\right)e^{-2s}, \quad s > 0.$

16. Find $L\{B(t)\}$ where

$$B(t) = \sin 2t, \quad 0 < t < \pi,$$
$$= 0, \quad t > \pi.$$

ANS. $\dfrac{2(1 - e^{-\pi s})}{s^2 + 4}, \quad s > 0.$

57. Sectionally continuous functions

It soon becomes tiresome to test each $F(t)$ we encounter to determine whether the integral

$$(1) \qquad\qquad \int_0^\infty e^{-st}F(t)\, dt$$

exists for some range of values of s. We therefore seek a fairly large class of functions for which we can prove once and for all that the integral (1) exists.

One of our avowed interests in the Laplace transform is in its usefulness as a tool in solving problems in more or less elementary applications, particularly boundary value problems in differential equations. Therefore we do not hesitate to restrict our study to functions $F(t)$ that are continuous or even differentiable, except possibly at a discrete set of points, in the semi-infinite range $t \geqq 0$.

For such functions, the existence of the integral (1) can be endangered only at points of discontinuity of $F(t)$ or by divergence due to behavior of the integrand as $t \to \infty$.

In elementary calculus we found that finite discontinuities, or finite jumps, of the integrand did not interfere with the existence of the integral. We therefore introduce a term to describe functions that are continuous except for such jumps.

DEFINITION: *The function $F(t)$ is said to be sectionally continuous over the closed interval $a \leqq t \leqq b$ if that interval can be divided into a finite number of subintervals $c \leqq t \leqq d$ such that in each subinterval:*

1. $F(t)$ is continuous in the open interval $c < t < d$,

2. $F(t)$ approaches a limit as t approaches each endpoint from within the interval; that is, $\operatorname*{Lim}_{t \to c^{+}} F(t)$ and $\operatorname*{Lim}_{t \to d^{-}} F(t)$ exist.

FIGURE 17

Figure 17 shows an $F(t)$ that is sectionally continuous over the interval

$$0 \leqq t \leqq 6.$$

The student should realize that there is no implication that $F(t)$ must be sectionally continuous for $L\{F(t)\}$ to exist. Indeed, we shall meet several counterexamples to any such notion. The concept of sectionally continuous functions will, in Section 59, play a role in a set of conditions sufficient for the existence of the transform.

58. Functions of exponential order

If the integral of $e^{-st}F(t)$ between the limits 0 and t_0 exists for every finite positive t_0, the only remaining threat to the existence of the transform

$$(1) \qquad \int_0^{\infty} e^{-st}F(t)\, dt$$

is the behavior of the integrand as $t \to \infty$.

We know that

$$(2) \qquad \int_0^{\infty} e^{-ct}\, dt$$

converges for $c > 0$. This arouses our interest in functions $F(t)$ that are, for large $t(t \geqq t_0)$, essentially bounded by some exponential e^{bt} so that the integrand in (1) will behave like the integrand in (2) for s large enough.

DEFINITION: *The function $F(t)$ is said to be of exponential order as $t \to \infty$ if there exist constants M and b and a fixed t-value t_0 such that*

$$(3) \qquad |F(t)| < Me^{bt}, \qquad for\ t \geqq t_0.$$

If b is to be emphasized, we say that $F(t)$ is of the order of e^{bt} as $t \to \infty$. We also write

$$(4) \qquad F(t) = O(e^{bt}), \qquad t \to \infty,$$

to mean that $F(t)$ is of exponential order, the exponential being e^{bt}, as $t \to \infty$. That is, (4) is another way of expressing (3).

The integral in (1) may be split into parts as follows:

$$(5) \qquad \int_0^\infty e^{-st}F(t)\, dt = \int_0^{t_0} e^{-st}F(t)dt + \int_{t_0}^\infty e^{-st}F(t)\, dt.$$

If $F(t)$ is of exponential order, $F(t) = O(e^{bt})$, the last integral in equation (5) exists because from the inequality (3) it follows that for $s > b$,

$$(6) \qquad \int_{t_0}^\infty |e^{-st}F(t)|\, dt < M \int_{t_0}^\infty e^{-st} \cdot e^{bt}\, dt = \frac{M \exp [-t_0(s - b)]}{s - b}.$$

For $s > b$, the last member of (6) approaches zero as $t_0 \to \infty$. Therefore the last integral in (5) is absolutely convergent* for $s > b$. We have proved the following result.

THEOREM 5: *If the integral of $e^{-st}F(t)$ between the limits 0 and t_0 exists for every finite positive t_0, and if $F(t)$ is of exponential order, $F(t) = O(e^{bt})$ as $t \to \infty$, the Laplace transform*

$$(7) \qquad L\{F(t)\} = \int_0^\infty e^{-st}F(t)\, dt = f(s)$$

exists for $s > b$.

We know that a function that is sectionally continuous over an interval is integrable over that interval. This leads us to the following useful special case of Theorem 5.

THEOREM 6: *If $F(t)$ is sectionally continuous over every finite interval in the range $t \geq 0$, and if $F(t)$ is of exponential order, $F(t) = O(e^{bt})$ as $t \to \infty$, the Laplace transform $L\{F(t)\}$ exists for $s > b$.*

Functions of exponential order play a dominant role throughout our work. It is therefore wise to develop proficiency in determining whether or not a specified function is of exponential order.

Surely if a constant b exists such that

$$(8) \qquad \lim_{t \to \infty} [e^{-bt}|F(t)|]$$

---

* If complex s is to be used, the integral converges for $\mathrm{Re}(s) > b$.

exists, the function $F(t)$ is of exponential order, indeed of the order of e^{bt}. To see this, let the value of the limit (8) be $K \neq 0$. Then, for t large enough, $|e^{-bt}F(t)|$ can be made as close to K as is desired, so certainly

$$|e^{-bt}F(t)| < 2K.$$

Therefore, for t sufficiently large,

$$(9) \qquad\qquad |F(t)| < Me^{bt},$$

with $M = 2K$. If the limit in (8) is zero, we may write (9) with $M = 1$.

On the other hand, if for every fixed c,

$$(10) \qquad\qquad \lim_{t \to \infty} [e^{-ct}|F(t)|] = \infty,$$

the function $F(t)$ is not of exponential order. For, assume b exists such that

$$(11) \qquad\qquad |F(t)| < Me^{bt}, \qquad t \geqq t_0;$$

then the choice $c = 2b$ would yield, by (11),

$$|e^{-2bt}F(t)| < Me^{-bt},$$

so $e^{-2bt}F(t) \to 0$ as $t \to \infty$, which disagrees with (10).

EXAMPLE (a): Show that t^3 is of exponential order as $t \to \infty$.
We consider, with b as yet unspecified,

$$(12) \qquad\qquad \lim_{t \to \infty} (e^{-bt}t^3) = \lim_{t \to \infty} \frac{t^3}{e^{bt}}.$$

If $b > 0$, the limit in (12) is of a type treated in calculus. In fact,

$$\lim_{t \to \infty} \frac{t^3}{e^{bt}} = \lim_{t \to \infty} \frac{3t^2}{be^{bt}} = \lim_{t \to \infty} \frac{6t}{b^2 e^{bt}} = \lim_{t \to \infty} \frac{6}{b^3 e^{bt}} = 0.$$

Therefore t^3 is of exponential order,

$$t^3 = O(e^{bt}), \qquad t \to \infty,$$

for any fixed positive b.

EXAMPLE (b): Show that $\exp(t^2)$ is not of exponential order as $t \to \infty$.
Consider

$$(13) \qquad\qquad \lim_{t \to \infty} \frac{\exp(t^2)}{\exp(bt)}.$$

If $b \leqq 0$, the limit in (13) is infinite. If $b > 0$,

$$\lim_{t \to \infty} \frac{\exp{(t^2)}}{\exp{(bt)}} = \lim_{t \to \infty} \exp{[t(t - b)]} = \infty.$$

Thus, no matter what fixed b we use, the limit in (13) is infinite and $\exp{(t^2)}$ cannot be of exponential order.

The exercises at the end of the next section give additional opportunities for practice in determining whether or not a function is of exponential order.

59. Functions of class A

For brevity we shall hereafter use the term "a function of class A" for any function that

(a) is sectionally continuous over every finite interval in the range $t \geqq 0$, and

(b) is of exponential order as $t \to \infty$.

We may then reword Theorem 6 as follows.

THEOREM 7: *If $F(t)$ is a function of class A, $L\{F(t)\}$ exists.*

It is important to realize that Theorem 7 states only that for $L\{F(t)\}$ to exist, it is sufficient that $F(t)$ be of class A. The condition is not necessary. A classic example showing that functions other than those of class A do have Laplace transforms is

$$F(t) = t^{-\frac{1}{2}}.$$

This function is not sectionally continuous in every finite interval in the range $t \geqq 0$, because $F \to \infty$ as $t \to 0^+$. But $t^{-\frac{1}{2}}$ is integrable from 0 to any positive t_0. Also $t^{-\frac{1}{2}} \to 0$ as $t \to \infty$, so $t^{-\frac{1}{2}}$ is of exponential order, with $M = 1$ and $b = 0$ in the inequality (3), page 168. Hence, by Theorem 5, page 169, $L\{t^{-\frac{1}{2}}\}$ exists.

Indeed, for $s > 0$,

$$L\{t^{-\frac{1}{2}}\} = \int_0^\infty e^{-st} t^{-\frac{1}{2}}\, dt,$$

in which the change of variable $t^{\frac{1}{2}} = \beta$ leads to

$$L\{t^{-\frac{1}{2}}\} = 2 \int_0^\infty \exp{(-s\beta^2)}\, d\beta, \qquad s > 0.$$

Another change of variable of integration, $s^{\frac{1}{2}}\beta = y$, yields

$$L\{t^{-\frac{1}{2}}\} = 2s^{-\frac{1}{2}} \int_0^{\infty} \exp\left(-y^2\right) dy, \qquad s > 0.$$

In elementary calculus* we found that $\int_0^{\infty} \exp\left(-y^2\right) dy = \frac{1}{2}\sqrt{\pi}$.
Therefore

$$(1) \qquad\qquad L\{t^{-\frac{1}{2}}\} = 2s^{-\frac{1}{2}} \cdot \frac{1}{2}\sqrt{\pi}$$
$$= \left(\frac{\pi}{s}\right)^{\frac{1}{2}}, \qquad s > 0,$$

even though $t^{-\frac{1}{2}} \to \infty$ as $t \to 0^+$. Additional examples are easily constructed and we shall meet some of them later in the book.

If $F(t)$ is of class A, $F(t)$ is bounded over the range $0 \le t \le t_0$,

$$(2) \qquad\qquad |F(t)| < M_1, \qquad 0 \le t \le t_0.$$

But $F(t)$ is also of exponential order,

$$(3) \qquad\qquad |F(t)| < M_2 e^{bt}, \qquad t \ge t_0.$$

If we choose M as the larger of M_1 and M_2 and c as the larger of b and
zero, we may write

$$(4) \qquad\qquad |F(t)| < M e^{ct}, \qquad t \ge 0.$$

Therefore, for any function $F(t)$ of class A,

$$(5) \qquad \left| \int_0^{\infty} e^{-st} F(t)\, dt \right| < M \int_0^{\infty} e^{-st} \cdot e^{ct}\, dt = \frac{M}{s - c}, \qquad s > c.$$

Since the right member of (5) approaches zero as $s \to \infty$, we have proved
the following useful result.

THEOREM 8: *If $F(t)$ is of class A and if $L\{F(t)\} = f(s)$,*

$$\operatorname*{Lim}_{s \to \infty} f(s) = 0.$$

From (5) we may also conclude the stronger result that the transform
$f(s)$ of a function $F(t)$ of class A must be such that $sf(s)$ is bounded as
$s \to \infty$.

---

* E. D. Rainville, *Unified Calculus and Analytic Geometry* (New York: The
Macmillan Co., 1961), p. 531.

Exercises

1. Prove that if $F_1(t)$ and $F_2(t)$ are each of exponential order as $t \to \infty$, then $F_1(t) \cdot F_2(t)$ and $F_1(t) + F_2(t)$ are also of exponential order as $t \to \infty$.

2. Prove that if $F_1(t)$ and $F_2(t)$ are of class A, page 171, then $F_1(t) + F_2(t)$ and $F_1(t) \cdot F_2(t)$ are also of class A.

3. Show that t^x is of exponential order as $t \to \infty$ for all real x.

In Exs. 4–17, show that the given function is of class A. In these exercises, n denotes a non-negative integer, k any real number.

4. $\sin kt$.

5. $\cos kt$.

6. $\cosh kt$.

7. $\sinh kt$.

8. t^n.

9. $t^n e^{kt}$.

10. $t^n \sin kt$.

11. $t^n \cos kt$.

12. $t^n \sinh kt$.

13. $t^n \cosh kt$.

14. $\dfrac{\sin kt}{t}$.

15. $\dfrac{1 - \exp(-t)}{t}$.

16. $\dfrac{1 - \cos kt}{t}$.

17. $\dfrac{\cos t - \cosh t}{t}$.

60. Transforms of derivatives

Any function of class A, page 171, has a Laplace transform, but the derivative of such a function may or may not be of class A. For the function
$$F_1(t) = \sin[\exp(t)]$$
with derivative
$$F_1'(t) = \exp(t) \cos[\exp(t)],$$
both F_1 and F_1' are of exponential order as $t \to \infty$. Here F_1 is bounded so it is of the order of $\exp(0 \cdot t)$; F_1' is of the order of $\exp(t)$. On the other hand, the function
$$F_2(t) = \sin[\exp(t^2)]$$
with derivative
$$F_2'(t) = 2t \exp(t^2) \cos[\exp(t^2)]$$
is such that F_2 is of the order of $\exp(0 \cdot t)$, but F_2' is not of exponential order. From Example (b), page 170,
$$\lim_{t \to \infty} \frac{\exp(t^2)}{\exp(bt)} = \infty$$

for any real b. Since the factors $2t \cos [\exp (t^2)]$ do not even approach zero as $t \to \infty$, the product $F_2' \exp (-ct)$ cannot be bounded as $t \to \infty$ no matter how large a fixed c is chosen.

Therefore, in studying the transforms of derivatives, we shall stipulate that the derivatives themselves be of class A.

If $F(t)$ is continuous for $t \geqq 0$ and of exponential order as $t \to \infty$, and if $F'(t)$ is of class A, the integral in

$$(1) \qquad L\{F'(t)\} = \int_0^\infty e^{-st} F'(t) \, dt$$

may be simplified by integration by parts with the choice exhibited in the table.

e^{-st}	$F'(t) \, dt$
$-se^{-st} \, dt$	$F(t)$

We thus obtain, for s greater than some fixed s_0,

$$\int_0^\infty e^{-st} F'(t) \, dt = \left[e^{-st} F(t) \right]_0^\infty + s \int_0^\infty e^{-st} F(t) \, dt,$$

or

$$(2) \qquad L\{F'(t)\} = -F(0) + sL\{F(t)\}.$$

THEOREM 9: *If $F(t)$ is continuous for $t \geqq 0$ and of exponential order as $t \to \infty$, and if $F'(t)$ is of class A, page 171, it follows from $L\{F(t)\} = f(s)$ that*

$$(3) \qquad L\{F'(t)\} = sf(s) - F(0).$$

In treating a differential equation of order n, we seek solutions for which the highest-ordered derivative present is reasonably well behaved, say sectionally continuous. The integral of a sectionally continuous function is continuous. Hence, we lose nothing by requiring continuity for all derivatives of order lower than n. The requirement that the various derivatives be of exponential order is forced upon us by our desire to use the Laplace transform as a tool. For our purposes, iteration of Theorem 9 to obtain transforms of higher derivatives makes sense.

From (3) we obtain, if F, F', F'' are suitably restricted,

$$L\{F''(t)\} = sL\{F'(t)\} - F'(0),$$

or

$$(4) \qquad L\{F''(t)\} = s^2 f(s) - sF(0) - F'(0),$$

and the process can be repeated as many times as we wish.

THEOREM 10: *If* $F(t), F'(t), \cdots , F^{(n-1)}(t)$ *are continuous for* $t \geqq 0$ *and of exponential order as* $t \to \infty$, *and if* $F^{(n)}(t)$ *is of class* A, *then from*

$$L\{F(t)\} = f(s)$$

it follows that

(5) $$L\{F^{(n)}(t)\} = s^n f(s) - \sum_{k=0}^{n-1} s^{n-1-k} F^{(k)}(0).$$

Thus

$$L\{F^{(3)}(t)\} = s^3 f(s) - s^2 F(0) - s F'(0) - F''(0),$$

$$L\{F^{(4)}(t)\} = s^4 f(s) - s^3 F(0) - s^2 F'(0) - s F''(0) - F^{(3)}(0), \text{ etc.}$$

Theorem 10 is basic in employing the Laplace transform to solve linear differential equations with constant coefficients. The theorem permits us to transform such differential equations into algebraic ones.

The restriction that $F(t)$ be continuous can be relaxed, but discontinuities in $F(t)$ bring in additional terms in the transform of $F'(t)$. As an example, consider an $F(t)$ that is continuous for $t \geqq 0$ except for a finite jump at $t = t_1$, as in Figure 18. If $F(t)$ is also of exponential order as $t \to \infty$, and if $F'(t)$ is of class A, we may write

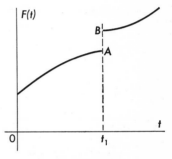

FIGURE 18

$$L\{F'(t)\} = \int_0^\infty e^{-st} F'(t)\, dt$$

$$= \int_0^{t_1} e^{-st} F'(t)\, dt + \int_{t_1}^\infty e^{-st} F'(t)\, dt.$$

Then, integration by parts applied to the last two integrals yields

$$L\{F'(t)\} = \left[e^{-st} F(t) \right]_0^{t_1} + s \int_0^{t_1} e^{-st} F(t)\, dt + \left[e^{-st} F(t) \right]_{t_1}^\infty$$

$$+ s \int_{t_1}^\infty e^{-st} F(t)\, dt$$

$$= s \int_0^\infty e^{-st} F(t)\, dt + \exp(-st_1) F(t_1^-) - F(0) + 0$$

$$- \exp(-st_1) F(t_1^+)$$

$$= s L\{F(t)\} - F(0) - \exp(-st_1)[F(t_1^+) - F(t_1^-)].$$

In Figure 18 the directed distance AB is of length $[F(t_1^+) - F(t_1^-)]$.

THEOREM 11: *If $F(t)$ is of exponential order as $t \to \infty$ and $F(t)$ is continuous for $t \geq 0$ except for a finite jump at $t = t_1$, and if $F'(t)$ is of class A, then from*

$$L\{F(t)\} = f(s)$$

it follows that

(6) $L\{F'(t)\} = sf(s) - F(0) - \exp(-st_1)[F(t_1^+) - F(t_1^-)].$

If $F(t)$ has more than one finite discontinuity, additional terms, similar to the last term in (6), enter the formula for $L\{F'(t)\}$.

61. Derivatives of transforms

For functions of class A, the methods of advanced calculus show that it is legitimate to differentiate the Laplace transform integral. That is, if $F(t)$ is of class A, from

(1) $$f(s) = \int_0^\infty e^{-st}F(t)\, dt$$

it follows that

(2) $$f'(s) = \int_0^\infty (-t)e^{-st}F(t)\, dt.$$

The integral on the right in (2) is the transform of the function $(-t)\,F(t)$.

THEOREM 12: *If $F(t)$ is a function of class A, it follows from*

$$L\{F(t)\} = f(s)$$

that

(3) $$f'(s) = L\{-tF(t)\}.$$

When $F(t)$ is of class A, $(-t)^k\,F(t)$ is also of class A for any positive integer k.

THEOREM 13: *If $F(t)$ is of class A, it follows from $L\{F(t)\} = f(s)$ that for any positive integer n,*

(4) $$\frac{d^n}{ds^n} f(s) = L\{(-t)^n F(t)\}.$$

These theorems are useful in several ways. One immediate application is to add to our list of transforms with very little labor. We know that

(5) $$\frac{k}{s^2 + k^2} = L\{\sin kt\},$$

and therefore, by Theorem 12,

$$\frac{-2ks}{(s^2 + k^2)^2} = L\{-t \sin kt\}.$$

Thus we obtain

(6) $$\frac{s}{(s^2 + k^2)^2} = L\left\{\frac{t}{2k} \sin kt\right\}.$$

From the known formula

$$\frac{s}{s^2 + k^2} = L\{\cos kt\}$$

we obtain, by differentiation with respect to s,

(7) $$\frac{k^2 - s^2}{(s^2 + k^2)^2} = L\{-t \cos kt\}.$$

Let us add to each side of (7) the corresponding member of

$$\frac{1}{s^2 + k^2} = L\left\{\frac{1}{k} \sin kt\right\}$$

to get

$$\frac{s^2 + k^2 + k^2 - s^2}{(s^2 + k^2)^2} = L\left\{\frac{1}{k} \sin kt - t \cos kt\right\},$$

from which it follows that

(8) $$\frac{1}{(s^2 + k^2)^2} = L\left\{\frac{1}{2k^3} (\sin kt - kt \cos kt)\right\}.$$

62. The gamma function

For obtaining the Laplace transform of nonintegral powers of t, we need a function not usually discussed in elementary mathematics. The Gamma function $\Gamma(x)$ is defined by

(1) $$\Gamma(x) = \int_0^\infty e^{-\beta} \beta^{x-1} \, d\beta, \qquad x > 0.$$

Substitution of $(x + 1)$ for x in (1) gives

(2) $$\Gamma(x + 1) = \int_0^\infty e^{-\beta} \beta^x \, d\beta.$$

An integration by parts, integrating $e^{-\beta} d\beta$ and differentiating β^x, yields

(3) $\Gamma(x + 1) = \left[-e^{-\beta}\beta^x \right]_0^\infty + x \int_0^\infty e^{-\beta}\beta^{x-1} d\beta.$

Since $x > 0$, $\beta^x \to 0$ as $\beta \to 0$. Since x is fixed, $e^{-\beta}\beta^x \to 0$ as $\beta \to \infty$. Thus

(4) $\Gamma(x + 1) = x \int_0^\infty e^{-\beta}\beta^{x-1} d\beta = x\Gamma(x).$

THEOREM 14: *For $x > 0$, $\Gamma(x + 1) = x\Gamma(x)$.*

Suppose n is a positive integer. Iteration of Theorem 14 gives us

$$\Gamma(n + 1) = n\Gamma(n)$$
$$= n(n - 1)\Gamma(n - 1)$$
$$\cdot \; \cdot \; \cdot$$
$$= n(n - 1)(n - 2) \cdots 2 \cdot 1 \cdot \Gamma(1).$$
$$= n!\Gamma(1).$$

But, by definition,

$$\Gamma(1) = \int_0^\infty e^{-\beta}\beta^0 d\beta = \left[-e^{-\beta} \right]_0^\infty = 1.$$

THEOREM 15: *For positive integral n, $\Gamma(n + 1) = n!$.*

In the integral for $\Gamma(x + 1)$ in (2), let us put $\beta = st$ with $s > 0$ and t as the new variable of integration. This yields, since $t \to 0$ as $\beta \to 0$ and $t \to \infty$ as $\beta \to \infty$,

(5) $\Gamma(x + 1) = \int_0^\infty e^{-st}s^x t^x s \, dt = s^{x+1} \int_0^\infty e^{-st}t^x \, dt,$

which is valid for $x + 1 > 0$. We thus obtain

$$\frac{\Gamma(x + 1)}{s^{x+1}} = \int_0^\infty e^{-st}t^x \, dt, \qquad s > 0, x > -1,$$

which in our Laplace transform notation says that

(6) $L\{t^x\} = \dfrac{\Gamma(x + 1)}{s^{x+1}}, \qquad s > 0, \quad x > -1.$

If in (6) we put $x = -\frac{1}{2}$, we get

$$L\{t^{-\frac{1}{2}}\} = \frac{\Gamma(\frac{1}{2})}{s^{\frac{1}{2}}}.$$

But we already know that $L\{t^{-\frac{1}{2}}\} = \left(\dfrac{\pi}{s}\right)^{\frac{1}{2}} \cdot$ Hence

(7) $$\Gamma(\tfrac{1}{2}) = \sqrt{\pi}.$$

63. Periodic functions

Suppose the function $F(t)$ is periodic with period ω:

(1) $$F(t + \omega) = F(t).$$

The function is completely determined by (1) once the nature of $F(t)$ throughout one period, $0 \leqq t < \omega$, is given. If $F(t)$ has a transform,

(2) $$L\{F(t)\} = \int_0^\infty e^{-st}F(t) \, dt,$$

the integral can be written as a sum of integrals,

(3) $$L\{F(t)\} = \sum_{n=0}^\infty \int_{n\omega}^{(n+1)\omega} e^{-st}F(t) \, dt.$$

Let us put $t = n\omega + \beta$. Then (3) becomes

$$L\{F(t)\} = \sum_{n=0}^\infty \int_0^\omega \exp\left(-sn\omega - s\beta\right)F(\beta + n\omega) \, d\beta.$$

But $F(\beta + n\omega) = F(\beta)$, by iteration of (1). Hence

(4) $$L\{F(t)\} = \sum_{n=0}^\infty \exp\left(-sn\omega\right) \int_0^\omega \exp\left(-s\beta\right)F(\beta) \, d\beta.$$

The integral on the right in (4) is independent of n and we can sum the series on the right;

$$\sum_{n=0}^\infty \exp\left(-sn\omega\right) = \sum_{n=0}^\infty \left[\exp\left(-s\omega\right)\right]^n = \frac{1}{1 - e^{-s\omega}} \cdot$$

THEOREM 16: *If $F(t)$ has a Laplace transform and if $F(t + \omega) = F(t)$,*

(5) $$L\{F(t)\} = \frac{\int_0^\omega e^{-s\beta}F(\beta) \, d\beta}{1 - e^{-s\omega}} \cdot$$

Next suppose that a function $H(t)$ has a period $2c$ and that we demand that $H(t)$ be zero throughout the right half of each period. That is,

(6) $$H(t + 2c) = H(t),$$

(7) $$H(t) = g(t), \qquad 0 \leq t < c,$$
$$= 0, \qquad c \leq t < 2c.$$

Then we say that $H(t)$ is a half-wave rectification of $g(t)$. Using (5) we may conclude that for the $H(t)$ defined by (6) and (7),

(8) $$L\{H(t)\} = \frac{\int_0^c \exp{(-s\beta)}g(\beta)\, d\beta}{1 - \exp{(-2cs)}}.$$

EXAMPLE (a): Find the transform of the function $\psi(t, c)$ shown in Figure 19 and defined by

FIGURE 19

(9) $\psi(t, c) = 1, \qquad 0 < t < c,$
$ = 0, \qquad c < t < 2c;$

(10) $\psi(t + 2c, c) = \psi(t, c).$

We may use equation (8) and the fact that

$$\int_0^c \exp{(-s\beta)}\, d\beta = \frac{1 - \exp{(-sc)}}{s}$$

to conclude that

(11) $$L\{\psi(t, c)\} = \frac{1}{s} \cdot \frac{1 - \exp{(-sc)}}{1 - \exp{(-2sc)}} = \frac{1}{s} \cdot \frac{1}{1 + \exp{(-sc)}}.$$

EXAMPLE (b): Find the transform of the square-wave function $Q(t, c)$ shown in Figure 20 and defined by

(12) $Q(t, c) = 1, \qquad 0 < t < c,$
$ = -1, \qquad c < t < 2c;$

(13) $Q(t + 2c, c) = Q(t, c).$

This transform can be obtained by using Theorem 16, but also

FIGURE 20

(14) $$Q(t, c) = 2\psi(t, c) - 1;$$

hence, from (11),

(15) $$L\{Q(t, c)\} = \frac{1}{s}\left[\frac{2}{1 + \exp{(-sc)}} - 1\right] = \frac{1}{s} \cdot \frac{1 - \exp{(-sc)}}{1 + \exp{(-sc)}}.$$

By multiplying numerator and denominator of the last fraction above by $\exp\left(\tfrac{1}{2}sc\right)$, we may put (15) in the form

$$(16) \qquad L\{Q(t, c)\} = \frac{1}{s} \tanh \frac{cs}{2}.$$

Exercises

1. Show that $L\{t^{\frac{1}{2}}\} = \dfrac{1}{2s}\left(\dfrac{\pi}{s}\right)^{\frac{1}{2}}$, $s > 0$.

2. Show that $L\{t^{\frac{5}{2}}\} = \dfrac{15}{8s^3}\left(\dfrac{\pi}{s}\right)^{\frac{1}{2}}$, $s > 0$.

3. Use equation (4), page 174, to derive $L\{\sin kt\}$.

4. Use equation (4), page 174, to derive $L\{\cos kt\}$.

5. Check the known transforms of $\sin kt$ and $\cos kt$ against one another by using Theorem 9, page 174.

6. If n is a positive integer, obtain $L\{t^n e^{kt}\}$ from the known $L\{e^{kt}\}$ by using Theorem 13, page 176   ANS. $\dfrac{n!}{(s-k)^{n+1}}$, $s > k$.

7. Find $L\{t^2 \sin kt\}$·   ANS. $\dfrac{2k(3s^2 - k^2)}{(s^2 + k^2)^3}$, $s > 0$.

8. Find $L\{t^2 \cos kt\}$ ·   ANS. $\dfrac{2s(s^2 - 3k^2)}{(s^2 + k^2)^3}$, $s > 0$.

9. For the function

$$\begin{aligned} F(t) &= t + 1, \qquad 0 \leqq t \leqq 2, \\ &= 3, \qquad\qquad t > 2, \end{aligned}$$

graph $F(t)$ and $F'(t)$. Find $L\{F(t)\}$. Find $L\{F'(t)\}$ in two ways.
ANS. $L\{F'(t)\} = s^{-1}(1 - e^{-2s})$, $s > 0$.

10. For the function

$$\begin{aligned} H(t) &= t + 1, \qquad 0 \leqq t \leqq 2, \\ &= 6, \qquad\qquad t > 2, \end{aligned}$$

parallel Ex. 9 above.

11. Define a triangular-wave function $T(t, c)$ by

$$\begin{aligned} T(t, c) &= t, \qquad\qquad 0 \leqq t \leqq c, \\ &= 2c - t, \qquad c < t < 2c; \end{aligned}$$

$$T(t + 2c, c) = T(t, c).$$

Sketch $T(t, c)$ and find its Laplace transform.   ANS. $\dfrac{1}{s^2} \tanh \dfrac{cs}{2}$.

12. Show that the derivative of the function $T(t, c)$ of Ex. 11 is, except at certain points, the function $Q(t, c)$ of Example (b), Section 63. Obtain $L\{T(t, c)\}$ from $L\{Q(t, c)\}$.

13. Sketch a half-wave rectification of the function $\sin \omega t$, as described below, and find its transform.

$$F(t) = \sin \omega t, \qquad 0 \leq t \leq \frac{\pi}{\omega},$$

$$= 0, \qquad\qquad \frac{\pi}{\omega} < t < \frac{2\pi}{\omega} \; ;$$

$$F\left(t + \frac{2\pi}{\omega}\right) = F(t).$$

$$\text{ANS.} \quad \frac{\omega}{s^2 + \omega^2} \cdot \frac{1}{1 - \exp\left(-\dfrac{s\pi}{\omega}\right)}.$$

14. Find $L\{F(t)\}$ where $F(t) = t$ for $0 < t < \omega$ and $F(t + \omega) = F(t)$.

$$\text{ANS.} \quad \frac{1}{s^2} - \frac{\omega}{s} \frac{\exp(-s\omega)}{1 - \exp(-s\omega)} = \frac{1}{s^2} + \frac{\omega}{2s}\left(1 - \coth\frac{\omega s}{2}\right).$$

15. Prove that if $L\{F(t)\} = f(s)$ and if $\dfrac{F(t)}{t}$ is of class A,

$$L\left\{\frac{F(t)}{t}\right\} = \int_s^\infty f(\beta) \, d\beta.$$

Hint: Use Theorem 12, page 176.

CHAPTER 12

Inverse Transforms

64. Definition of an inverse transform

Suppose the function $F(t)$ is to be determined from a differential equation with boundary conditions. The Laplace operator L is used to transform the original problem into a new problem from which the transform $f(s)$ is to be found. If the Laplace transformation is to be effective, the new problem must be simpler than the original problem. We first find $f(s)$ and then must obtain $F(t)$ from $f(s)$. It is therefore desirable to develop methods for finding the object function $F(t)$ when its transform $f(s)$ is known.

If

(1) $$L\{F(t)\} = f(s),$$

we say that $F(t)$ is an *inverse Laplace transform*, or an inverse transform, of $f(s)$ and we write

(2) $$F(t) = L^{-1}\{f(s)\}.$$

Since (1) means that

(3) $$\int_0^\infty e^{-st}F(t)\,dt = f(s),$$

it follows at once that an inverse transform is not unique. For example, if $F_1(t)$ and $F_2(t)$ are identical except at a discrete set of points and differ at

183

those points, the value of the integral in (3) is the same for the two functions; their transforms are identical.

Let us employ the term *null function* for any function $N(t)$ for which

$$(4) \qquad\qquad \int_0^{t_0} N(t)\, dt = 0$$

for every positive t_0. Lerch's theorem (not proved here) states that if $L\{F_1(t)\} = L\{F_2(t)\}$, then $F_1(t) - F_2(t) = N(t)$. That is, an inverse Laplace transform is unique except for the addition of an arbitrary null function.

The only continuous null function is zero. If an $f(s)$ has a continuous inverse $F(t)$, then $F(t)$ is the only continuous inverse of $f(s)$. If $f(s)$ has an inverse $F_1(t)$ continuous over a specified closed interval, every inverse that is also continuous over that interval is identical with $F_1(t)$ on that interval. Essentially, inverses of the same $f(s)$ differ at most at their points of discontinuity.

In applications, failure of uniqueness caused by addition of a null function is not vital, because the effect of that null function on physical properties of the solution is null. In the problems we treat, the inverse $F(t)$ is required either to be continuous for $t \geqq 0$ or to be sectionally continuous with the values of $F(t)$ at the points of discontinuity specified by each problem. The $F(t)$ is then unique.

A crude, but sometimes effective, method for finding inverse Laplace transforms is to construct a table of transforms (page 210) and then to use it in reverse to find inverse transforms.

We know from Ex. 1, page 166, that

$$(5) \qquad\qquad L\{\cos kt\} = \frac{s}{s^2 + k^2}.$$

Therefore

$$(6) \qquad\qquad L^{-1}\left\{\frac{s}{s^2 + k^2}\right\} = \cos kt.$$

We shall refine the above method, and actually make it quite powerful, by developing theorems by which a given $f(s)$ may be expanded into component parts whose inverses are known (found in the table). Other theorems will permit us to write $f(s)$ in alternate forms which yield the desired inverse. The most fundamental of such theorems is one that states that the inverse transformation is a linear operation.

THEOREM 17: *If c_1 and c_2 are constants,*

$$L^{-1}\{c_1 f_1(s) + c_2 f_2(s)\} = c_1 L^{-1}\{f_1(s)\} + c_2 L^{-1}\{f_2(s)\}.$$

Next let us prove a simple, but extremely useful, theorem on the manipulation of inverse transforms. From

(7) $$f(s) = \int_0^\infty e^{-st}F(t)\,dt,$$

we obtain

$$f(s - a) = \int_0^\infty e^{-(s-a)t}F(t)\,dt$$
$$= \int_0^\infty e^{-st}[e^{at}F(t)]\,dt.$$

Thus, from $L^{-1}\{f(s)\} = F(t)$ it follows that

$$L^{-1}\{f(s - a)\} = e^{at}F(t),$$

or

(8) $$L^{-1}\{f(s - a)\} = e^{at}L^{-1}\{f(s)\}.$$

Equation (8) may be rewritten with the exponential transferred to the other side of the equation. We thus obtain the following result.

THEOREM 18: $L^{-1}\{f(s)\} = e^{-at}L^{-1}\{f(s - a)\}.$

EXAMPLE (a): Find $L^{-1}\left\{\dfrac{15}{s^2 + 4s + 13}\right\}.$

First complete the square in the denominator.

$$L^{-1}\left\{\frac{15}{s^2 + 4s + 13}\right\} = L^{-1}\left\{\frac{15}{(s + 2)^2 + 9}\right\}.$$

Since we know that $L^{-1}\left\{\dfrac{k}{s^2 + k^2}\right\} = \sin kt$, we proceed as follows:

$$L^{-1}\left\{\frac{15}{s^2 + 4s + 13}\right\} = 5L^{-1}\left\{\frac{3}{(s + 2)^2 + 9}\right\} = 5e^{-2t}L^{-1}\left\{\frac{3}{s^2 + 9}\right\}$$
$$= 5e^{-2t}\sin 3t,$$

in which we have used Theorem 18.

EXAMPLE (b): Evaluate $L^{-1}\left\{\dfrac{s + 1}{s^2 + 6s + 25}\right\}.$

We write

$$L^{-1}\left\{\frac{s + 1}{s^2 + 6s + 25}\right\} = L^{-1}\left\{\frac{s + 1}{(s + 3)^2 + 16}\right\}.$$

Then

$$L^{-1}\left\{\frac{s+1}{s^2+6s+25}\right\} = e^{-3t}L^{-1}\left\{\frac{s-2}{s^2+16}\right\}$$

$$= e^{-3t}\left[L^{-1}\left\{\frac{s}{s^2+16}\right\} - \tfrac{1}{2}L^{-1}\left\{\frac{4}{s^2+16}\right\}\right]$$

$$= e^{-3t}\left(\cos 4t - \tfrac{1}{2}\sin 4t\right).$$

Exercises

In Exs. 1–10, obtain $L^{-1}\{f(s)\}$ from the given $f(s)$.

1. $\dfrac{1}{s^2+2s+5}$.   ANS. $\tfrac{1}{2}e^{-t}\sin 2t$.

2. $\dfrac{1}{s^2-6s+10}$.   ANS. $e^{3t}\sin t$.

3. $\dfrac{s}{s^2+2s+5}$.   ANS. $e^{-t}(\cos 2t - \tfrac{1}{2}\sin 2t)$.

4. $\dfrac{s}{s^2-6s+13}$.   ANS. $e^{3t}(\cos 2t + \tfrac{3}{2}\sin 2t)$.

5. $\dfrac{1}{s^2+8s+16}$.   ANS. te^{-4t}.

6. $\dfrac{s}{s^2+8s+16}$.   ANS. $e^{-4t}(1 - 4t)$.

7. $\dfrac{s-5}{s^2+6s+13}$.   ANS. $e^{-3t}(\cos 2t - 4\sin 2t)$.

8. $\dfrac{2s-1}{s^2+4s+29}$.   ANS. $e^{-2t}(2\cos 5t - \sin 5t)$.

9. $\dfrac{3s+1}{(s+1)^4}$.   ANS. $e^{-t}\left(\dfrac{3}{2}t^2 - \dfrac{1}{3}t^3\right)$.

10. $\dfrac{s^2}{(s+2)^3}$.   ANS. $e^{-2t}(1 - 4t + 2t^2)$.

11. Show that for n a non-negative integer

$$L^{-1}\left\{\frac{1}{(s+a)^{n+1}}\right\} = \frac{t^n e^{-at}}{n!}.$$

12. Show that for $m > -1$,

$$L^{-1}\left\{\frac{1}{(s+a)^{m+1}}\right\} = \frac{t^m e^{-at}}{\Gamma(m+1)}.$$

13. Show that

$$L^{-1}\left\{\frac{1}{(s+a)^2+b^2}\right\} = \frac{1}{b}e^{-at}\sin bt.$$

14. Show that

$$L^{-1}\left\{\frac{s}{(s+a)^2+b^2}\right\} = \frac{1}{b}\,e^{-at}\,(b\cos bt - a\sin bt).$$

15. For $a > 0$, show that from $L^{-1}\{f(s)\} = F(t)$ it follows that

$$L^{-1}\{f(as)\} = \frac{1}{a}F\left(\frac{t}{a}\right).$$

16. For $a > 0$, show that from $L^{-1}\{f(s)\} = F(t)$ it follows that

$$L^{-1}\{f(as+b)\} = \frac{1}{a}\exp\left(-\frac{bt}{a}\right)F\left(\frac{t}{a}\right).$$

65. A step function

Applications frequently deal with situations that change abruptly at specified times. We need a notation for a function that will suppress a given term up to a certain value of t and insert the term for all larger t. The function we are about to introduce leads us to a powerful tool for the constructing of inverse transforms.

Let us define function $\alpha(t)$ by

(1) $\alpha(t) = 0, \qquad t < 0,$
         $\quad\;\; = 1, \qquad t \geq 0.$

The graph of $\alpha(t)$ is shown in Figure 21.

The definition (1) says that $\alpha(t)$ is zero when the argument is negative and $\alpha(t)$ is unity when the argument is positive or is zero. It follows that

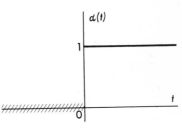

FIGURE 21

(2) $\alpha(t - c) = 0, \qquad t < c,$
         $\qquad\quad\;\; = 1, \qquad t \geq c.$

The α function permits easy designation of the result of translating the graph of $F(t)$. If the graph of

(3) $y = F(t), \qquad t \geq 0,$

is as shown in Figure 22, page 188, the graph of

(4) $y = \alpha(t - c)F(t - c), \qquad t \geq c,$

is that shown in Figure 23. Furthermore, if $F(x)$ is defined for $-c \leqq x < 0$, $F(t - c)$ is defined for $0 \leqq t < c$ and the y of (4) is zero for $0 \leqq t < c$

FIGURE 22   FIGURE 23

because of the negative argument in $\alpha(t - c)$. Notice that the values of $F(x)$ for negative x have no bearing on this result because each value is multiplied by zero (from the α); only the existence of F for negative arguments is needed.

The Laplace transform of $\alpha(t - c)F(t - c)$ is related to that of $F(t)$. Consider

$$L\{\alpha(t - c)F(t - c)\} = \int_0^\infty e^{-st}\alpha(t - c)F(t - c)\, dt.$$

Since $\alpha(t - c) = 0$ for $0 \leqq t < c$ and $\alpha(t - c) = 1$ for $t \geqq c$, we get

$$L\{\alpha(t - c)F(t - c)\} = \int_c^\infty e^{-st}F(t - c)\, dt.$$

Now put $t - c = v$ in the integral to obtain

$$L\{\alpha(t - c)F(t - c)\} = \int_0^\infty e^{-s(c+v)}F(v)\, dv$$

$$= e^{-cs}\int_0^\infty e^{-sv}F(v)\, dv.$$

Since a definite integral is independent of the variable of integration,

$$\int_0^\infty e^{-sv}F(v)\, dv = \int_0^\infty e^{-st}F(t)\, dt = L\{F(t)\} = f(s).$$

Therefore we have shown that

(5) $$L\{\alpha(t - c)F(t - c)\} = e^{-cs}L\{F(t)\} = e^{-cs}f(s).$$

THEOREM 19: *If $L^{-1}\{f(s)\} = F(t)$, if $c \geqq 0$, and if $F(t)$ be assigned values (no matter what ones) for $-c \leqq t < 0$,*

(6) $$L^{-1}\{e^{-cs}f(s)\} = F(t - c)\alpha(t - c).$$

EXAMPLE (a): Find $L\{y(t)\}$ where (Figure 24)

$$y(t) = t^2, \quad 0 < t < 2,$$
$$= 6, \quad t > 2.$$

Here, direct use of the definition of a transform yields

$$L\{y(t)\} = \int_0^2 t^2 e^{-st}\,dt + \int_2^\infty 6e^{-st}\,dt.$$

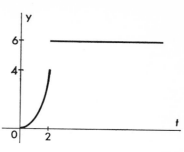

FIGURE 24

Although the above integrations are not difficult, one of them may (or may not, depending on the skill of the operator) involve two integrations by parts. We prefer to use the α function.

Since $\alpha(t - 2) = 0$ for $t < 2$ and $\alpha(t - 2) = 1$ for $t \geqq 2$, we build the $y(t)$ in the following way. The crude trial

$$y_1 = t^2$$

works for $0 < t < 2$, but we wish to knock out the t^2 when $t > 2$. Hence we write

$$y_2 = t^2 - t^2\alpha(t - 2).$$

This gives t^2 for $t < 2$ and zero for $t > 2$. Then we add the term $6\alpha(t - 2)$ and finally arrive at

$$(7) \qquad y(t) = t^2 - t^2\alpha(t - 2) + 6\alpha(t - 2).$$

The y of (7) is the y of our example and, of course, it can be written at once after a little practice with the α function. No intermediate steps such as forming y_1 and y_2 need be used.

Unfortunately, the y of (7) is not yet in the best form for our purpose. The theorem we wish to use gives us

$$L\{F(t - c)\alpha(t - c)\} = e^{-cs}f(s).$$

Therefore we must have the coefficient of $\alpha(t - 2)$ expressed as a function of $(t - 2)$. Since

$$-t^2 + 6 = -(t^2 - 4t + 4) - 4(t - 2) + 2,$$

$$(8) \quad y(t) = t^2 - (t - 2)^2\alpha(t - 2) - 4(t - 2)\alpha(t - 2) + 2\alpha(t - 2),$$

from which it follows at once that

$$L\{y(t)\} = \frac{2}{s^3} - \frac{2e^{-2s}}{s^3} - \frac{4e^{-2s}}{s^2} + \frac{2e^{-2s}}{s}.$$

EXAMPLE (b): Find and sketch a function $g(t)$ for which

$$g(t) = L^{-1}\left\{\frac{3}{s} - \frac{4e^{-s}}{s^2} + \frac{4e^{-3s}}{s^2}\right\}.$$

We know that $L^{-1}\left\{\dfrac{4}{s^2}\right\} = 4t$. By Theorem 19 we then get

$$L^{-1}\left\{\frac{4e^{-s}}{s^2}\right\} = 4(t-1)\alpha(t-1)$$

and

$$L^{-1}\left\{\frac{4e^{-3s}}{s^2}\right\} = 4(t-3)\alpha(t-3).$$

FIGURE 25

We may therefore write

(9) $\qquad g(t) = 3 - 4(t-1)\alpha(t-1) + 4(t-3)\alpha(t-3).$

To write $g(t)$ without the α function, consider first the interval

$$0 \leqq t < 1$$

in which $\alpha(t-1) = 0$ and $\alpha(t-3) = 0$. We find

(10) $\qquad\qquad\qquad g(t) = 3, \qquad 0 \leqq t < 1.$

For $1 \leqq t < 3$, $\alpha(t-1) = 1$, and $\alpha(t-3) = 0$. Hence

(11) $\qquad\qquad g(t) = 3 - 4(t-1) = 7 - 4t, \qquad 1 \leqq t < 3.$

For $t \geqq 3$, $\alpha(t-1) = 1$ and $\alpha(t-3) = 1$, so

(12) $\qquad g(t) = 3 - 4(t-1) + 4(t-3) = -5, \qquad t \geqq 3.$

Equations (10), (11), and (12) are equivalent to equation (9). The graph of $g(t)$ is shown in Figure 25.

Exercises

In Exs. 1–8, express $F(t)$ in terms of the α function and find $L\{F(t)\}$.

1. $F(t) = 2, \qquad 0 < t < 1,$
   $\quad\;\; = t, \qquad\qquad t > 1.$
        ANS. $\dfrac{2}{s} + e^{-s}\left(\dfrac{1}{s^2} - \dfrac{1}{s}\right).$

2. $F(t) = 6, \qquad 0 < t < 4,$
   $\quad\;\; = 2t + 1, \qquad t > 4.$
        ANS. $\dfrac{6}{s} + e^{-4s}\left(\dfrac{2}{s^2} + \dfrac{3}{s}\right).$

3. $F(t) = t^2, \qquad 0 < t < 1,$
   $\quad\;\; = 4, \qquad\qquad t > 1.$
        ANS. $\dfrac{2}{s^3} + e^{-s}\left(\dfrac{3}{s} - \dfrac{2}{s^2} - \dfrac{2}{s^3}\right).$

4. $F(t) = t^2$, $0 < t < 2$,
        $= 4$, $2 \leqq t \leqq 4$,   ANS. $\dfrac{2}{s^3} - e^{-2s}\left(\dfrac{4}{s^2} + \dfrac{2}{s^3}\right) - \dfrac{4}{s} e^{-4s}$.
        $= 0$, $t > 4$.

5. $F(t) = t^2$, $0 < t < 2$,
        $= t - 1$, $2 < t < 3$,
        $= 7$, $t > 3$.

ANS. $\dfrac{2}{s^3} - e^{-2s}\left(\dfrac{3}{s} + \dfrac{3}{s^2} + \dfrac{2}{s^3}\right) + e^{-3s}\left(\dfrac{5}{s} - \dfrac{1}{s^2}\right)$.

6. $F(t) = e^{-t}$, $0 < t < 2$,   ANS. $\dfrac{1 - \exp(-2s - 2)}{s + 1}$.
        $= 0$, $t > 2$.

7. $F(t) = \sin 3t$, $0 < t < \frac{1}{2}\pi$,   ANS. $\dfrac{3 + s \exp(-\frac{1}{2}\pi s)}{s^2 + 9}$.
        $= 0$, $t > \frac{1}{2}\pi$.

8. $F(t) = \sin 3t$, $0 < t < \pi$,   ANS. $\dfrac{3(1 + e^{-\pi s})}{s^2 + 9}$.
        $= 0$, $t > \pi$.

9. Find and sketch an inverse Laplace transform of

$$\frac{5e^{-3s}}{s} - \frac{e^{-s}}{s}.$$

ANS. $F(t) = 5\alpha(t - 3) - \alpha(t - 1)$.

10. Evaluate $L^{-1}\left\{\dfrac{e^{-4s}}{(s + 2)^3}\right\}$.

ANS. $\frac{1}{2}(t - 4)^2 \exp[-2(t - 4)] \alpha(t - 4)$.

11. If $F(t)$ is to be continuous for $t \geqq 0$ and

$$F(t) = L^{-1}\left\{\frac{e^{-3s}}{(s + 1)^3}\right\},$$

evaluate $F(2)$, $F(5)$, $F(7)$.

ANS. $F(2) = 0$, $F(5) = 2e^{-2}$, $F(7) = 8e^{-4}$.

12. If $F(t)$ is to be continuous for $t \geqq 0$ and

$$F(t) = L^{-1}\left\{\frac{(1 - e^{-2s})(1 - 3e^{-2s})}{s^2}\right\},$$

evaluate $F(1)$, $F(3)$, $F(5)$.   ANS. $F(1) = 1$, $F(3) = -1$, $F(5) = -4$.

13. Prove that $\psi(t, c) = \displaystyle\sum_{n=0}^{\infty} (-1)^n \alpha(t - nc)$ is the same function as was

used in Example (a), Section 63. Note that for any specific t, the series is finite; no question of convergence is involved.

14. Obtain the transform of the half-wave rectification $F(t)$ of $\sin t$ by writing

$$F(t) = \sin t \, \psi(t, \pi)$$

in terms of the ψ of Ex. 13 above. Use the fact that

$$(-1)^n \sin t = \sin (t - n\pi).$$

Check your result with that in Ex. 13, page 182.

66. A convolution theorem

We now seek a formula for the inverse transform of a product of transforms. Given

$$(1) \qquad\qquad L^{-1}\{f(s)\} = F(t), \qquad L^{-1}\{g(s)\} = G(t),$$

in which $F(t)$ and $G(t)$ are assumed to be functions of class A, we shall obtain a formula for

$$(2) \qquad\qquad\qquad\qquad L^{-1}\{f(s)g(s)\}.$$

Since $f(s)$ is the transform of $F(t)$, we may write

$$(3) \qquad\qquad\qquad f(s) = \int_0^\infty e^{-st}F(t)\, dt.$$

Since $g(s)$ is the transform of $G(t)$,

$$(4) \qquad\qquad\qquad g(s) = \int_0^\infty e^{-s\beta}G(\beta)\, d\beta,$$

in which, to avoid confusion, we have used β (rather than t) as the variable of integration in the definite integral.

By equation (4), we have

$$(5) \qquad\qquad\qquad f(s)g(s) = \int_0^\infty e^{-s\beta}f(s)G(\beta)\, d\beta.$$

On the right in (5) we encounter the product $e^{-s\beta}f(s)$. By Theorem 19, page 188, we know that from

$$(6) \qquad\qquad\qquad L^{-1}\{f(s)\} = F(t)$$

it follows that

$$(7) \qquad\qquad L^{-1}\{e^{-s\beta}f(s)\} = F(t - \beta)\alpha(t - \beta),$$

in which α is the step function discussed in Section 65. Equation (7) means that

$$(8) \qquad\qquad e^{-s\beta}f(s) = \int_0^\infty e^{-st}F(t - \beta)\alpha(t - \beta)\, dt.$$

With the aid of (8) we may put equation (5) in the form

(9) $$f(s)g(s) = \int_0^\infty \int_0^\infty e^{-st}G(\beta)F(t - \beta)\alpha(t - \beta) \, dt \, d\beta.$$

Since $\alpha(t - \beta) = 0$ for $0 < t < \beta$ and $\alpha(t - \beta) = 1$ for $t \geq \beta$, equation (9) may be rewritten as

(10) $$f(s)g(s) = \int_0^\infty \int_\beta^\infty e^{-st}G(\beta)F(t - \beta) \, dt \, d\beta.$$

In (10), the integration in the $t\beta$-plane covers the shaded region shown in Figure 26. The elements are summed from $t = \beta$ to $t = \infty$ and then from $\beta = 0$ to $\beta = \infty$.

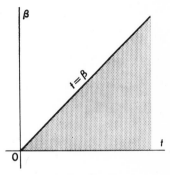

FIGURE 26

By the methods of advanced calculus it can be shown that, because $F(t)$ and $G(t)$ are functions of class A, it is legitimate to interchange the order of integration on the right in equation (10). From Figure 26 we see that in the new order of integration, the elements are to be summed from $\beta = 0$ to $\beta = t$ and then from $t = 0$ to $t = \infty$. We thus obtain

$$f(s)g(s) = \int_0^\infty \int_0^t e^{-st}G(\beta)F(t - \beta) \, d\beta \, dt,$$

or

(11) $$f(s)g(s) = \int_0^\infty e^{-st} \left[\int_0^t G(\beta)F(t - \beta) \, d\beta \right] dt.$$

Since the right member of (11) is precisely the Laplace transform of

$$\int_0^t G(\beta)F(t - \beta) \, d\beta,$$

we have arrived at the desired result, which is called the convolution theorem for the Laplace transform.

THEOREM 20: *If $L^{-1}\{f(s)\} = F(t)$, if $L^{-1}\{g(s)\} = G(t)$, and if $F(t)$ and $G(t)$ are functions of class A, page* 171, *then*

(12) $$L^{-1}\{f(s)g(s)\} = \int_0^t G(\beta)F(t - \beta) \, d\beta.$$

It is easy to show that the right member of equation (12) is also a function of class A.

Of course F and G are interchangeable in (12), since f and g enter (12) symmetrically. We may replace (12) by

$$(13) \qquad L^{-1}\{f(s)g(s)\} = \int_0^t F(\beta)G(t - \beta)\, d\beta,$$

a result which also follows from (12) by a change of variable of integration.

EXAMPLE: Evaluate $L^{-1}\left\{\dfrac{f(s)}{s}\right\}$.

Let $L^{-1}\{f(s)\} = F(t)$. Since

$$L^{-1}\left\{\frac{1}{s}\right\} = 1,$$

we use Theorem 20 to conclude that

$$L^{-1}\left\{\frac{f(s)}{s}\right\} = \int_0^t F(\beta)\, d\beta.$$

67. Partial fractions

In using the Laplace transform to solve differential equations, we often need to obtain the inverse transform of a rational fraction

$$(1) \qquad \frac{N(s)}{D(s)}.$$

The numerator and denominator in (1) are polynomials in s and the degree of $D(s)$ is larger than the degree of $N(s)$. The fraction (1) has the partial fractions expansion used in calculus.* Because of the linearity of the inverse operator L^{-1}, the partial fractions expansion of (1) permits us to replace a complicated problem in obtaining an inverse transform with a set of simpler problems.

EXAMPLE (a): Obtain $L^{-1}\left\{\dfrac{s^2 - 6}{s^3 + 4s^2 + 3s}\right\}$.

Since the denominator is a product of distinct linear factors, we know that constants A, B, C exist such that

---

* See, for example, E. D. Rainville, *Unified Calculus and Analytic Geometry* (New York: The Macmillan Co., 1961), pp. 357–364.

$$\frac{s^2 - 6}{s^3 + 4s^2 + 3s} = \frac{s^2 - 6}{s(s + 1)(s + 3)} = \frac{A}{s} + \frac{B}{s + 1} + \frac{C}{s + 3}.$$

Multiplying each term by the lowest common denominator, we obtain the identity

(2) $s^2 - 6 = A(s + 1)(s + 3) + Bs(s + 3) + Cs(s + 1),$

from which we need to determine A, B, and C. Using the values $s = 0$, -1, -3 successively in (2), we get

$$s = 0:   \qquad -6 = A(1)(3),$$
$$s = -1:   \qquad -5 = B(-1)(2),$$
$$s = -3:   \qquad 3 = C(-3)(-2),$$

from which $A = -2$, $B = \frac{5}{2}$, $C = \frac{1}{2}$. Therefore

$$\frac{s^2 - 6}{s^3 + 4s^2 + 3s} = \frac{-2}{s} + \frac{\frac{5}{2}}{s + 1} + \frac{\frac{1}{2}}{s + 3}.$$

Since $L^{-1}\left\{\frac{1}{s}\right\} = 1$ and $L^{-1}\left\{\frac{1}{s + a}\right\} = e^{-at}$, we get the desired result,

$$L^{-1}\left\{\frac{s^2 - 6}{s^3 + 4s^2 + 3s}\right\} = -2 + \frac{5}{2}e^{-t} + \frac{1}{2}e^{-3t}.$$

EXAMPLE (b): Obtain $L^{-1}\left\{\dfrac{5s^3 - 6s - 3}{s^3(s + 1)^2}\right\}.$

Since the denominator contains repeated linear factors, we must assume partial fractions of the form shown:

(3) $\dfrac{5s^3 - 6s - 3}{s^3(s + 1)^2} = \dfrac{A_1}{s} + \dfrac{A_2}{s^2} + \dfrac{A_3}{s^3} + \dfrac{B_1}{s + 1} + \dfrac{B_2}{(s + 1)^2}.$

Corresponding to a denominator factor $(x - \gamma)^r$, we must in general assume r partial fractions of the form

$$\frac{A_1}{x - \gamma} + \frac{A_2}{(x - \gamma)^2} + \cdots + \frac{A_r}{(x - \gamma)^r}.$$

From (3) we get

(4) $5s^3 - 6s - 3 = A_1 s^2(s + 1)^2 + A_2 s(s + 1)^2$
$$+ A_3(s + 1)^2 + B_1 s^3(s + 1) + B_2 s^3,$$

which must be an identity in s. To get the necessary five equations for the determination of A_1, A_2, A_3, B_1, B_2, two elementary methods are popular.

Specific values of s can be used in (4), or the coefficients of like powers of s in the two members of (4) may be equated. We employ whatever combination of these methods yields simple equations to be solved for A_1, A_2, $\cdots$, B_2. From (4) we obtain

$$
\begin{aligned}
s = 0: \qquad & -3 = A_3(1), \\
s = -1: \qquad & -2 = B_2(-1), \\
\text{coeff. of } s^4: \qquad & 0 = A_1 + B_1, \\
\text{coeff. of } s^3: \qquad & 5 = 2A_1 + A_2 + B_1 + B_2, \\
\text{coeff. of } s: \qquad & -6 = A_2 + 2A_3.
\end{aligned}
$$

The above equations yield $A_1 = 3$, $A_2 = 0$, $A_3 = -3$, $B_1 = -3$, $B_2 = 2$. Therefore we find that

$$
L^{-1} \left\{ \frac{5s^3 - 6s - 3}{s^3(s+1)^2} \right\} = L^{-1} \left\{ \frac{3}{s} - \frac{3}{s^3} - \frac{3}{s+1} + \frac{2}{(s+1)^2} \right\}
$$

$$
= 3 - \tfrac{3}{2}t^2 - 3e^{-t} + 2te^{-t}.
$$

EXAMPLE (c): Obtain $L^{-1} \left\{ \dfrac{16}{s(s^2+4)^2} \right\}$.

Since quadratic factors require the corresponding partial fractions to have linear numerators, we start with an expansion of the form

$$
\frac{16}{s(s^2+4)^2} = \frac{A}{s} + \frac{B_1 s + C_1}{s^2 + 4} + \frac{B_2 s + C_2}{(s^2+4)^2}.
$$

From the identity

$$
16 = A(s^2+4)^2 + (B_1 s + C_1)s(s^2+4) + (B_2 s + C_2)s,
$$

it is not difficult to find the values $A = 1$, $B_1 = -1$, $B_2 = -4$, $C_1 = 0$, $C_2 = 0$. We thus obtain

$$
L^{-1} \left\{ \frac{16}{s(s^2+4)^2} \right\} = L^{-1} \left\{ \frac{1}{s} - \frac{s}{s^2+4} - \frac{4s}{(s^2+4)^2} \right\}
$$

$$
= 1 - \cos 2t - t \sin 2t.
$$

It is possible to obtain formulas for the partial fractions expansion of the rational fractions being treated in this section. Such formulas are useful in theory and not particularly inefficient in practice. The elementary techniques above, if used intelligently, are efficient in numerical problems and are the only partial fractions methods presented in this short treatment of the subject.

Exercises

In Exs. 1–10, find an inverse transform of the given $f(s)$.

1. $\dfrac{1}{s^2 + as}$.   ANS. $\dfrac{1}{a}(1 - e^{-at})$.

2. $\dfrac{s + 2}{s^2 - 6s + 8}$.   ANS. $3e^{4t} - 2e^{2t}$.

3. $\dfrac{2s^2 + 5s - 4}{s^3 + s^2 - 2s}$.   ANS. $2 + e^t - e^{-2t}$.

4. $\dfrac{2s^2 + 1}{s(s + 1)^2}$.   ANS. $1 + e^{-t} - 3te^{-t}$.

5. $\dfrac{4s + 4}{s^2(s - 2)}$.   ANS. $3e^{2t} - 3 - 2t$.

6. $\dfrac{1}{s^3(s^2 + 1)}$.   ANS. $\frac{1}{2}t^2 - 1 + \cos t$.

7. $\dfrac{5s - 2}{s^2(s + 2)(s - 1)}$.   ANS. $t - 2 + e^t + e^{-2t}$.

8. $\dfrac{1}{(s^2 + a^2)(s^2 + b^2)}$, $a^2 \neq b^2,\ ab \neq 0$.   ANS. $\dfrac{b \sin at - a \sin bt}{ab(b^2 - a^2)}$.

9. $\dfrac{s}{(s^2 + a^2)(s^2 + b^2)}$, $a^2 \neq b^2,\ ab \neq 0$.   ANS. $\dfrac{\cos at - \cos bt}{b^2 - a^2}$.

10. $\dfrac{s^2}{(s^2 + a^2)(s^2 + b^2)}$, $a^2 \neq b^2,\ ab \neq 0$.   ANS. $\dfrac{a \sin at - b \sin bt}{a^2 - b^2}$.

11. Obtain the answers to Exs. 9 and 10 from that for Ex. 8.

12. Use equation (8), page 177, and the convolution, Theorem 20, to obtain

$$L^{-1}\left\{\frac{16}{s(s^2 + 4)^2}\right\} = \int_0^t (\sin 2\beta - 2\beta \cos 2\beta)\, d\beta,$$

and then perform the integration to check the answer to Example (c), page 196.

68. Simple boundary value problems

Because of Theorem 10, page 175, the Laplace operator will transform a differential equation with constant coefficients into an algebraic equation in the transformed function. Several examples will be treated in detail so that we can get some feeling for the advantages and disadvantages of the transform method. One fact is apparent from the start: this method is at its best when the boundary conditions are actually initial conditions, those giving the value of the function and its derivatives at time zero.

EXAMPLE (a): Solve the problem

(1) $y''(t) + \beta^2 y(t) = A \sin \omega t;$ $y(0) = 1,$ $y'(0) = 0.$

Here A, β, ω are constants. Since $\beta = 0$ would make the problem one of elementary calculus and since a change in sign of β or ω would not alter the character of the problem, we may assume that β and ω are positive.

Let $L\{y(t)\} = u(s).$

Then $L\{y'(t)\} = su(s) - 1,$
               $L\{y''(t)\} = s^2 u(s) - s \cdot 1 - 0,$

and application of the operator L transforms the problem (1) into

$$s^2 u(s) - s + \beta^2 u(s) = \frac{A\omega}{s^2 + \omega^2},$$

from which

(2) $$u(s) = \frac{s}{s^2 + \beta^2} + \frac{A\omega}{(s^2 + \beta^2)(s^2 + \omega^2)}.$$

We need the inverse transform of the right member of (2). The form of that inverse depends upon whether β and ω are equal or unequal.

If $\omega \neq \beta$,

$$u(s) = \frac{s}{s^2 + \beta^2} + \frac{A\omega}{\beta^2 - \omega^2}\left(\frac{1}{s^2 + \omega^2} - \frac{1}{s^2 + \beta^2}\right)$$

$$= \frac{s}{s^2 + \beta^2} + \frac{A}{\beta(\beta^2 - \omega^2)}\left(\frac{\omega\beta}{s^2 + \omega^2} - \frac{\omega\beta}{s^2 + \beta^2}\right).$$

Now $y(t) = L^{-1}\{u(s)\}$ so, for $\omega \neq \beta$,

(3) $$y(t) = \cos \beta t + \frac{A}{\beta(\beta^2 - \omega^2)}(\beta \sin \omega t - \omega \sin \beta t).$$

If $\omega = \beta$, the transform (2) becomes

(4) $$u(s) = \frac{s}{s^2 + \beta^2} + \frac{A\beta}{(s^2 + \beta^2)^2}.$$

We know that

$$L^{-1}\left\{\frac{1}{(s^2 + \beta^2)^2}\right\} = \frac{1}{2\beta^3}(\sin \beta t - \beta t \cos \beta t).$$

Hence, for $\omega = \beta$,

(5) $$y(t) = \cos \beta t + \frac{A}{2\beta^2}(\sin \beta t - \beta t \cos \beta t).$$

Note that the initial conditions were satisfied automatically by this method when Theorem 10 was applied. We get, not the general soultion with arbitrary constants still to be determined, but that particular solution which satisfies the desired initial conditions. The transform method also gives us some insight into the reason that the solution takes different forms according to whether ω and β are equal or unequal.

EXAMPLE (b): Solve the problem

$$(6)\qquad x''(t) + 2x'(t) + x(t) = 3te^{-t}; \qquad x(0) = 4, \quad x'(0) = 2.$$

Let $L\{x(t)\} = y(s)$. Then the operator L converts (6) into

$$s^2y(s) - 4s - 2 + 2[sy(s) - 4] + y(s) = \frac{3}{(s+1)^2},$$

or

$$(7)\qquad\qquad y(s) = \frac{4s + 10}{(s+1)^2} + \frac{3}{(s+1)^4}.$$

We may write

$$y(s) = \frac{4(s+1) + 6}{(s+1)^2} + \frac{3}{(s+1)^4}$$

$$= \frac{4}{s+1} + \frac{6}{(s+1)^2} + \frac{3}{(s+1)^4}.$$

Employing the inverse transform, we obtain

$$(8)\qquad\qquad x(t) = (4 + 6t + \tfrac{1}{2}t^3)e^{-t}.$$

Again the presence of initial conditions contributed to the efficiency of our method. In obtaining and in using equation (7), those terms that came from the initial values $x(0)$ and $x'(0)$ were not combined with the term that came from the transform of the right member of the differential equation. To combine such terms rarely simplifies and frequently complicates the task of obtaining the inverse transform.

From the solution

$$(8)\qquad\qquad x(t) = (4 + 6t + \tfrac{1}{2}t^3)e^{-t}$$

the student should obtain the derivatives

$$x'(t) = (2 - 6t + \tfrac{3}{2}t^2 - \tfrac{1}{2}t^3)e^{-t},$$

$$x''(t) = (-8 + 9t - 3t^2 + \tfrac{1}{2}t^3)e^{-t},$$

and thus verify that the x of (8) satisfies both the differential equation and the initial conditions of the problem (6). Such verification not only checks our work but also removes any need to justify temporary assumptions about the right to use the Laplace transform theorems on the function $x(t)$ during the time that the function is still unknown.

EXAMPLE (c): Solve the problem

(9) $\qquad x''(t) + 4x(t) = \psi(t); \qquad x(0) = 1, \qquad x'(0) = 0,$

in which $\psi(t)$ is defined by

(10) $\qquad\qquad\qquad \psi(t) = 4t, \qquad 0 \leqq t \leqq 1,$

$\qquad\qquad\qquad\qquad = 4, \qquad t > 1.$

We seek, of course, a solution valid in the range $t \geqq 0$ in which the right member $\psi(t)$ is defined.

In this problem another phase of the power of the Laplace transform method begins to emerge. The fact that the function $\psi(t)$ in the differential equation has discontinuous derivatives makes the use of the classical method of undetermined coefficients somewhat awkward, but such discontinuities do not interfere at all with the simplicity of the Laplace transform method.

In attacking this problem, let us put $L\{x(t)\} = h(s)$. We need to obtain $L\{\psi(t)\}$. In terms of the α function we may write, from (10),

(11) $\qquad\qquad \psi(t) = 4t - 4(t - 1)\alpha(t - 1), \qquad t \geqq 0.$

From (11) it follows that

$$L\{\psi(t)\} = \frac{4}{s^2} - \frac{4e^{-s}}{s^2}.$$

Therefore the application of the operator L transforms problem (9) into

$$s^2 h(s) - s - 0 + 4h(s) = \frac{4}{s^2} - \frac{4e^{-s}}{s^2},$$

from which

(12) $\qquad\qquad h(s) = \frac{s}{s^2 + 4} + \frac{4}{s^2(s^2 + 4)} - \frac{4e^{-s}}{s^2(s^2 + 4)}.$

Now

$$\frac{4}{s^2(s^2 + 4)} = \frac{1}{s^2} - \frac{1}{s^2 + 4},$$

so (12) becomes

(13) $\qquad h(s) = \frac{s}{s^2 + 4} + \frac{1}{s^2} - \frac{1}{s^2 + 4} - \left(\frac{1}{s^2} - \frac{1}{s^2 + 4}\right)e^{-s}.$

Since $x(t) = L^{-1}\{h(s)\}$, we obtain the desired solution

(14) $x(t) = \cos 2t + t - \frac{1}{2}\sin 2t - [(t-1) - \frac{1}{2}\sin 2(t-1)]\,\alpha(t-1).$

It is easy to verify our solution. From (14) it follows that

(15) $x'(t) = -2\sin 2t + 1 - \cos 2t - [1 - \cos 2(t-1)]\,\alpha(t-1),$

(16) $x''(t) = -4\cos 2t + 2\sin 2t - 2\sin 2(t-1)\,\alpha(t-1).$

Therefore $x(0) = 1$ and $x'(0) = 0$, as desired. Also, from (14), and (16), we get

$$x''(t) + 4x(t) = 4t - 4(t-1)\alpha(t-1) = \psi(t), \qquad t \geqq 0.$$

EXAMPLE (d): Solve the problem

(17) $x''(t) + k^2 x(t) = F(t); \qquad x(0) = A, \qquad x'(0) = B.$

Here k, A, B are constants and $F(t)$ is a known but unstipulated function. For the time being, think of $F(t)$ as a function whose Laplace transform exists. Let

$$L\{x(t)\} = u(s), \qquad L\{F(t)\} = f(s).$$

Then the Laplace operator transforms problem (17) into

$$s^2 u(s) - As - B + k^2 u(s) = f(s),$$

(18) $$u(s) = \frac{As + B}{s^2 + k^2} + \frac{f(s)}{s^2 + k^2}.$$

To get the inverse transform of the last term in (18), we use the convolution theorem. Thus we arrive at

$$x(t) = A\cos kt + \frac{B}{k}\sin kt + \frac{1}{k}\int_0^t F(t - \beta)\sin k\beta \, d\beta,$$

or

(19) $$x(t) = A\cos kt + \frac{B}{k}\sin kt + \frac{1}{k}\int_0^t F(\beta)\sin k(t - \beta)\, d\beta.$$

For the student who has had advanced calculus and knows how to differentiate a definite integral with respect to a parameter (Leibniz' rule), verification of the solution (19) is simple. Once that check has been performed, the need for the assumption that $F(t)$ has a Laplace transform is removed. It does not matter what method we use to get a solution (with certain exceptions naturally imposed during college examinations) if the validity of the result can be verified from the result itself.

EXAMPLE (e): Solve the problem

(20) $w''(x) + 2w'(x) + w(x) = x;$ $w(0) = -3,$ $w(1) = -1.$

In this example the boundary conditions are not both of the initial condition type. Using x, rather than t, as independent variable, let

(21) $L\{w(x)\} = g(s).$

We know $w(0) = -3$, but we also need $w'(0)$ in order to write the transform of $w''(x)$. Hence we put

(22) $w'(0) = B$

and expect to determine B later by using the condition that $w(1) = -1$.
    The transformed problem is

$$s^2g(s) - s(-3) - B + 2[sg(s) - (-3)] + g(s) = \frac{1}{s^2}.$$

from which

(23) $g(s) = \dfrac{-3(s+1) + B - 3}{(s+1)^2} + \dfrac{1}{s^2(s+1)^2}.$

But, by the usual partial fractions expansion,

$$\frac{1}{s^2(s+1)^2} = -\frac{2}{s} + \frac{1}{s^2} + \frac{2}{s+1} + \frac{1}{(s+1)^2},$$

so

(24) $g(s) = \dfrac{1}{s^2} - \dfrac{2}{s} - \dfrac{1}{s+1} + \dfrac{B-2}{(s+1)^2},$

from which we obtain

(25) $w(x) = x - 2 - e^{-x} + (B-2)xe^{-x}.$

We have yet to impose the condition that $w(1) = -1$. From (25) with $x = 1$, we get

$$-1 = 1 - 2 - e^{-1} + (B-2)e^{-1},$$

so $B = 3$.
    Thus our final result is

(26) $w(x) = x - 2 - e^{-x} + xe^{-x}.$

The problem in Example (e) may be solved efficiently by the methods of Chapter 9. See also Exs. 21–42 below.

Exercises

In Exs. 1–14, solve the problem by the Laplace transform method. Verify that your solution satisfies the differential equation and the boundary conditions.

1. $x''(t) + 4x'(t) + 4x(t) = 4e^{-2t}$; $x(0) = -1$, $x'(0) = 4$.

> ANS. $x(t) = e^{-2t}(2t^2 + 2t - 1)$.

2. $x''(t) + x(t) = 6 \cos 2t$; $x(0) = 3$, $x'(0) = 1$.

> ANS. $x(t) = 5 \cos t + \sin t - 2 \cos 2t$.

3. $y''(t) - y(t) = 5 \sin 2t$; $y(0) = 0$, $y'(0) = 1$.

> ANS. $y(t) = 3 \sinh t - \sin 2t$.

4. $y''(t) + 6y'(t) + 9y(t) = 6t^2 e^{-3t}$; $y(0) = 0$, $y'(0) = 0$.

> ANS. $y(t) = \frac{1}{2}t^4 e^{-3t}$.

5. $x''(t) + 4x(t) = 2t - 8$; $x(0) = 1$, $x'(0) = 0$.

> ANS. $x(t) = 3 \cos 2t - \frac{1}{4} \sin 2t + \frac{1}{2}t - 2$.

6. $x''(t) + 2x'(t) = 8t$; $x(0) = 0$, $x'(0) = 0$.

> ANS. $x(t) = 2t^2 - 2t + 1 - e^{-2t}$.

7. $u''(t) + 4u(t) = 15e^t$; $u(0) = 1$, $u'(0) = 3$.

> ANS. $u(t) = 3e^t - 2 \cos 2t$.

8. $u''(t) + 4u'(t) + 3u(t) = 12$; $u(0) = 7$, $u'(0) = 1$.

> ANS. $u(t) = 4 + 5e^{-t} - 2e^{-3t}$.

9. $y''(x) + 9y(x) = 40e^x$; $y(0) = 5$, $y'(0) = -2$.

> ANS. $y(x) = 4e^x + \cos 3x - 2 \sin 3x$.

10. $y''(x) + y(x) = 4e^x$; $y(0) = 0$, $y'(0) = 0$.

> ANS. $y(x) = 2(e^x - \cos x - \sin x)$.

11. $x''(t) + 3x'(t) + 2x(t) = 4t^2$; $x(0) = 0$, $x'(0) = 0$.

> ANS. $x(t) = 2t^2 - 6t + 7 - 8e^{-t} + e^{-2t}$.

12. $x''(t) + 4x'(t) + 4x(t) = 4 \cos 2t$; $x(0) = 2$, $x'(0) = 5$.

> ANS. $x(t) = 2e^{2t}(1 + t) - \frac{1}{2} \sin 2t$.

13. $x''(t) + x(t) = F(t)$; $x(0) = 0$, $x'(0) = 0$, in which

$$F(t) = 4, \qquad 0 \leq t \leq 2,$$
$$= t + 2, \qquad t > 2.$$

> ANS. $x(t) = 4 - 4 \cos t + [(t - 2) - \sin (t - 2)] \alpha(t - 2)$.

14. $x''(t) + x(t) = H(t)$; $x(0) = 1$, $x'(0) = 0$, in which

$$H(t) = 3, \qquad 0 \leq t \leq 4,$$
$$= 2t - 5, \qquad t > 4.$$

> ANS. $x(t) = 3 - 2 \cos t + 2[t - 4 - \sin (t - 4)] \alpha(t - 4)$.

15. Compute $y(\tfrac{1}{2}\pi)$ and $y(2 + \tfrac{1}{2}\pi)$ for the function $y(x)$ that satisfies the boundary value problem

$$y''(x) + y(x) = (x - 2)\alpha(x - 2); \; y(0) = 0, \; y'(0) = 0.$$

ANS. $y(\tfrac{1}{2}\pi) = 0, \; y(2 + \tfrac{1}{2}\pi) = \tfrac{1}{2}\pi - 1.$

16. Compute $x(1)$ and $x(4)$ for the function $x(t)$ that satisfies the boundary value problem

$$x''(t) + 2x'(t) + x(t) = 2 + (t - 3)\alpha(t - 3); \; x(0) = 2, \; x'(0) = 1.$$

ANS. $x(1) = 2 + e^{-1}, \; x(4) = 1 + 3e^{-1} + 4e^{-4}.$

17. Solve the problem

$$x''(t) + 2x'(t) + x(t) = F(t); x(0) = 0, \; x'(0) = 0.$$

ANS. $x(t) = \displaystyle\int_0^t \beta e^{-\beta} F(t - \beta) \, d\beta.$

18. Solve the problem

$$y''(t) - k^2 y(t) = H(t); \; y(0) = 0, \; y'(0) = 0.$$

ANS. $y(t) = \dfrac{1}{k} \displaystyle\int_0^t H(t - \beta) \sinh k\beta \, d\beta.$

19. Solve the problem

$$y''(t) + 4y'(t) + 13y(t) = F(t); \; y(0) = 0, \; y'(0) = 0.$$

20. Solve the problem

$$x''(t) + 6x'(t) + 9x(t) = F(t); \; x(0) = A, \; x'(0) = B.$$

ANS. $x(t) = e^{-3t}[A + (B + 3A)t] + \displaystyle\int_0^t \beta e^{-3\beta} F(t - \beta) \, d\beta.$

In Exs. 21–42, use the Laplace transform method with the realization that these exercises were not constructed with the Laplace transform technique in mind. Compare your work with that done in solving the same problems by the methods of Chapter 9.

21. Ex. 1, page 136.	**22.** Ex. 2, page 136.
23. Ex. 3, page 136.	**24.** Ex. 11, page 136.
25. Ex. 14, page 137.	**26.** Ex. 20, page 137.
27. Ex. 21, page 137.	**28.** Ex. 22, page 137.
29. Ex. 23, page 137.	**30.** Ex. 36, page 137.
31. Ex. 37, page 137.	**32.** Ex. 38, page 137.
33. Ex. 39, page 138.	**34.** Ex. 40, page 138.
35. Ex. 41, page 138.	**36.** Ex. 42, page 138.
37. Ex. 43, page 138.	**38.** Ex. 44, page 138.

39. Ex. 45, page 138.   **40.** Ex. 46, page 138.

41. Solve the problem

$$x''(t) - 4x'(t) + 4x(t) = e^{2t}; \; x'(0) = 0, \; x(1) = 0.$$

$$\text{ANS.} \quad x(t) = \tfrac{1}{2}(1 - t)^2 e^{2t}.$$

42. Solve the problem

$$x''(t) + 4x(t) = -8t^2; \; x(0) = 3, \; x(\tfrac{1}{4}\pi) = 0.$$

$$\text{ANS.} \quad x(t) = 2 \cos 2t + \left(\frac{1}{8}\pi^2 - 1\right) \sin 2t + 1 - 2t^2.$$

69. Special integral equations

A differential equation may be loosely described as one that contains a derivative of a dependent variable; the equation contains a dependent variable under a derivative sign. An equation that contains a dependent variable under an integral sign is called an integral equation.

Because of the convolution theorem, the Laplace transform is an excellent tool for solving a very special class of integral equations. We know from Theorem 20 that if

$$L\{F(t)\} = f(s)$$

and

$$L\{G(t)\} = g(s),$$

then

(1) $$L\left\{\int_0^t F(\beta)G(t - \beta) \, d\beta\right\} = f(s)g(s).$$

The relation (1) suggests the use of the Laplace transform on equations that contain convolution integrals.

EXAMPLE (a): Find $F(t)$ from the integral equation

(2) $$F(t) = 4t - 3 \int_0^t F(\beta) \sin (t - \beta) \, d\beta.$$

The integral in (2) is in precisely the right form to permit the use of the convolution theorem. Let

$$L\{F(t)\} = f(s).$$

Then, since

$$L\{\sin t\} = \frac{1}{s^2 + 1},$$

application of Theorem 20, page 193, yields

$$L\left\{\int_0^t F(\beta) \sin (t - \beta)\, d\beta\right\} = \frac{f(s)}{s^2 + 1}.$$

Therefore, the Laplace operator converts equation (2) into

(3) $$f(s) = \frac{4}{s^2} - \frac{3f(s)}{s^2 + 1}.$$

We need to obtain $f(s)$ from (3) and then $F(t)$ from $f(s)$. From (3) we get

$$\left(1 + \frac{3}{s^2 + 1}\right)f(s) = \frac{4}{s^2},$$

or

$$f(s) = \frac{4(s^2 + 1)}{s^2(s^2 + 4)}.$$

Then, by the methods of Section 67, or by inspection,

$$f(s) = \frac{1}{s^2} + \frac{3}{s^2 + 4}.$$

Therefore

$$F(t) = L^{-1}\left\{\frac{1}{s^2} + \frac{3}{s^2 + 4}\right\},$$

(4) $$F(t) = t + \tfrac{3}{2} \sin 2t.$$

That the $F(t)$ of (4) is a solution of equation (2) may be verified directly. Such a check is frequently tedious. We shall show that for the F of (4), the right-hand side of equation (2) reduces to the left-hand side of (2). Since

$$RHS = 4t - 3 \int_0^t (\beta + \tfrac{3}{2} \sin 2\beta) \sin (t - \beta)\, d\beta,$$

we integrate by parts with the choice shown in the table.

$(\beta + \tfrac{3}{2} \sin 2\beta)$	$\sin (t - \beta)\, d\beta$
$(1 + 3 \cos 2\beta)\, d\beta$	$\cos (t - \beta)$

It thus follows that

$$RHS = 4t - 3\left[(\beta + \tfrac{3}{2} \sin 2\beta) \cos (t - \beta)\right]_0^t$$

$$+ 3 \int_0^t (1 + 3 \cos 2\beta) \cos (t - \beta)\, d\beta,$$

from which

$$RHS = 4t - 3(t + \tfrac{3}{2} \sin 2t) + 3 \int_0^t \cos (t - \beta) \, d\beta$$

$$+ 9 \int_0^t \cos 2\beta \cos (t - \beta) \, d\beta,$$

or

$$RHS = t - \tfrac{9}{2} \sin 2t - 3 \left[\sin (t - \beta) \right]_0^t$$

$$+ \tfrac{9}{2} \int_0^t [\cos (t + \beta) + \cos (t - 3\beta)] \, d\beta.$$

This leads us to the result

$$RHS = t - \tfrac{9}{2} \sin 2t + 3 \sin t + \tfrac{9}{2} \left[\sin (t + \beta) - \tfrac{1}{3} \sin (t - 3\beta) \right]_0^t$$

$$= t - \tfrac{9}{2} \sin 2t + 3 \sin t + \tfrac{9}{2} \sin 2t + \tfrac{3}{2} \sin 2t - \tfrac{9}{2} \sin t + \tfrac{3}{2} \sin t,$$

or

$$RHS = t + \tfrac{3}{2} \sin 2t = F(t) = LHS,$$

as desired.

It is important to realize that the original equation

$$(2) \qquad F(t) = 4t - 3 \int_0^t F(\beta) \sin (t - \beta) \, d\beta$$

could equally well have been encountered in the equivalent form

$$F(t) = 4t - 3 \int_0^t F(t - \beta) \sin \beta \, d\beta.$$

An essential ingredient for the success of the method being used is that the integral involved be in exactly the convolution integral form. We must have zero to the independent variable as limits of integration, and an integrand that is the product of a function of the variable of integration by a function of the difference between the independent variable and the variable of integration. The fact that integrals of that form appear with some frequency in physical problems is all that keeps the topic of this section from being relegated to the role of a mathematical parlor game.

EXAMPLE (b): Solve the equation

$$(5) \qquad g(x) = \tfrac{1}{2}x^2 - \int_0^x (x - y)g(y) \, dy.$$

Again the integral involved is one of the convolution type with x playing the role of the independent variable. Let the Laplace transform of $g(x)$ be some as yet unknown function $h(z)$:

(6) $$L\{g(x)\} = h(z).$$

Since $L\{\frac{1}{2}x^2\} = \dfrac{1}{z^3}$ and $L\{x\} = \dfrac{1}{z^2}$, we may apply the operator L throughout (5) and obtain

$$h(z) = \frac{1}{z^3} - \frac{h(z)}{z^2},$$

from which

$$\left(1 + \frac{1}{z^2}\right)h(z) = \frac{1}{z^3},$$

or

$$h(z) = \frac{1}{z(z^2+1)} = \frac{z^2+1-z^2}{z(z^2+1)} = \frac{1}{z} - \frac{z}{z^2+1}.$$

Then

$$g(x) = L^{-1}\left\{\frac{1}{z} - \frac{z}{z^2+1}\right\}$$

or

(7) $$g(x) = 1 - \cos x.$$

Verification of (7) is simple. For the right member of (5) we get

$$RHS = \tfrac{1}{2}x^2 - \int_0^x (x-y)(1-\cos y)\,dy$$

$$= \tfrac{1}{2}x^2 - \left[(x-y)(y-\sin y)\right]_0^x - \int_0^x (y-\sin y)\,dy$$

$$= \tfrac{1}{2}x^2 - 0 - \left[\tfrac{1}{2}y^2 + \cos y\right]_0^x$$

$$= \tfrac{1}{2}x^2 - \tfrac{1}{2}x^2 - \cos x + 1 = 1 - \cos x = LHS.$$

Exercises

In Exs. 1–4, solve the given equation and verify your solution.

1. $F(t) = 1 + 2\displaystyle\int_0^t F(t-\beta)e^{-2\beta}\,d\beta.$ ANS. $F(t) = 1 + 2t.$

2. $F(t) = 1 + \displaystyle\int_0^t F(\beta)\sin(t-\beta)\,d\beta.$ ANS. $F(t) = 1 + \tfrac{1}{2}t^2.$

3. $F(t) = t + \displaystyle\int_0^t F(t-\beta)e^{-\beta}\,d\beta.$ ANS. $F(t) = t + \tfrac{1}{2}t^2.$

4. $F(t) = 4t^2 - \displaystyle\int_0^t F(t-\beta)e^{-\beta}\,d\beta.$

          ANS. $F(t) = -1 + 2t + 2t^2 + e^{-2t}.$

In Exs. 5–8, solve the given equation. If sufficient time is available, verify your solution.

5. $F(t) = t^3 + \int_0^t F(\beta) \sin (t - \beta) \, d\beta.$ ANS. $F(t) = t^3 + \dfrac{1}{20} t^5.$

6. $F(t) = 8t^2 - 3 \int_0^t F(\beta) \sin (t - \beta) \, d\beta.$

7. $F(t) = t^2 - 2 \int_0^t F(t - \beta) \sinh 2\beta \, d\beta.$ ANS. $F(t) = t^2 - \dfrac{1}{3} t^4.$

8. $F(t) = 1 + 2 \int_0^t F(t - \beta) \cos \beta \, d\beta.$ ANS. $F(t) = 1 + 2te^t.$

In Exs. 9–12, solve the given equation.

9. $H(t) = 9e^{2t} - 2 \int_0^t H(t - \beta) \cos \beta \, d\beta.$

10. $H(y) = y^2 + \int_0^y H(x) \sin (y - x) \, dx.$ ANS. $H(y) = y^2 + \dfrac{1}{12} y^4.$

11. $g(x) = e^{-x} - 2 \int_0^x g(\beta) \cos (x - \beta) \, d\beta.$ ANS. $g(x) = e^{-x}(1 - x)^2.$

12. $y(t) = 6t + 4 \int_0^t (\beta - t)^2 y(\beta) \, d\beta.$

ANS. $y(t) = e^{2t} - e^{-t} (\cos \sqrt{3}\, t - \sqrt{3} \sin \sqrt{3}\, t).$

13. Solve the following equation for $F(t)$ with the condition that $F(0) = 4$:

$F'(t) = t + \int_0^t F(t - \beta) \cos \beta \, d\beta.$ ANS. $F(t) = 4 + \dfrac{5}{2} t^2 + \dfrac{1}{24} t^4.$

14. Solve the following equation for $F(t)$ with the condition that $F(0) = 0$:

$F'(t) = \sin t + \int_0^t F(t - \beta) \cos \beta \, d\beta.$ ANS. $F(t) = \tfrac{1}{2} t^2.$

15. Show that the equation of Ex. 3 above can be put in the form

(A) $e^t F(t) = te^t + \int_0^t e^\beta F(\beta) \, d\beta.$

Differentiate each member of (A) with respect to t and thus replace the integral equation with a differential equation. Note that $F(0) = 0$. Find $F(t)$ by this method.

16. Solve the equation

$$\int_0^t F(t - \beta) \, e^{-\beta} \, d\beta = t$$

by two methods; use the convolution theorem and the basic idea introduced in Ex. 15. Note that no differential equation need be solved in this instance.

Table of Transforms

Whenever n is used, it denotes a non-negative integer.

The range of validity may be determined from the appropriate text material. Many other transforms will be found in the examples and exercises.

$f(s) = L\{F(t)\}$	$F(t)$
$f(s - a)$	$e^{at}F(t)$
$f(as + b)$	$\dfrac{1}{a}\exp\left(-\dfrac{bt}{a}\right)F\left(\dfrac{t}{a}\right)$
$\dfrac{1}{s}e^{-cs}, \quad c > 0$	$\alpha(t - c) = 0, \quad 0 \leqq t < c,$ $= 1, \; t \geqq c$
$e^{-cs}f(s), \quad c > 0$	$F(t - c)\alpha(t - c)$
$f_1(s)\,f_2(s)$	$\displaystyle\int_0^t F_1(\beta)\,F_2(t - \beta)\,d\beta$
$\dfrac{1}{s}$	1
$\dfrac{1}{s^{n+1}}$	$\dfrac{t^n}{n!}$
$\dfrac{1}{s^{x+1}}, \quad x > -1$	$\dfrac{t^x}{\Gamma(x + 1)}$
$s^{-\frac{1}{2}}$	$(\pi t)^{-\frac{1}{2}}$
$\dfrac{1}{s + a}$	e^{-at}

$f(s) = L\{F(t)\}$	$F(t)$
$\dfrac{1}{(s+a)^{n+1}}$	$\dfrac{t^n e^{-at}}{n!}$
$\dfrac{k}{s^2 + k^2}$	$\sin kt$
$\dfrac{s}{s^2 + k^2}$	$\cos kt$
$\dfrac{k}{s^2 - k^2}$	$\sinh kt$
$\dfrac{s}{s^2 - k^2}$	$\cosh kt$
$\dfrac{2k^3}{(s^2 + k^2)^2}$	$\sin kt - kt \cos kt$
$\dfrac{2ks}{(s^2 + k^2)^2}$	$t \sin kt$
$\ln\left(1 + \dfrac{1}{s}\right)$	$\dfrac{1 - e^{-t}}{t}$
$\ln\dfrac{s + k}{s - k}$	$\dfrac{2 \sinh kt}{t}$
$\ln\left(1 - \dfrac{k^2}{s^2}\right)$	$\dfrac{2}{t}(1 - \cosh kt)$
$\ln\left(1 + \dfrac{k^2}{s^2}\right)$	$\dfrac{2}{t}(1 - \cos kt)$
$\text{Arctan}\,\dfrac{k}{s}$	$\dfrac{\sin kt}{t}$

CHAPTER 13

Applications

70. Vibration of a spring

Consider a steel spring attached to a support and hanging downward. Within certain elastic limits the spring will obey Hooke's law: if the spring is stretched or compressed, its change in length will be proportional to the force exerted upon the spring and, when that force is removed, the spring will return to its original position with its length and other physical properties unchanged. There is, therefore, associated with each spring a numerical constant, the ratio of the force exerted to the displacement produced by that force. If a force of magnitude Q pounds stretches the spring c feet, the relation

$$(1) \qquad Q = kc$$

defines the spring constant k in units of pounds per foot.

Let a body B weighing w pounds be attached to the lower end of a spring (Figure 27) and brought to the point of equilibrium where it can remain at rest. Once the weight B is

FIGURE 27   FIGURE 28

moved from the point of equilibrium E in Figure 28, the motion of B will be determined by a differential equation and associated boundary conditions.

212

Let t be time measured in seconds after some initial moment when the motion begins. Let x, in feet, be distance measured positive downward (negative upward) from the point of equilibrium, as in Figure 28. We assume that the motion of B takes place entirely in a vertical line, so the velocity and acceleration are given by the first and second derivatives of x with respect to t.

In addition to the force proportional to displacement (Hooke's law), there will in general be a retarding force caused by resistance of the medium in which the motion takes place or by friction. We are interested here in only such retarding forces as can be well approximated by a term proportional to the velocity because we restrict our study to problems involving linear differential equations. Such a retarding force will contribute to the total force acting on B a term $bx'(t)$, in which b is a constant to be determined experimentally for the medium in which the motion takes place. Some common retarding forces, such as one proportional to the cube of the velocity, lead to nonlinear differential equations which are not amenable to treatment by the Laplace transform.

The weight of the spring is usually negligible compared to the weight B, so we use for the mass of our system the weight of B divided by g, the constant acceleration of gravity. If no forces other than those described above act upon the weight, the displacement x must satisfy the equation

$$(2) \qquad \frac{w}{g} x''(t) + bx'(t) + kx(t) = 0.$$

Suppose an additional vertical force, due to the motion of the support or to presence of a magnetic field, etc., is imposed upon the system. The new, impressed force, will depend upon time and we may use $F(t)$ to denote the acceleration which it alone would impart to the weight B. Then the impressed force is $\dfrac{w}{g} F(t)$ and equation (2) is replaced by

$$(3) \qquad \frac{w}{g} x''(t) + bx'(t) + kx(t) = \frac{w}{g} F(t).$$

At time zero, let the weight be displaced by an amount x_0 from the equilibrium point and let the weight be given an initial velocity v_0. Either or both of x_0 and v_0 may be zero in specific instances. The problem of determining the position of the weight at any time t becomes that of solving the boundary value problem consisting of the differential equation

$$(4) \qquad \frac{w}{g} x''(t) + bx'(t) + kx(t) = \frac{w}{g} F(t), \qquad \text{for } t > 0,$$

and the initial conditions

(5) $x(0) = x_0, \qquad x'(0) = v_0.$

It is convenient to rewrite equation (4) in the form

(6) $x''(t) + 2\gamma x'(t) + \beta^2 x(t) = F(t),$

in which we have put

$$\frac{bg}{w} = 2\gamma, \qquad \frac{kg}{w} = \beta^2.$$

We may choose $\beta > 0$ and we know $\gamma \geqq 0$. Note that $\gamma = 0$ corresponds to a negligible retarding force.

Impressed forces so ill-behaved that their Laplace transforms do not exist are hardly worth considering. We therefore let

(7) $L\{x(t)\} = u(s), \quad L\{F(t)\} = f(s),$

and obtain from the problem (5) and (6) the transformed problem

$$s^2 u(s) - sx_0 - v_0 + 2\gamma[su(s) - x_0] + \beta^2 u(s) = f(s),$$

$$u(s) = \frac{sx_0 + v_0 + 2\gamma x_0}{s^2 + 2\gamma s + \beta^2} + \frac{f(s)}{s^2 + 2\gamma s + \beta^2},$$

which we write as

(8) $u(s) = \dfrac{x_0(s + \gamma) + v_0 + \gamma x_0}{(s + \gamma)^2 + \beta^2 - \gamma^2} + \dfrac{f(s)}{(s + \gamma)^2 + \beta^2 - \gamma^2}.$

The desired $x(t)$ is the inverse transform of $u(s)$.

Here we begin to reap benefits from our use of the Laplace transform. Even before we get $x(t)$ we can see that its form will depend upon whether the denominator in (8) has distinct real linear factors, or equal factors, or is the sum of two squares. That is, the form of $x(t)$ will depend upon whether $\beta < \gamma$, $\beta = \gamma$, or $\beta > \gamma$. Furthermore, if $\gamma \neq 0$, we can predict the presence of a damping factor $e^{-\gamma t}$ in $x(t)$.

The inverse of the $u(s)$ of equation (8) can be obtained with our standard methods, including the convolution theorem. When the $F(t)$ is reasonably simple, one of the types which occur frequently in practice, the convolution theorem leads to forms less desirable than those obtained by the other methods in Chapter 12.

We shall now consider separately the various situations that arise according to the choice of parameters β and γ and the forcing function $F(t)$ in this problem of the vibrating spring.

In treating spring problems we are particularly interested in impressed forces that lead to $F(t)$ of forms such as those listed:

(a) No impressed force: $F(t) = 0$;

(b) Simple harmonic forcing function:

$$F(t) = A_1 \sin \omega t + A_2 \cos \omega t;$$

(c) Temporary constant force:

$$\begin{aligned} F(t) &= A, \quad 0 < t < t_0, \\ &= 0, \qquad t > t_0; \end{aligned}$$

(d) A delayed form of (c):

$$\begin{aligned} F(t) &= 0, \quad 0 < t < t_0, \\ &= A, \quad t_0 < t < t_1, \\ &= 0, \qquad t > t_1; \end{aligned}$$

(e) $F(t) =$ the half-wave rectification of a sine curve.

It will become apparent when we study electric circuits in Section 78 that all of our present work carries over to simple circuit problems with new meanings attached to the parameters and functions involved. In circuit theory we shall add to the forms of $F(t)$ listed above both $F(t)$ equal to a constant and $F(t)$ equal to the square-wave function that appeared in Section 63.

71. Undamped vibrations

If $\gamma = 0$ in the problem of Section 70, the transform becomes

(1) $$u(s) = \frac{x_0 s + v_0}{s^2 + \beta^2} + \frac{f(s)}{s^2 + \beta^2}.$$

The inverse transform of the first term on the right in (1) is

$$x_0 \cos \beta t + \frac{v_0}{\beta} \sin \beta t,$$

which contributes to $x(t)$ a simple harmonic motion, called the *natural component* of the motion, natural because it is independent of the forcing function $F(t)$. From the last term in (1) we obtain the forced component, the form of which is dependent upon $F(t)$.

Instead of jumping from (1) to the general solution

(2) $$x(t) = x_0 \cos \beta t + v_0 \beta^{-1} \sin \beta t + \beta^{-1} \int_0^t F(t - v) \sin \beta v \, dv,$$

we prefer to obtain $x(t)$ without a convolution integral for the specific types of $F(t)$ which occur often. Equation (2) was easily obtained but it leaves all the labor of simplification to the unfortunate user who has a particular $F(t)$ with which to deal.

EXAMPLE (a): Solve the spring problem with no damping but with a forcing function $F(t) = A \sin \omega t$.

The differential equation of motion is

$$\frac{w}{g} x''(t) + kx(t) = \frac{w}{g} A \sin \omega t$$

and is readily put into the form

$$(3) \qquad x''(t) + \beta^2 x(t) = A \sin \omega t$$

with the introduction of $\beta^2 = kg/w$. We shall assume initial conditions

$$(4) \qquad x(0) = x_0, \quad x'(0) = v_0.$$

Let $L\{x(t)\} = u(s)$. Then (3) and (4) yield

$$s^2 u(s) - sx_0 - v_0 + \beta^2 u(s) = \frac{A\omega}{s^2 + \omega^2},$$

or

$$(5) \qquad u(s) = \frac{sx_0 + v_0}{s^2 + \beta^2} + \frac{A\omega}{(s^2 + \beta^2)(s^2 + \omega^2)}.$$

The last term in (5) will lead to different inverse transforms according to whether $\omega = \beta$ or $\omega \neq \beta$. The case $\omega = \beta$ leads to resonance, which will be discussed in the next section.

If $\omega \neq \beta$, equation (5) yields

$$(6) \qquad u(s) = \frac{sx_0 + v_0}{s^2 + \beta^2} + \frac{A\omega}{\omega^2 - \beta^2}\left(\frac{1}{s^2 + \beta^2} - \frac{1}{s^2 + \omega^2}\right).$$

From (6) it follows at once that

$$(7) \quad x(t) = x_0 \cos \beta t + v_0 \beta^{-1} \sin \beta t + \frac{A\omega}{\beta(\omega^2 - \beta^2)} \sin \beta t - \frac{A}{\omega^2 - \beta^2} \sin \omega t.$$

That the x of (7) is a solution of the problem (3) and (4) is easily verified. A study of (7) is simple and leads at once to conclusions such as that $x(t)$ is bounded, etc. The first two terms on the right in (7) yield the natural harmonic component of the motion, the last two terms form the forced component.

EXAMPLE (b): A spring is such that it would be stretched 6 inches by a 12-pound weight. Let the weight be attached to the spring and pulled down 4 inches below the equilibrium point. If the weight is started with an upward velocity of 2 feet per second, describe the motion. No damping or impressed force is present.

We know that the acceleration of gravity enters our work in the expression for the mass. We wish to use the value $g = 32$ ft. per sec. per sec. and we must use consistent units, so we put all lengths into feet.

First we determine the spring constant k from the fact that the 12-pound weight stretches the spring 6 inches, $\frac{1}{2}$ ft. Thus $12 = \frac{1}{2}k$ so that $k = 24$ lb. per ft.

The differential equation of the motion is therefore

$$\text{(8)} \qquad\qquad \tfrac{12}{32}x''(t) + 24x(t) = 0.$$

At time zero the weight is 4 inches ($\frac{1}{3}$ ft.) below the equilibrium point, so $x(0) = \frac{1}{3}$. The initial velocity is negative (upward), so $x'(0) = -2$. Thus our problem is that of solving

$$\text{(9)} \qquad\quad x''(t) + 64x(t) = 0; \qquad x(0) = \tfrac{1}{3}, \quad x'(0) = -2.$$

We let $L\{x(t)\} = u(s)$ and conclude at once that

$$s^2 u(s) - \tfrac{1}{3}s + 2 + 64u(s) = 0,$$

from which

$$u(s) = \frac{\tfrac{1}{3}s - 2}{s^2 + 64}.$$

Then

$$\text{(10)} \qquad\qquad x(t) = \tfrac{1}{3}\cos 8t - \tfrac{1}{4}\sin 8t.$$

A detailed study of the motion is straightforward once (10) has been obtained. The amplitude of the motion is

$$\sqrt{(\tfrac{1}{3})^2 + (\tfrac{1}{4})^2} = \tfrac{5}{12};$$

that is, the weight oscillates between points 5 inches above and below E. The period is $\frac{1}{4}\pi$ sec.

EXAMPLE (c): A spring, with spring constant 0.75 lb. per ft., lies on a long smooth (frictionless) table. A 6-lb. weight is attached to the spring and is at rest (velocity zero) at the equilibrium position. A 1.5-lb. force is applied to the support along the line of action of the spring for 4 seconds and is then removed. Discuss the motion.

We must solve the problem

(11) $\frac{6}{32}x''(t) + \frac{3}{4}x(t) = H(t);$ $x(0) = 0,$ $x'(0) = 0,$

in which

$$H(t) = 1.5, \qquad 0 < t < 4,$$
$$= 0, \qquad\qquad t > 4.$$

Now $H(t) = 1.5[1 - \alpha(t - 4)]$ in terms of the α function of Section 65. Therefore we rewrite our problem (11) in the form

(12) $x''(t) + 4x(t) = 8[1 - \alpha(t - 4)];$ $x(0) = 0,$ $x'(0) = 0.$

Let $L\{x(t)\} = u(s)$. Then (12) yields

$$s^2 u(s) + 4u(s) = \frac{8}{s}(1 - e^{-4s}),$$

or

$$u(s) = \frac{8(1 - e^{-4s})}{s(s^2 + 4)}$$

$$= 2\left(\frac{1}{s} - \frac{s}{s^2 + 4}\right)(1 - e^{-4s}).$$

The desired solution is

(13) $x(t) = 2(1 - \cos 2t) - 2[1 - \cos 2(t - 4)]\alpha(t - 4).$

Of course, the solution (13) can be broken down into the two relations

(14)   For $0 \leq t \leq 4,$ $x(t) = 2(1 - \cos 2t),$

(15)   For $t > 4,$ $x(t) = 2[\cos 2(t - 4) - \cos 2t],$

if those forms seem simpler to use.

Verification of the solution (13), or (14) and (15), is direct. The student should show that

$$\underset{t\to4^-}{\text{Lim}}\; x(t) = \underset{t\to4^+}{\text{Lim}}\; x(t) = 2(1 - \cos 8) = 2.29$$

and

$$\underset{t\to4^-}{\text{Lim}}\; x'(t) = \underset{t\to4^+}{\text{Lim}}\; x'(t) = 4 \sin 8 = 3.96.$$

From (13) or (14) we see that in the range $0 < t < 4$, the maximum deviation of the weight from the starting point is $x = 4$ ft. and occurs at $t = \frac{1}{2}\pi = 1.57$ sec. At $t = 4$, $x = 2.29$ ft. as shown above. For $t > 4$, equation (15) takes over and thereafter the motion is simple harmonic with a maximum x of 3.03 ft. Indeed, for $t > 4$,

$$\max |x(t)| = 2 \sqrt{(1 - \cos 8)^2 + \sin^2 8}$$
$$= 2 \sqrt{2} \sqrt{1 - \cos 8}$$
$$= 2 \sqrt{2.2910} = 3.03.$$

Example (c) is one type of problem for which the Laplace transform technique is particularly useful. Such problems can be solved by the older classical methods, but with much less simplicity and dispatch.

72. Resonance

In the problem of undamped vibrations of a spring, one of the examples we encountered was

(1) $\qquad x''(t) + \beta^2 x(t) = A \sin \omega t; \qquad x(0) = x_0, \quad x'(0) = v_0.$

The solution of (1) was obtained by putting $L\{x(t)\} = u(s)$ and getting

(2) $\qquad u(s) = \dfrac{sx_0 + v_0}{s^2 + \beta^2} + \dfrac{A\omega}{(s^2 + \beta^2)(s^2 + \omega^2)}.$

From (2) we see that the inverse transform differs according to whether $\omega = \beta$ or $\omega \neq \beta$. The latter has been studied. Let us now assume $\omega = \beta$.

Our problem is to solve

(3) $\qquad x''(t) + \beta^2 x(t) = A \sin \beta t; \qquad x(0) = x_0, \quad x'(0) = v_0,$

with the aid of

(4) $\qquad u(s) = \dfrac{sx_0 + v_0}{s^2 + \beta^2} + \dfrac{A\beta}{(s^2 + \beta^2)^2}.$

We already know, from page 177, that

$$L^{-1} \left\{ \frac{1}{(s^2 + \beta^2)^2} \right\} = \frac{1}{2\beta^3} (\sin \beta t - \beta t \cos \beta t).$$

Therefore (4) leads us to the solution

(5) $\qquad x(t) = x_0 \cos \beta t + \dfrac{v_0}{\beta} \sin \beta t + \dfrac{A}{2\beta^2} (\sin \beta t - \beta t \cos \beta t).$

That (5) satisfies all the conditions of (3) is readily verified.

In the solution (5) the terms proportional to $\cos \beta t$ and $\sin \beta t$ are bounded, but the term with $\beta t \cos \beta t$ can be made as large as we wish by proper choice of t. This building up of large amplitudes in the vibration when $\omega = \beta$ in (1) is called *resonance*.

Exercises

1. A spring is such that a 5-pound weight stretches it 6 inches. The 5-pound weight is attached, the spring reaches equilibrium, then the weight is pulled down 3 inches below the equilibrium point and started off with an upward velocity of 6 ft. per sec. Find an equation giving the position of the weight at all subsequent times.

   ANS. $x = \frac{1}{4}(\cos 8t - 3 \sin 8t)$.

2. A spring is stretched 1.5 inches by a 2-pound weight. Let the weight be pushed up 3 inches above E and then released. Describe the motion.

   ANS. $x = -\frac{1}{4}\cos 16t$.

3. For the spring and weight of Ex. 2, let the weight be pulled down 4 inches below E and given a downward initial velocity of 8 ft. per sec. Describe the motion.   ANS. $x = \frac{1}{3}\cos 16t + \frac{1}{2}\sin 16t$.

4. Show that the answer to Ex. 3 can be written $x = 0.60 \sin (16t + \varphi)$ where $\varphi = $ Arctan $\frac{2}{3}$.

5. A spring is such that a 4-pound weight stretches it 6 inches. An impressed force $\frac{1}{2}\cos 8t$ is acting on the spring. If the 4-pound weight is started from the equilibrium point with an imparted upward velocity of 4 ft. per sec., determine the position of the weight as a function of time.   ANS. $x = \frac{1}{4}(t - 2) \sin 8t$.

6. A spring is such that it is stretched 6 inches by a 12-pound weight. The 12-pound weight is pulled down 3 inches below the equilibrium point and then released. If there is an impressed force of magnitude $9 \sin 4t$ pounds, describe the motion. Assume that the impressed force acts downward for very small t.

   ANS. $x = \frac{1}{4}\cos 8t - \frac{1}{4}\sin 8t + \frac{1}{2}\sin 4t$.

7. Show that the answer to Ex. 6 can be written

   $$x = \frac{1}{4}\sqrt{2}\cos (8t + \pi/4) + \frac{1}{2}\sin 4t.$$

8. A spring is such that a 2-pound weight stretches it $\frac{1}{2}$ ft. An impressed force $\frac{1}{4}\sin 8t$ is acting upon the spring. If the 2-pound weight is released from a point 3 inches below the equilibrium point, determine the equation of motion.   ANS. $x = \frac{1}{4}(1 - t) \cos 8t + \frac{1}{32}\sin 8t$ (ft.).

9. For the motion of Ex. 8, find the first four times at which stops occur and find the position at each stop. ANS. $t = \pi/8, \pi/4, 1, 3\pi/8$ (sec.) and $x = -0.15, +0.05, +0.03, +0.04$ (ft.), respectively.

10. Determine the position to be expected, if nothing such as breakage interferes, at the time of the 65th stop, when $t = 8\pi$ (sec.), in Ex. 8.

    ANS. $x = -6.0$ (ft.).

11. A spring is such that a 16-pound weight stretches it 1.5 inches. The weight is pulled down to a point 4 inches below the equilibrium point and given an initial downward velocity of 4 ft. per sec. There is an impressed force of 360 cos 4t pounds. Find the position and velocity of the weight at time $t = \pi/8$ seconds.

ANS.   At $t = \pi/8$(sec.), $x = -\frac{8}{3}$ (ft.), $v = -8$ (ft./sec.).

12. A spring is stretched 3 inches by a 5-pound weight. Let the weight be started from E with an upward velocity of 12 ft. per sec. Describe the motion.   ANS. $x = -1.06 \sin 11.3t$.

13. For the spring and weight of Ex. 12, let the weight be pulled down 4 inches below E and then given an upward velocity of 8 ft. per sec. Describe the motion.   ANS. $x = 0.33 \cos 11.3t - 0.71 \sin 11.3t$.

14. Find the amplitude of the motion in Ex. 13.   ANS.   0.78 ft.

15. A 20-pound weight stretches a certain spring 10 inches. Let the spring first be compressed 4 inches, and then the 20-pound weight attached and given an initial downward velocity of 8 ft. per sec. Find how far the weight would drop.   ANS.   35 in.

16. A spring is such that an 8-pound weight would stretch it 6 inches. Let a 4-pound weight be attached to the spring, pushed up 2 inches above its equilibrium point and then released. Describe the motion.

ANS. $x = -\frac{1}{6} \cos 11.3t$.

17. If the 4-pound weight of Ex. 16 starts at the same point, 2 inches above E, but with an upward velocity of 15 ft. per sec., when will the weight reach its lowest point?   ANS.   At $t =$ approximately 0.4 sec.

18. A spring is such that it is stretched 4 inches by a 10-pound weight. Suppose the 10-pound weight to be pulled down 5 inches below E and then given a downward velocity of 15 ft. per sec. Describe the motion.

ANS. $x = 0.42 \cos 9.8t + 1.53 \sin 9.8t$
$= 1.59 \cos (9.8t - \varphi)$, where $\varphi =$ Arctan 3.64.

19. A spring is such that it is stretched 4 inches by an 8-pound weight. Suppose the weight to be pulled down 6 inches below E and then given an upward velocity of 8 ft. per sec. Describe the motion.

ANS. $x = 0.50 \cos 9.8t - 0.82 \sin 9.8t$.

20. Show that the answer to Ex. 19 can be written $x = 0.96 \cos (9.8t + \varphi)$ where $\varphi =$ Arctan 1.64.

21. A spring is such that a 4-pound weight stretches it 6 inches. The 4-pound weight is attached to the vertical spring and reaches its equilibrium point. The weight is then ($t = 0$) drawn downward 3 inches and released. There is a simple harmonic exterior force equal to sin 8t impressed upon the whole system. Find the time for each of the first

four stops following $t = 0$. Put the stops in chronological order.

ANS. $t = \pi/8, \frac{1}{2}, \pi/4, 3\pi/8$ (sec.).

22. A spring is stretched 1.5 inches by a 4-pound weight. Let the weight be pulled down 3 inches below equilibrium and released. If there is an impressed force 8 sin $16t$ acting upon the spring, describe the motion.

ANS. $x = \frac{1}{4}(1 - 8t) \cos 16t + \frac{1}{8} \sin 16t$.

23. For the motion of Ex. 22, find the first four times at which stops occur and find the position at each stop.

ANS. $t = \frac{1}{8}, \pi/16, \pi/8, 3\pi/16$ (sec.) and
$x = +0.11, +0.14, -0.54, +0.93$ (ft.), respectively.

73. Damped vibrations

In the general linear spring problem of Section 70, we were confronted with

(1) $x''(t) + 2\gamma x'(t) + \beta^2 x(t) = F(t);$ $x(0) = x_0,$ $x'(0) = v_0,$

in which $\gamma = \dfrac{bg}{w}$ and $\beta^2 = \dfrac{kg}{w}$, $\beta > 0$. We let

$$L\{x(t)\} = u(s), \qquad L\{F(t)\} = f(s)$$

and obtained

(2) $u(s) = \dfrac{x_0(s + \gamma) + v_0 + \gamma x_0}{(s + \gamma)^2 + \beta^2 - \gamma^2} + \dfrac{f(s)}{(s + \gamma)^2 + \beta^2 - \gamma^2}.$

We are now concerned with $\gamma > 0$; a non-negligible retarding force is present. We know that the form of the inverse transform of $u(s)$ depends upon whether $\beta > \gamma$, $\beta = \gamma$, or $\beta < \gamma$.

If $\beta > \gamma$, $\beta^2 - \gamma^2 > 0$, so let us put

(3) $\beta^2 - \gamma^2 = \delta^2.$

Then (2) becomes

(4) $u(s) = \dfrac{x_0(s + \gamma) + v_0 + \gamma x_0}{(s + \gamma)^2 + \delta^2} + \dfrac{f(s)}{(s + \gamma)^2 + \delta^2}$

and we arrive at

(5) $x(t) = e^{-\gamma t}[x_0 \cos \delta t + (v_0 + \gamma x_0)\delta^{-1} \sin \delta t] + \psi_1(t)$

in which $\psi_1(t)$ is an inverse transform of the last term in (4). The function $\psi_1(t)$ can always be written in terms of $F(t)$ by the convolution theorem, but that leads to undesirable complications for the most common choices of $F(t)$. In the solution (5), the presence of the damping factor $e^{-\gamma t}$ shows that the natural component of the motion approaches zero as $t \to \infty$.

If in (1) and (2) we have $\beta = \gamma$, the transform

(6) $$u(s) = \frac{x_0(s + \gamma) + v_0 + \gamma x_0}{(s + \gamma)^2} + \frac{f(s)}{(s + \gamma)^2}$$

leads us to the solution

(7) $$x(t) = e^{-\gamma t}[x_0 + (v_0 + \gamma x_0)t] + \psi_2(t),$$

in which $\psi_2(t)$ is an inverse of $(s + \gamma)^{-2}f(s)$ and is easily determined once $F(t)$ is stipulated. Again the natural component has the damping factor $e^{-\gamma t}$ in it.

If in (1) and (2) we have $\beta < \gamma$, $\gamma^2 - \beta^2 > 0$, and we put

(8) $$\gamma^2 - \beta^2 = \sigma^2.$$

Then (2) becomes

(9) $$u(s) = \frac{x_0(s + \gamma) + v_0 + \gamma x_0}{(s + \gamma)^2 - \sigma^2} + \frac{f(s)}{(s + \gamma)^2 - \sigma^2},$$

which leads to the solution

(10) $$x(t) = e^{-\gamma t}[x_0 \cosh \sigma t + (v_0 + \gamma x_0)\sigma^{-1} \sinh \sigma t] + \psi_3(t),$$

in which $\psi_3(t)$ is an inverse of the last term in (9). By (8) we see that $\gamma > \sigma$, so that once more the natural component of the $x(t)$ in (10) approaches zero as $t \to \infty$.

Suppose for the moment that we have $F(t) \equiv 0$, so the natural component of the motion is all that is under consideration. If $\beta > \gamma$, equation (5) holds and the motion is a *damped oscillatory* one. If $\beta = \gamma$, equation (7) holds and the motion is not oscillatory; it is called *critically damped* motion. If $\beta < \gamma$, (10) holds and the motion is said to be *overdamped;* the parameter γ is larger than it needs to be to remove the oscillations. Figure 29 shows a representative graph of each type

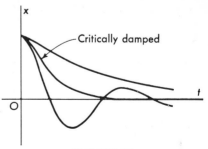

Critically damped

FIGURE 29

of motion mentioned in this paragraph, a damped oscillatory motion, a critically damped motion, and an overdamped motion.

EXAMPLE: Solve the problem of Example (b), Section 71, with an added damping force of magnitude $0.6|v|$. Such a damping force can be realized by immersing the weight B in a thick liquid.

The boundary value problem to be solved is

(11) $\frac{12}{32}x''(t) + 0.6x'(t) + 24x(t) = 0;$ $x(0) = \frac{1}{3},$ $x'(0) = -2.$

Put $L\{x(t)\} = u(s)$. Then (11) yields

$$(s^2 + 1.6s + 64)u(s) = \tfrac{1}{3}(s - 4.4),$$

from which we obtain

$$x(t) = \tfrac{1}{3}L^{-1}\left\{\frac{s - 4.4}{(s + 0.8)^2 + 63.36}\right\}$$

$$= \tfrac{1}{3}\exp(-0.8t)L^{-1}\left\{\frac{s - 5.2}{s^2 + 63.36}\right\}.$$

Therefore the desired solution is

(12) $x(t) = \exp(-0.8t)(0.33 \cos 8.0t - 0.22 \sin 8.0t),$

a portion of its graph being shown in Figure 30.

FIGURE 30

Exercises

1. A certain straight-line motion is determined by the differential equation

$$\frac{d^2x}{dt^2} + 2\gamma \frac{dx}{dt} + 169x = 0$$

and the conditions that when $t = 0$, $x = 0$ and $v = 8$ ft. per sec.

     (a) Find the value of γ that leads to critical damping, determine x in terms of t, and draw the graph for $0 \leqq t \leqq 0.2$.

                            ANS. $\gamma = 13(1/\text{sec.}),\ x = 8te^{-13t}.$

     (b) Use $\gamma = 12$. Find x in terms of t and draw the graph.

                                 ANS. $x = 1.6e^{-12t} \sin 5t.$

(c) Use $\gamma = 14$. Find x in terms of t and draw the graph.

$$\text{ANS.} \quad x = 0.77(e^{-8.8t} - e^{-19.2t}).$$

2. A spring is such that a 2-pound weight stretches it $\frac{1}{2}$ foot. An impressed force $\frac{1}{4} \sin 8t$ and a damping force of magnitude $|v|$ are both acting on the spring. The weight starts $\frac{1}{4}$ foot below the equilibrium point with an imparted upward velocity of 3 ft. per sec. Find a formula for the position of the weight at time t.

$$\text{ANS.} \quad x = \tfrac{3}{32}e^{-8t}(3 - 8t) - \tfrac{1}{32}\cos 8t.$$

3. A spring is such that a 4-pound weight stretches it 0.64 feet. The 4-pound weight is pushed up $\frac{1}{3}$ foot above the point of equilibrium and then started with a downward velocity of 5 ft. per sec. The motion takes place in a medium which furnishes a damping force of magnitude $\frac{1}{4}|v|$ at all times. Find the equation describing the position of the weight at time t. $\text{ANS.} \quad x = \frac{1}{3}e^{-t}(2 \sin 7t - \cos 7t)$.

4. A spring is such that a 4-pound weight stretches it 0.32 feet. The weight is attached to the spring and moves in a medium which furnishes a damping force of magnitude $\frac{3}{2}|v|$. The weight is drawn down $\frac{1}{2}$ foot below the equilibrium point and given an initial upward velocity of 4 ft. per sec. Find the position of the weight thereafter.

$$\text{ANS.} \quad x = \tfrac{1}{8}e^{-6t}(4 \cos 8t - \sin 8t).$$

5. A spring is such that a 4-pound weight stretches the spring 0.4 feet. The 4-pound weight is attached to the spring (suspended from a fixed support) and the system is allowed to reach equilibrium. Then the weight is started from equilibrium position with an imparted upward velocity of 2 ft. per sec. Assume that the motion takes place in a medium which furnishes a retarding force of magnitude numerically equal to the speed, in feet per second, of the moving weight. Determine the position of the weight as a function of time.

$$\text{ANS.} \quad x = -\tfrac{1}{4}e^{-4t}\sin 8t.$$

6. A spring is stretched 6 inches by a 3-pound weight. The 3-pound weight is attached to the spring and then started from equilibrium with an imparted upward velocity of 12 ft. per sec. Air resistance furnishes a retarding force equal in magnitude to $0.03|v|$. Find the equation of motion. $\text{ANS.} \quad x = -1.5e^{-0.16t}\sin 8t$.

7. A spring is such that a 2-pound weight stretches it 6 inches. There is a damping force present, with magnitude the same as the magnitude of the velocity. An impressed force $(2 \sin 8t)$ is acting on the spring. If, at $t = 0$, the weight is released from a point 3 inches below the equilibrium point, find its position for $t > 0$.

$$\text{ANS.} \quad x = (\tfrac{1}{2} + 4t)e^{-8t} - \tfrac{1}{4}\cos 8t.$$

8. A spring is stretched 10 inches by a 4-pound weight. The weight is started 6 inches below the equilibrium point with an upward velocity of 8 ft. per sec. If a resisting medium furnishes a retarding force of magnitude $\frac{1}{4}|v|$, describe the motion.

ANS. $x = e^{-t}[0.50 \cos 6.1t - 1.23 \sin 6.1t]$.

9. For Ex. 8, find the times of the first three stops and the position (to the nearest inch) of the weight at each stop.

ANS. $t_1 = 0.3$ sec., $x_1 = -12$ in.; $t_2 = 0.8$ sec.,
$x_2 = +6$ in.; $t_3 = 1.3$ sec., $x_3 = -4$ in.

10. A spring is stretched 4 inches by a 2-pound weight. The 2-pound weight is started from the equilibrium point with a downward velocity of 12 ft. per sec. If air resistance furnishes a retarding force of magnitude 0.02 of the velocity, describe the motion.

ANS. $x = 1.22e^{-0.16t} \sin 9.8t$.

11. For Ex. 10, find how long it takes the damping factor to drop to one-tenth its initial value.   ANS.   14.4 sec.

12. For Ex. 10, find the position of the weight at: (a) the first stop; (b) the second stop.   ANS.   (a) $x = 1.2$ ft.; (b) $x = -1.1$ ft.

13. Let the motion of Ex. 8, page 220, be retarded by a damping force of magnitude $0.6|v|$. Find the equation of motion.

ANS. $x = 0.30e^{-4.8t} \cos 6.4t + 0.22e^{-4.8t} \sin 6.4t - 0.05 \cos 8t$ (ft.).

14. Show that whenever $t > 1$ (sec.), the solution of Ex. 13 can be replaced (to the nearest 0.01 ft.) by $x = -0.05 \cos 8t$.

15. Let the motion of Ex. 8, page 220, be retarded by a damping force of magnitude $|v|$. Find the equation of motion and also determine its form (to the nearest 0.01 ft.) for $t > 1$ (sec.).

ANS. $x = \frac{9}{32}(8t + 1)e^{-8t} - \frac{1}{32} \cos 8t$ (ft.); for $t > 1$, $x = -\frac{1}{32} \cos 8t$.

16. Let the motion of Ex. 8, page 220, be retarded by a damping force of magnitude $\frac{5}{3}|v|$. Find the equation of motion.

ANS. $x = 0.30e^{-(8/3)t} - 0.03e^{-24t} - 0.02 \cos 8t$.

17. Alter Ex. 6, page 220, by inserting a damping force of magnitude one-half that of the velocity and then determine x.

ANS. $x = \exp\left(-\frac{2}{3}t\right)(0.30 \cos 8.0t - 0.22 \sin 8.0t)$
$- 0.05 \cos 4t + 0.49 \sin 4t$.

18. A spring is stretched 6 inches by a 4-pound weight. Let the weight be pulled down 6 inches below equilibrium and given an initial upward velocity of 7 ft. per sec. Assuming a damping force twice the magnitude of the velocity, describe the motion and sketch the graph at intervals of 0.05 sec. for $0 \leq t \leq 0.3$ (sec.).   ANS. $x = \frac{1}{2}e^{-8t}(1 - 6t)$.

19. An object weighing w pounds is dropped from a height h feet above the

earth. At time t (sec.) after the object is dropped, let its distance from the starting point be x (ft.), measured positive downward. Assuming air resistance to be negligible, show that x must satisfy the equation

$$\frac{w}{g}\frac{d^2x}{dt^2} = w$$

as long as $x < h$. Find x.   ANS. $x = \frac{1}{2}gt^2$.

20. Let the weight of Ex. 19 be given an initial velocity v_0. Let v be the velocity at time t. Determine v and x.

ANS. $v = gt + v_0$, $x = \frac{1}{2}gt^2 + v_0t$.

21. From the results in Ex. 20, find a relation that does not contain t explicitly.   ANS. $v^2 = v_0^2 + 2gx$.

22. If air resistance furnishes an additional force proportional to the velocity in the motion studied in Ex. 19 and 20, show that the equation of motion becomes

(A) $$\frac{w}{g}\frac{d^2x}{dt^2} + b\frac{dx}{dt} = w.$$

Solve equation (A) given the conditions

(B)   when $t = 0$, $x = 0$ and $v = v_0$.

Use $a = bg/w$.   ANS. $x = a^{-1}gt + a^{-2}(av_0 - g)(1 - e^{-at})$.

23. To compare the results of Ex. 20 and 22 when $a = bg/w$ is small, use the power series for e^{-at} in the answer for Ex. 22 and discard all terms involving a^n for $n \geq 3$.

ANS. $x = \frac{1}{2}gt^2 + v_0t - \frac{1}{6}at^2(3v_0 + gt) + \frac{1}{24}a^2t^3(4v_0 + gt)$.

24. The equation of motion of the vertical fall of a man with a parachute may be roughly approximated by equation (A) of Ex. 22. Suppose a 180-pound man drops from a great height and attains a velocity of 20 miles per hour after a long time. Determine the implied coefficient b of equation (A).   ANS.   6.1 (lb.)(sec.) per ft.

25. A particle is moving along the x-axis according to the law

$$\frac{d^2x}{dt^2} + 6\frac{dx}{dt} + 25x = 0.$$

If the particle started at $x = 0$ with an initial velocity of 12 ft. per sec. to the left, determine: (a) x in terms of t; (b) the times at which stops occur; and (c) the ratio between the numerical values of x at successive stops.   ANS.   (a) $x = -3e^{-3t}\sin 4t$,

(b) $t = 0.23 + \frac{1}{4}n\pi$, $n = 0, 1, 2, 3, \cdots$, (c) 0.095.

74. The simple pendulum

A rod of length C feet is suspended by one end so it can swing freely in a vertical plane. Let a weight B (the bob) of w pounds be attached to the free end of the rod, and let the weight of the rod be negligible compared to the weight of the bob.

Let θ (radians) be the angular displacement from the vertical, as shown in Figure 31, of the rod at time t (sec.). The tangential component of the force w (lb.) is $w \sin \theta$ and it tends to decrease θ. Then, neglecting the weight of the rod and using $S = C\theta$ as a measure of arc length from the vertical position, we may conclude that

$$(1) \qquad \frac{w}{g}\frac{d^2S}{dt^2} = -w \sin \theta.$$

Since $S = C\theta$ and C is constant, (1) becomes

FIGURE 31 (2) $\dfrac{d^2\theta}{dt^2} + \dfrac{g}{C}\sin\theta = 0.$

The solution of equation (2) is not elementary; it involves an elliptic integral. If θ is small, however, $\sin \theta$ and θ are nearly equal and (2) is closely approximated by the much simpler equation

$$(3) \qquad \frac{d^2\theta}{dt^2} + \beta^2\theta = 0; \; \beta^2 = \frac{g}{C}.$$

The solution of (3) with pertinent boundary conditions gives usable results whenever those conditions are such that θ remains small, say $|\theta| < 0.3$ (radians).

75. Beams

Consider a beam of length $2c$, as shown in Figure 32. Denote distance from one end of the beam by x, the deflection of the beam by y. If the beam is subjected to a vertical load $W(x)$, the deflection y must satisfy the equation

$$(1) \qquad EI\frac{d^4y}{dx^4} = W(x), \qquad \text{for } 0 < x < 2c,$$

in which E, the modulus of elasticity, and I, a moment of inertia, are known constants associated with the particular beam.

The slope of the curve of deflection is $y'(x)$, the bending moment is $EIy''(x)$, and the shearing force is $EIy'''(x)$. Common boundary conditions are of the following types:

(a) Beam imbedded in a support: $y = 0$ and $y' = 0$ at the point;

(b) Beam simply supported: $y = 0$ and $y'' = 0$ at the point;

(c) Beam free: $y'' = 0$ and $y''' = 0$ at the point.

Problems in the transverse displacement of a beam take the form of the differential equation (1) with boundary conditions at each end of the beam. Such problems can be solved by integration with the use of a little algebra. There are however two reasons for employing our transform method in such problems. Frequently the load function, or its derivative, is discontinuous. Beam problems also give us a chance to examine a useful device in which a problem over a finite range is solved with the aid of an associated problem over an infinite range.

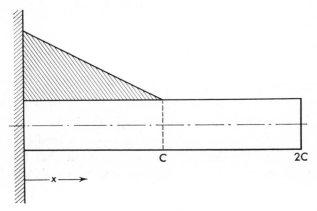

FIGURE 32

E X A M P L E : Find the displacement y throughout the beam of Figure 32, in which the load is assumed to decrease uniformly from w_0 at $x = 0$ to zero at $x = c$ and to remain zero from $x = c$ to $x = 2c$. The weight of the beam is to be negligible. The beam is imbedded at $x = 0$ and free at $x = 2c$.

We are to solve the problem

$$(2) \qquad EI \frac{d^4y}{dx^4} = \frac{w_0}{c}[c - x + (x - c)\alpha(x - c)], \qquad \text{for } 0 < x < 2c;$$

$$(3) \qquad\qquad y(0) = 0, \qquad y'(0) = 0;$$

$$(4) \qquad\qquad y''(2c) = 0, \qquad y'''(2c) = 0.$$

The student should verify that the right member of (2) is the stipulated load function

$$(5) \qquad W(x) = \frac{w_0}{c}(c - x), \qquad \text{for } 0 \leq x \leq c,$$

$$= 0, \qquad \text{for } c < x \leq 2c.$$

To apply the transform technique, with x playing the role for which we usually employ t, we need first to extend the range of x so it will run from 0 to ∞. That is, instead of the problem (2), (3), (4), we shall solve the problem consisting of

$$(6) \qquad EI\frac{d^4y}{dx^4} = H(x), \qquad \text{for } 0 < x < \infty,$$

and the conditions (3) and (4). In (6) the function $H(x)$ is to be chosen by us except that $H(x)$ must agree with $W(x)$ over the range $0 < x < 2c$. The solution of the problem (6), (3), (4) will then be used only in the range $0 \leq x \leq 2c$. Of the various choices for $H(x)$, it seems simplest to use

$$(7) \qquad H(x) = \frac{w_0}{c}[c - x + (x - c)\alpha(x - c)], \qquad \text{for } 0 < x < \infty.$$

That is, in practice we ordinarily retain the equation (2) and merely extend the range from $0 < x < 2c$ to $0 < x < \infty$. The student must, however, keep in mind that we cannot apply the Laplace operator to the function $W(x)$ of (5), since that function is not defined over the entire range $0 < x < \infty$. We shall solve (6) and conclude that the solution is valid for (2) on the range $0 \leq x \leq 2c$, over which (2) and (6) are identical.

Let

$$L\{EIy(x)\} = u(s);$$

$$(8) \qquad u(s) = EI\int_0^\infty e^{-sx}y(x)\,dx.$$

To transform $EIy^{(4)}(x)$ we need to use the values of $EIy(x)$ and its first three derivatives at $x = 0$. From (3) we know that

$$EIy(0) = 0, \qquad EIy'(0) = 0.$$

Put

$$(9) \qquad EIy''(0) = A, \qquad EIy'''(0) = B.$$

The constants A and B must be determined by using the conditions (4).

By our usual methods we obtain, for the $H(x)$ of (7),

$$L\{H(x)\} = \frac{w_0}{c} L\{c - x + (x - c)\alpha(x - c)\}$$

$$= \frac{w_0}{c} \left(\frac{c}{s} - \frac{1}{s^2} + \frac{e^{-cs}}{s^2}\right).$$

Thus the differential equation (6) is transformed into

$$s^4 u(s) - s^3 \cdot 0 - s^2 \cdot 0 - s \cdot A - B = \frac{w_0}{c} \left(\frac{c}{s} - \frac{1}{s^2} + \frac{e^{-cs}}{s^2}\right),$$

from which we get

(10) $$u(s) = \frac{A}{s^3} + \frac{B}{s^4} + \frac{w_0}{c} \left(\frac{c}{s^5} - \frac{1}{s^6} + \frac{e^{-cs}}{s^6}\right).$$

Now $L^{-1}\{u(s)\} = EIy(x)$. Hence

(11) $\quad EIy(x) = \frac{1}{2}Ax^2 + \frac{1}{6}Bx^3 + \frac{w_0}{120c} [5cx^4 - x^5 + (x - c)^5\alpha(x - c)].$

From (11) we obtain

(12) $\quad EIy'(x) = Ax + \frac{1}{2}Bx^2 + \frac{w_0}{24c} [4cx^3 - x^4 + (x - 4)^4\alpha(x - c)],$

(13) $\quad EIy''(x) = A + Bx + \frac{w_0}{6c} [3cx^2 - x^3 + (x - c)^3\alpha(x - c)],$

(14) $\quad EIy'''(x) = B + \frac{w_0}{2c} [2cx - x^2 + (x - c)^2\alpha(x - c)].$

By differentiating both members of equation (14), we can see that the y of (11) is a solution of (6) over the infinite range and, more important, a solution of (2) over the range $0 < x < 2c$.

With the aid of equations (11) through (14) we can now determine A and B to make the y satisfy appropriate conditions at $x = 2c$, whether the beam be free, imbedded, or pin-supported there. In our example the beam is to be free at $x = 2c$; the solution is to satisfy the conditions

(4) $$y''(2c) = 0, \qquad y'''(2c) = 0.$$

Using (13) and (14), and a little work, we find that (4) requires $A = \frac{1}{6}w_0c^2$, $B = -\frac{1}{2}w_0c$. We are thus led to the solution

(15) $\quad EIy(x) = \frac{1}{12}w_0c^2x^2 - \frac{1}{12}w_0cx^3$

$$+ \frac{w_0}{120c} [5cx^4 - x^5 + (x - c)^5\alpha(x - c)],$$

for $0 \leq x \leq 2c$.

The student should verify by differentiations and appropriate substitutions that the y of (15) satisfies the original differential equation (2) and boundary conditions (3) and (4).

From (15) we can obtain whatever information we wish. For example, at $x = \frac{1}{2}c$ the bending moment is

$$EIy''(\tfrac{1}{2}c) = w_0c^2[\tfrac{1}{6} - \tfrac{1}{4} + \tfrac{1}{6}(-\tfrac{1}{8} + \tfrac{3}{4} + 0)] = \tfrac{1}{48}w_0c^2.$$

Exercises

1. A clock has a 6-inch pendulum. The clock ticks once for each time that the pendulum completes a swing, returning to its original position. How many times does the clock tick in 30 seconds?   ANS.   38 times.

2. A 6-inch pendulum is released from rest at an angle one-tenth of a radian from the vertical. Using $g = 32$ (ft. per sec. per sec.), describe the motion.   ANS. $\theta = 0.1 \cos 8t$ (radians).

3. For the pendulum of Ex. 2, find the maximum angular speed and its first time of occurrence.   ANS.   0.8 (rad. per sec.) at 0.2 sec.

4. A 6-inch pendulum is started with a velocity of one radian per second, toward the vertical, from a position one-tenth radian from the vertical. Describe the motion.   ANS. $\theta = \tfrac{1}{10} \cos 8t - \tfrac{1}{8} \sin 8t$ (radians).

5. For Ex. 4, find to the nearest degree the maximum angular displacement from the vertical.   ANS.   9°.

6. Interpret as a pendulum problem and solve:

(A) $$\frac{d^2\theta}{dt^2} + \beta^2\theta = 0 : \beta^2 = \frac{g}{C},$$

(B)   when $t = 0$, $\theta = \theta_0$ and $\omega = \frac{d\theta}{dt} = \omega_0$.

                        ANS. $\theta = \theta_0 \cos \beta t + \beta^{-1}\omega_0 \sin \beta t$ (radians).

7. Find the maximum angular displacement from the vertical for the pendulum of Ex. 6.   ANS. $\theta_{\max} = (\theta_0{}^2 + \beta^{-2}\omega_0{}^2)^{\frac{1}{2}}$.

In Exs. 8–11, find the y that satisfies equation (1), page 228, with the given load function $W(x)$ and the given conditions at the ends of the beam. (See (a), (b), (c), page 229.) Verify your solutions.

8. $W(x)$ as in the example introduced on page 229; beam imbedded at both $x = 0$ and $x = 2c$.

    ANS. $EIy(x) = \tfrac{23}{480}w_0c^2x^2 - \tfrac{3}{40}w_0cx^3$

$$+ \frac{w_0}{120c} [5cx^4 - x^5 + (x - c)^5\alpha(x - c)].$$

9. $W(x) = 0$,   for $0 < x < \frac{1}{2}c$,

     $= w_0$,   for $\frac{1}{2}c < x < \frac{3}{2}c$,

     $= 0$,   for $\frac{3}{2}c < x < 2c$;

beam imbedded at $x = 0$, free at $x = 2c$.

ANS. $EIy(x) = \frac{1}{2}w_0c^2x^2 - \frac{1}{6}w_0cx^3$

$$+ \tfrac{1}{24}w_0[(x - \tfrac{1}{2}c)^4\alpha(x - \tfrac{1}{2}c) - (x - \tfrac{3}{2}c)^4\alpha(x - \tfrac{3}{2}c)].$$

10. $W(x) = w_0[1 - \alpha(x - c)]$ (describe the load); beam to be imbedded at $x = 0$ and pin-supported (simply supported) at $x = 2c$.

ANS. $EIy(x) = \tfrac{9}{64}w_0c^2x^2 - \tfrac{19}{128}w_0cx^3 + \tfrac{1}{24}w_0[x^4 - (x - c)^4\alpha(x - c)].$

11. $W(x) = \dfrac{w_0}{c}(2c - x)$, for $0 < x < c$,

     $= w_0$,   for $c < x < 2c$;

beam to be imbedded at $x = 0$ and free at $x = 2c$.

ANS. $EIy(x) = \tfrac{13}{12}w_0c^2x^2 - \tfrac{5}{12}w_0cx^3 + \tfrac{1}{24}w_0x^4$

$$+ \frac{w_0}{120c}[5cx^4 - x^5 + (x - c)^5\alpha(x - c)].$$

CHAPTER 14

Systems of Equations

76. The Laplace transform method

The Laplace operator can be used to transform a system of linear differential equations with constant coefficients into a system of algebraic equations.

EXAMPLE: Solve the system of equations

(1) $$x''(t) - x(t) + 5y'(t) = t,$$

(2) $$y''(t) - 4y(t) - 2x'(t) = -2,$$

with the initial conditions

(3) $$x(0) = 0, \quad x'(0) = 0, \quad y(0) = 0, \quad y'(0) = 0.$$

Let $L\{x(t)\} = u(s)$ and $L\{y(t)\} = v(s)$. Then, application of the Laplace operator transforms the problem into that of solving a pair of simultaneous algebraic equations:

(4) $$(s^2 - 1)u(s) + 5sv(s) = \frac{1}{s^2},$$

(5) $$-2su(s) + (s^2 - 4)v(s) = -\frac{2}{s}.$$

We solve equations (4) and (5) to obtain

(6) $$u(s) = \frac{11s^2 - 4}{s^2(s^2 + 1)(s^2 + 4)},$$

(7) $$v(s) = \frac{-2s^2 + 4}{s(s^2 + 1)(s^2 + 4)}.$$

Seeking the inverse transforms of u and v, we first expand the right members of (6) and (7) into partial fractions:

(8) $$u(s) = -\frac{1}{s^2} + \frac{5}{s^2 + 1} - \frac{4}{s^2 + 4},$$

(9) $$v(s) = \frac{1}{s} - \frac{2s}{s^2 + 1} + \frac{s}{s^2 + 4}.$$

Since $x(t) = L^{-1}\{u(s)\}$ and $y(t) = L^{-1}\{v(s)\}$, we get the desired results

(10) $$x(t) = -t + 5 \sin t - 2 \sin 2t,$$

(11) $$y(t) = 1 - 2 \cos t + \cos 2t,$$

which are easily verified by direct substitution into (1), (2), and (3).

The above procedure is simple in concept and powerful in theoretical studies, but of only moderate efficiency for numerical problems. The student should not overlook the sometimes tedious algebra used in passing from (6) and (7) to (8) and (9). The example was deliberately constructed to make the work simple.

77. The differential operator method

In solving systems of simultaneous linear equations, the differential operator notation is another convenient tool. Consider the system

(1) $$y'' - y + 5v' = x,$$
$$2y' - v'' + 4v = 2,$$

with independent variable x and dependent variables y and v. It is natural to attack the system (1) by eliminating one dependent variable to obtain a single equation for the other dependent variable. Using $D = \dfrac{d}{dx}$, write the system (1) in the form

(2) $$(D^2 - 1)y + 5Dv = x,$$
$$2Dy - (D^2 - 4)v = 2.$$

Then, elimination of one dependent variable is straightforward. We may, for instance, operate upon the first equation with $2D$ and upon the second equation with $(D^2 - 1)$, and then subtract one from the other, obtaining

$$[10D^2 + (D^2 - 1)(D^2 - 4)]v = 2Dx - (D^2 - 1)2,$$

or

(3) $$(D^4 + 5D^2 + 4)v = 4.$$

In a similar manner v may be eliminated; the resultant equation for y is

$$[(D^2 - 1)(D^2 - 4) + 10D^2]y = (D^2 - 4)x + 5D(2),$$

or

(4) $$(D^4 + 5D^2 + 4)y = -4x.$$

From equations (3) and (4) it follows at once that

(5) $$v = 1 + a_1 \cos x + a_2 \sin x + a_3 \cos 2x + a_4 \sin 2x$$

and

(6) $$y = -x + b_1 \cos x + b_2 \sin x + b_3 \cos 2x + b_4 \sin 2x.$$

The a's and b's have yet to be adjusted to make (5) and (6) satisfy the original equations, rather than just the equations (3) and (4), which resulted from the original ones after certain eliminations were performed.

Combining (by substitution) the v of (5) and the y of (6) with the first equation of the system (2) leads to the identity

(7) $$x - 2b_1 \cos x - 2b_2 \sin x - 5b_3 \cos 2x - 5b_4 \sin 2x$$
$$- 5a_1 \sin x + 5a_2 \cos x - 10a_3 \sin 2x + 10a_4 \cos 2x \equiv x.$$

That (7) be an identity in x demands that

(8) $$-2b_1 + 5a_2 = 0,$$
$$-2b_2 - 5a_1 = 0,$$
$$-5b_3 + 10a_4 = 0,$$
$$-5b_4 - 10a_3 = 0.$$

Relations between the a's and b's equivalent to the relations (8) follow from substitution of the v of (5) and the y of (6) into the second equation of the system (2).

We conclude that the general solution of the system (2) is

(9) $v = 1 + a_1 \cos x + a_2 \sin x + a_3 \cos 2x + a_4 \sin 2x,$

     $y = -x + \frac{5}{2}a_2 \cos x - \frac{5}{2}a_1 \sin x + 2a_4 \cos 2x - 2a_3 \sin 2x,$

in which a_1, a_2, a_3, a_4 are arbitrary constants.

The equations (3) and (4) for v and y can be written with the aid of determinants. From the system (2) above we may write at once

$$\begin{vmatrix} (D^2 - 1) & 5D \\ 2D & -(D^2 - 4) \end{vmatrix} v = \begin{vmatrix} (D^2 - 1) & x \\ 2D & 2 \end{vmatrix},$$

which reduces to equation (3) above, if care is used in the interpretation of the right-hand member. The determinant on the right is to be interpreted as

$$(D^2 - 1)(2) - 2D(x),$$

not as the differential operator $2(D^2 - 1) - x(2D)$.

Determinants are extremely useful in any treatment of the theory of systems of linear equations. For many simple systems which arise in practice, no such powerful tool is needed.

There are other techniques for treating a system such as (2). For example, we may first obtain (3) and from it v as in equation (5). Next we wish to find an equation giving y in terms of v; that is, we seek to eliminate from the system (2) those terms that involve derivatives of y. From (2) we obtain the two equations

(10) $(2D^2 - 2)y + 10Dv = 2x,$

(11) $2D^2y - (D^3 - 4D)v = 0,$

the latter by operating with D on each member of the second equation of the system (2). From (10) and (11) it follows at once that

$$2y - D^3v - 6Dv = -2x,$$

or

(12) $y = -x + \frac{1}{2}D^3v + 3Dv.$

The v of equation (5) may now be used in (12) to compute the y which was given in the solution (9). In this method of solution there is no need to obtain (4), (6), (7), or (8).

Both methods outlined here are available whenever the system is linear with constant coefficients. Such systems appear naturally in the study of electric networks, which will be discussed in the next chapter.

Systems of nonlinear equations and systems of linear equations with variable coefficients will not be studied in this book.

Exercises

In Exs. 1–8, use the Laplace transform method.

1. $x''(t) - 3x'(t) - y'(t) + 2y(t) = 14t + 3$,
   $x'(t) - 3x(t) + y'(t) = 1; x(0) = 0, x'(0) = 0, y(0) = 6.5$.

$$\text{ANS.} \quad x(t) = 2 - \tfrac{1}{2}e^t - \tfrac{1}{2}e^{3t} - e^{-2t},$$
$$y(t) = 7t + 5 - e^t + \tfrac{5}{2}e^{-2t}.$$

2. $2x'(t) + 2x(t) + y'(t) - y(t) = 3t$,
   $x'(t) + x(t) + y'(t) + y(t) = 1; x(0) = 1, y(0) = 3$.

$$\text{ANS.} \quad x(t) = t + 3e^{-t} - 2e^{-3t},$$
$$y(t) = 1 - t + 2e^{-3t}.$$

3. $x'(t) - 2x(t) - y'(t) - y(t) = 6e^{3t}$,
   $2x'(t) - 3x(t) + y'(t) - 3y(t) = 6e^{3t}; x(0) = 3, y(0) = 0$.

$$\text{ANS.} \quad x(t) = (1 + 2t)e^t + 2e^{3t},$$
$$y(t) = (1 - t)e^t - e^{3t}.$$

4. $x''(t) + 2x(t) - y'(t) = 2t + 5$,
   $x'(t) - x(t) + y'(t) + y(t) = -2t - 1; x(0) = 3, x'(0) = 0, y(0) = -3$.

$$\text{ANS.} \quad x(t) = t + 2 + e^{-2t} + \sin t,$$
$$y(t) = 1 - t - 3e^{-2t} - \cos t.$$

5. The equations of the example of Section 76, page 234, with initial conditions $x(0) = 0$, $x'(0) = 0$, $y(0) = 1$, $y'(0) = 0$.

$$\text{ANS.} \quad x(t) = -t - \tfrac{5}{3}\sin t + \tfrac{4}{3}\sin 2t,$$
$$y(t) = 1 + \tfrac{2}{3}\cos t - \tfrac{2}{3}\cos 2t.$$

6. The equations of the example of Section 76, page 234, with initial conditions $x(0) = 9$, $x'(0) = 2$, $y(0) = 1$, $y'(0) = 0$.

$$\text{ANS.} \quad x(t) = -t + 15\cos t - 5\sin t - 6\cos 2t + 4\sin 2t,$$
$$y(t) = 1 + 2\cos t + 6\sin t - 2\cos 2t - 3\sin 2t.$$

7. $x''(t) + y'(t) - y(t) = 0$,
   $2x'(t) - x(t) + z'(t) - z(t) = 0$,
   $x'(t) + 3x(t) + y'(t) - 4y(t) + 3z(t) = 0$;
   $x(0) = 0, x'(0) = 1, y(0) = 0, z(0) = 0$.

8. $x''(t) - x(t) + 5y'(t) = \beta(t)$,
   $y''(t) - 4y(t) - 2x'(t) = 0$,
   in which $\beta(t) = 6t, \quad 0 \leqq t \leqq 2$,
   $\qquad\qquad = 12, \qquad t > 2$;
   $x(0) = 0, x'(0) = 0, y(0) = 0, y'(0) = 0$.

$$\text{ANS.} \quad x(t) = -2(3t - 5\sin t + \sin 2t)$$
$$+ 2[3(t - 2) - 5\sin (t - 2) + \sin 2(t - 2)]\alpha(t - 2),$$
$$y(t) = 3 - 4\cos t + \cos 2t$$
$$- [3 - 4\cos(t - 2) + \cos 2(t - 2)]\alpha(t - 2).$$

In Exs. 9–12, use the differential operator method.

9. Ex. 1.   10. Ex. 2.
11. Ex. 3.   12. Ex. 4.

In Exs. 13–24, use whichever method you prefer. Obtain the general solution except where otherwise directed.

13. $v' - 2v + 2w' = 2 - 4e^{2x}$,
    $2v' - 3v + 3w' - w = 0$.   ANS. $v = a_1e^x + a_2e^{-2x} + 5e^{2x} - 1$,
                                              $w = \frac{1}{2}a_1e^x - a_2e^{-2x} - e^{2x} + 3$.

14. $(3D + 2)v + (D - 6)w = 5e^x$,
    $(4D + 2)v + (D - 8)w = 5e^x + 2x - 3$.
                            ANS. $v = a_1 \cos 2x + a_2 \sin 2x + 2e^x - 3x + 5$,
                                   $w = a_2 \cos 2x - a_1 \sin 2x + e^x - x$.

15. $(D^2 + 6)y + Dv = 0$,
    $(D + 2)y + (D - 2)v = 2$.
                            ANS. $y = c_1e^{3x} + c_2 \cos 2x + c_3 \sin 2x$,
                                   $v = -1 - 5c_1e^{3x} + c_3 \cos 2x - c_2 \sin 2x$.

16. $D^2y - (2D - 1)v = 1$,
    $(2D + 1)y + (D^2 - 4)v = 0$.
        ANS. $v = 1 + a_1e^x + a_2e^{-x} + a_3 \cos x + a_4 \sin x$,
               $y = 4 + a_1e^x - 3a_2e^{-x} + (a_3 - 2a_4) \cos x + (2a_3 + a_4) \sin x$.

17. $(D^2 - 3D)y - (D - 2)z = 14x + 7$,
    $(D - 3)y + Dz = 1$.
                            ANS. $y = 2 + a_1e^x + a_2e^{3x} + a_3e^{-2x}$,
                                   $z = 7 + 7x + 2a_1e^x - \frac{5}{2}a_3e^{-2x}$.

18. $(D^3 + D^2 - 1)u + (D^3 + 2D^2 + 3D + 1)v = 3 - x$,
    $(D - 1)u + (D + 1)v = 3 - x$.
                        ANS. $u = 2x + a_1 + a_2 \cos x + a_3 \sin x$,
                               $v = x + a_1 - a_3 \cos x + a_2 \sin x$.

19. $(D^2 + 1)y + 4(D - 1)v = 4e^x$,
    $(D - 1)y + (D + 9)v = 0$; when $x = 0$, $y = 5$, $y' = 0$, $v = \frac{1}{2}$.
                        ANS. $y = 2e^x + 2e^{-x} + e^{-2x}(\cos x + 2 \sin x)$,
                               $v = \frac{1}{2}e^{-x} + e^{-2x} \sin x$.

20. $\dfrac{d^2x}{dt^2} + x - 2\dfrac{dy}{dt} = 2t$,

    $2\dfrac{dx}{dt} - x + \dfrac{dy}{dt} - 2y = 7$.
                        ANS. $x = 2t - 2 + b_1e^t + b_2e^{-t} + b_3e^{-2t}$,
                               $y = -t - 1 + b_1e^t - b_2e^{-t} - \frac{5}{4}b_3e^{-2t}$.

21. $2(D + 1)y + (D - 1)w = x + 1$,
$(D + 3)y + (D + 1)w = 4x + 14$.

ANS. $y = x + 2 + c_1e^{-x} \cos 2x + c_2e^{-x} \sin 2x$,

$w = x + 6 + (c_2 - c_1)e^{-x} \cos 2x - (c_1 + c_2)e^{-x} \sin 2x$.

22. $(D + 1)y + (D - 4)v = 6 \cos x$,
$(D - 1)y + (D^2 + 4)v = -6 \sin x$.

ANS. $y = 3 \cos x + 3 \sin x + a_1 + a_2 \cos 3x + a_3 \sin 3x$,

$v = \tfrac{1}{4}a_1 - \tfrac{1}{5}(a_2 - 3a_3) \cos 3x - \tfrac{1}{5}(3a_2 + a_3) \sin 3x$.

23. $2Du + (D - 1)v + (D + 2)w = 0$,
$(D + 2)u + (2D - 3)v - (D - 6)w = 0$,
$2Du - (D + 3)v - Dw = 0$.

ANS. $u = 3c_1e^{2x} + 3c_2e^{-x} + 3c_3e^{x/2}$,

$v = 4c_1e^{2x} - 5c_2e^{-x} + c_3e^{x/2}$,

$w = -4c_1e^{2x} - 4c_2e^{-x} - c_3e^{x/2}$.

24. $D^2y + (D - 1)v = 0$,
$(2D - 1)y + (D - 1)w = 0$,
$(D + 3)y + (D - 4)v + 3w = 0$.

ANS. $y = a_1 + a_2e^x + 3a_3e^{4x}$,

$v = b_2e^x - a_2xe^x - 16a_3e^{4x}$,

$w = -a_1 + (b_2 - a_2)e^x - a_2xe^x - 7a_3e^{4x}$.

25. Solve the problem of Section 77 by the method of Section 76.

CHAPTER 15

Electric Circuits and Networks

78. Circuits

The basic laws governing the flow of electric current in a circuit or a network will be given here without derivation. The notation used is common to most texts in electrical engineering and is:

t (sec.) = time
Q (coulombs) = quantity of electricity; e.g., charge on a capacitor
I (amperes) = current, time rate of flow of electricity
E (volts) = electromotive force or voltage
R (ohms) = resistance
L (henrys) = inductance
C (farads) = capacitance.

By the definition of Q and I it follows that

$$I(t) = Q'(t).$$

The current at each point in a network may be determined by solving the equations that result from applying Kirchhoff's laws:

(a) *The sum of the currents into (or away from) any point is zero,* and

(b) *Around any closed path the sum of the instantaneous voltage drops in a specified direction is zero.*

241

A circuit is treated as a network containing only one closed path. Figure 33 exhibits an "*RLC* circuit" with some of the customary conventions for indicating various elements.

For a circuit, Kirchhoff's current law (a) indicates merely that the current is the same throughout. That law plays a larger role in networks, as we shall see later.

To apply Kirchhoff's voltage law (b), it is necessary to know the contributions of each of the idealized elements in Figure 33. The voltage drop across the resistance is RI, that across the inductance is $LI'(t)$, and that across the capacitor is $C^{-1}Q(t)$. The impressed electromotive force $E(t)$ is contributing a voltage rise.

FIGURE 33

Assume that at time $t = 0$ the switch shown in Figure 33 is to be closed. At $t = 0$ there is no current flowing, $I(0) = 0$, and if the capacitor is initially without charge, $Q(0) = 0$. From Kirchhoff's law (b), we get the differential equation

$$(1) \qquad LI'(t) + RI(t) + C^{-1}Q(t) = E(t),$$

in which

$$(2) \qquad I(t) = Q'(t).$$

Equations (1) and (2), with the initial conditions

$$(3) \qquad I(0) = 0, \qquad Q(0) = 0,$$

constitute the problem to be solved.

To retain the conventional symbol L for the number of henrys inductance of the circuit, we shall in this section denote by L_t the Laplace operator for which L is used in all other sections of the book.

Let the transforms of $I(t)$, $Q(t)$, $E(t)$ be denoted by lower case letters:

$$(4) \qquad L_t\{I(t)\} = i(s), \qquad L_t\{Q(t)\} = q(s), \qquad L_t\{E(t)\} = e(s).$$

The problem (1), (2), and (3) is then transformed into

$$(5) \qquad L\, si(s) + Ri(s) + C^{-1}q(s) = e(s),$$
$$(6) \qquad i(s) = sq(s).$$

From (5) and (6) we find either or both of $i(s)$ and $q(s)$,

$$(7) \qquad i(s) = \frac{se(s)}{Ls^2 + Rs + C^{-1}},$$

(8)
$$q(s) = \frac{e(s)}{Ls^2 + Rs + C^{-1}}.$$

Then $I(t)$ and $Q(t)$ are obtained as inverse transforms from (7) and (8). From (7), (8), or the differential equation

(9)
$$LQ''(t) + RQ'(t) + C^{-1}Q(t) = E(t),$$

it follows that the circuit problem is equivalent to a problem in damped vibrations of a spring (Section 73). The resistance term $RQ'(t)$ parallels the damping term in vibration problems. The analogies between electrical and mechanical systems are useful in practice.

EXAMPLE: In the RL circuit with the schematic diagram shown in Figure 34, let the switch be closed at $t = 0$. At some later time, $t = t_0$, the direct current element, the constant E, is to be removed from the circuit, which remains closed. Find the current for all $t > 0$.

FIGURE 34

The boundary value problem to be solved is

(10) $LI'(t) + RI(t) = E(t);\quad I(0) = 0,$
(11) $E(t) = E[1 - \alpha(t - t_0)].$

Let the transform of $I(t)$ be $i(s)$. We know the transform of $E(t)$. Therefore we obtain the transformed problem

(12)
$$sL\,i(s) + Ri(s) = \frac{E}{s}[1 - \exp(-t_0 s)],$$

from which

(13)
$$i(s) = \frac{E[1 - \exp(-t_0 s)]}{s(sL + R)}.$$

Now
$$\frac{1}{s(sL + R)} = \frac{1}{R}\left(\frac{1}{s} - \frac{1}{s + RL^{-1}}\right),$$

so
$$i(s) = \frac{E}{R}\left(\frac{1}{s} - \frac{1}{s + RL^{-1}}\right)[1 - \exp(-t_0 s)].$$

Therefore

(14) $I(t) = \dfrac{E}{R}\bigg[1 - \alpha(t - t_0) - \exp\left(-\dfrac{R}{L}t\right)$
$$+ \exp\left\{-\frac{R}{L}(t - t_0)\right\}\alpha(t - t_0)\bigg].$$

The student should verify (14) and show that it can be written

(15)   For $0 \leqq t \leqq t_0$, $I(t) = \dfrac{E}{R}\left[1 - \exp\left(-\dfrac{Rt}{L}\right)\right];$

(16)   For $t > t_0$, $I(t) = I(t_0) \exp\left[-\dfrac{R}{L}(t - t_0)\right].$

79. Simple networks

Systems of differential equations occur naturally in the application of Kirchhoff's laws, page 241, to electric networks. The use of the Laplace operator makes the solution of such systems a straightforward, though often laborious, process. For the general theory of networks the Laplace operator (or its Heaviside equivalent) is a tool of great value. We restrict ourselves to extremely simple situations which should be sufficient to indicate the procedure commonly used.

EXAMPLE (a): Determine the character of the current $I_1(t)$ in the network having the schematic diagram in Figure 35, under the assumption that when the switch is closed the currents are each zero.

FIGURE 35

In a network, we apply Kirchhoff's laws, page 241, to obtain a system of equations to determine the currents. Since there are three dependent variables, I_1, I_2, I_3, we need three equations.

From the current law it follows that

(1) $I_1 = I_2 + I_3.$

Application of the voltage law to the circuit on the left in Figure 35 yields

(2) $R_1 I_1 + L_2 I_2' = E.$

Using the voltage law on the outside circuit, we get

(3) $R_1 I_1 + R_3 I_3 + L_3 I_3' = E.$

Still another equation can be obtained from the circuit on the right in Figure 35:

(4) $$R_3 I_3 + L_3 I_3' - L_2 I_2' = 0.$$

Equation (4) also follows at once from equations (2) and (3); it may be used instead of either (2) or (3).

We wish to obtain $I_1(t)$ from the boundary value problem consisting of equations (1), (2), (3), and the conditions $I_1(0) = 0$, $I_2(0) = 0$, $I_3(0) = 0$. One of the three initial conditions is redundant because of equation (1).

Let $L\{I_k(t)\} = i_k(s)$ for each of $k = 1, 2, 3$. Then use of the operator L transforms our problem into the algebraic one of solving the equations

(5) $$i_1 - i_2 - i_3 = 0,$$

(6) $$R_1 i_1 + sL_2 i_2 = \frac{E}{s}$$

(7) $$R_1 i_1 + (R_3 + sL_3) i_3 = \frac{E}{s}.$$

Since we desire only $i_1(s)$, let us use determinants to write the solution

(8) $$i_1(s) = \frac{\begin{vmatrix} 0 & -1 & -1 \\ \dfrac{E}{s} & sL_2 & 0 \\ \dfrac{E}{s} & 0 & (R_3 + sL_3) \end{vmatrix}}{\Delta} = \frac{E}{s} \cdot \frac{R_3 + s(L_2 + L_3)}{\Delta},$$

in which

$$\Delta = \begin{vmatrix} 1 & -1 & -1 \\ R_1 & sL_2 & 0 \\ R_1 & 0 & (R_3 + sL_3) \end{vmatrix} = \begin{vmatrix} 1 & 0 & 0 \\ R_1 & (sL_2 + R_1) & R_1 \\ R_1 & R_1 & (R_1 + R_3 + sL_3) \end{vmatrix}$$

Then

(9) $$\Delta = L_2 L_3 s^2 + (R_1 L_2 + R_3 L_2 + R_1 L_3)s + R_1 R_3.$$

We are interested in the factors of Δ. Consider the equation

(10) $$\Delta = 0.$$

Equation (10) has no positive roots. Its discriminant

$$(R_1 L_2 + R_3 L_2 + R_1 L_3)^2 - 4L_2 L_3 R_1 R_3$$

may be written

$$(R_1L_2)^2 + 2R_1L_2(R_3L_2 + R_1L_3) + (R_3L_2 + R_1L_3)^2 - 4L_2L_3R_1R_3,$$

which equals

$$(R_1L_2)^2 + 2R_1L_2(R_3L_2 + R_1L_3) + (R_3L_2 - R_1L_3)^2$$

and is therefore positive. Thus we see that equation (10) has two distinct negative roots. Call them $(-a_1)$ and $(-a_2)$. It follows that

$$\Delta = L_2L_3(s + a_1)(s + a_2),$$

and we have, from (8),

(11) $$i_1(s) = \frac{E}{s} \frac{R_3 + s(L_2 + L_3)}{L_2L_3(s + a_1)(s + a_2)}.$$

The right member of equation (11) has a partial fractions expansion

(12) $$i_1(s) = \frac{A_0}{s} + \frac{A_1}{s + a_1} + \frac{A_2}{s + a_2},$$

so

$$I_1(t) = A_0 + A_1 \exp(-a_1t) + A_2 \exp(-a_2t).$$

EXAMPLE (b): For the network shown in Figure 36, set up the equations for the determination of the currents I_1, I_2, I_3, and the charge Q_3. Assume that when the switch is closed all currents and charges are zero. Obtain the transformed problem.

FIGURE 36

Using Kirchhoff's laws we write the equations

(13) $$I_1 = I_2 + I_3,$$

(14) $$R_1I_1 + L_2\frac{dI_2}{dt} = E \sin \omega t,$$

(15) $$R_1I_1 + R_3I_3 + \frac{1}{C_3}Q_3 = E \sin \omega t;$$

and the definition of current as time rate of change of charge yields

$$(16) \qquad\qquad I_3 = \frac{dQ_3}{dt}.$$

Our problem consists of the four equations (13) through (16) with the initial conditions that

$$(17) \qquad I_2(0) = 0, \qquad I_3(0) = 0, \qquad Q_3(0) = 0.$$

Let $L\{I_k(t)\} = i_k(s)$, $k = 1, 2, 3$, and $L\{Q_3(t)\} = q_3(s)$. Then the transformed problem is the problem of solving the algebraic system

$$(18) \qquad\qquad i_1 - i_2 - i_3 = 0,$$

$$(19) \qquad\qquad R_1 i_1 + s L_2 i_2 = \frac{E\omega}{s^2 + \omega^2},$$

$$(20) \qquad\qquad R_1 i_1 + R_3 i_3 + \frac{1}{C_3} q_3 = \frac{E\omega}{s^2 + \omega^2},$$

$$(21) \qquad\qquad i_3 = s q_3.$$

Exercises

1. For the RL circuit of Figure 34, page 243, find the current I if the direct current element E is not removed from the circuit.
   ANS. $I = ER^{-1}[1 - \exp{(RtL^{-1})}]$.
2. Solve Ex. 1 if the direct-current element is replaced by an alternating-current element $E \cos \omega t$. For convenience, use the notation

$$Z^2 = R^2 + \omega^2 L^2,$$

   in which Z is called the steady-state impedance of this circuit.
   ANS. $I = EZ^{-2}[\omega L \sin \omega t + R \cos \omega t - R \exp{(-RtL^{-1})}]$.
3. Solve Ex. 2, replacing $E \cos \omega t$ with $E \sin \omega t$.
4. Figure 37 shows an RC circuit with an alternating-current element inserted. Assume that the switch is closed at $t = 0$ at which time $Q = 0$ and $I = 0$. Use the notation

$$Z^2 = R^2 + (\omega C)^{-2},$$

   FIGURE 37

   where Z is the steady-state impedance of this circuit. Find I for $t > 0$.
   ANS. $I = EZ^{-2}[R \sin \omega t + (\omega C)^{-1} \cos \omega t$
 $- (\omega C)^{-1} \exp{(-tR^{-1}C^{-1})}]$.

5. In Figure 37, replace the alternating-current element with a direct-current element $E = 50$ volts and use $R = 10$ ohms, $C = 4(10)^{-4}$ farad. Assume that when the switch is closed (at $t = 0$) the charge on the capacitor is 0.015 coulomb. Find the initial current in the circuit and the current for $t > 0$.

ANS. $I(0) = 1.25(\text{amp}), I(t) = 1.25 \exp(-250t)(\text{amp.}).$

6. In Figure 33, page 242, find $I(t)$ if $E(t) = 60$ volts, $R = 40$ ohms, $C = 5(10)^{-5}$ farad, $L = 0.02$ henry. Assume $I(0) = 0$, $Q(0) = 0$.

ANS. $I = 3000t \exp(-1000t)(\text{amp.}).$

7. In Ex. 6, find the maximum current.   ANS. $I_{max} = 3e^{-1}$ (amp.).

In Exs. 8–11, use Figure 33, page 242, with $E(t) = E \sin \omega t$ and with the following notations used to simplify the appearance of the formulas:

$$a = \frac{R}{2L}, b^2 = a^2 - \frac{1}{LC}, \beta^2 = \frac{1}{LC} - a^2,$$

$$\gamma = \omega L - \frac{1}{\omega C}, Z^2 = R^2 + \gamma^2.$$

The quantity Z is the steady-state impedance for an RLC circuit. In each of Exs. 8–11, find $I(t)$ assuming that $I(0) = 0$ and $Q(0) = 0$.

8. Assume that $4L < R^2C$.

ANS. $I = EZ^{-2}(R \sin \omega t - \gamma \cos \omega t) + \frac{1}{2}Eb^{-1}Z^{-2}[\{\gamma(a + b) - \omega R\}\exp\{-(a - b)t\} + \{\omega R - \gamma(a - b)\}\exp\{-(a + b)t\}].$

9. Assume that $R^2C < 4L$.

ANS. $I = EZ^{-2}(R \sin \omega t - \gamma \cos \omega t) + E\beta^{-1}Z^{-2}e^{-at}[\beta\gamma \cos \beta t - a(\gamma + 2\omega^{-1}C^{-1}) \sin \beta t].$

10. Assume that $R^2C = 4L$.

ANS. $I = EZ^{-2}(R \sin \omega t - \gamma \cos \omega t) + E\omega^{-1}Z^{-2}e^{-at}[\gamma\omega - a(\gamma\omega + aR)t].$

11. Show that the answer to Ex. 10 can be put in the form

$$I = EZ^{-2}(R \sin \omega t - \gamma \cos \omega t) + EZ^{-2}e^{-at}[\gamma + (a\gamma - R\omega)t].$$

12. In Ex. 4, replace the alternating current element $E \sin \omega t$ with

$$E[\alpha(t - t_0) - \alpha(t - t_1)], \quad t_1 > t_0 > 0.$$

Graph the new emf. Determine the current in the circuit.

ANS. $I(t) = \frac{E}{R}\left[\exp\left(-\frac{t - t_0}{RC}\right)\alpha(t - t_0) - \exp\left(-\frac{t - t_1}{RC}\right)\alpha(t - t_1)\right].$

13. In Figure 38, let $E = 60$ volts, $R_1 = 10$ ohms, $R_3 = 20$ ohms, and $C_2 = 5(10)^{-4}$ farad. Determine the currents if when the switch is closed the capacitor carries a charge of 0.03 coulomb.

ANS. $I_1 = 2(1 - e^{-300t})$, $I_2 = -3e^{-300t}$, $I_3 = 2 + e^{-300t}$.

FIGURE 38

14. In Ex. 13, let the initial charge on the capacitor be 0.01 coulomb, but leave the rest of the problem unchanged.

ANS. $I_1 = 2(1 + e^{-300t})$, $I_2 = 3e^{-300t}$, $I_3 = 2 - e^{-300t}$.

FIGURE 39

15. For the network in Figure 39, set up the equations for the determination of the charge Q_3 and the currents I_1, I_2, I_3. Assume all four of those quantities to be zero at time zero. Transform the problem into algebraic form.

FIGURE 40

16. For the network in Figure 40, set up the equations for the determination of the currents. Assume all currents to be zero at time zero. Find $i_1(s) = L\{I_1(t)\}$ and discuss the character of $I_1(t)$ without explicitly finding the function.

CHAPTER 16

Variation of Parameters
and Other Methods

80. Variation of parameters

In this chapter, three methods will be presented, any one of which will lead to the general solution of a linear differential equation with constant coefficients.

This time all that need be assumed about the right-hand member $R(x)$ in the equation

(1) $$f(D)y = R(x)$$

is that $R(x)$ be sufficiently well behaved that the integrals we encounter will exist.

For equation (1), once the roots of the auxiliary equation $f(m) = 0$ are known, the complementary function is written by inspection. Suppose, for instance, that (1) is of order two and its complementary function is given by

(2) $$y_c = c_1\varphi_1(x) + c_2\varphi_2(x),$$

where c_1 and c_2 are arbitrary constants (or parameters) and the $\varphi_1(x)$ and $\varphi_2(x)$ are, of course, known functions.

250

Then the method of variation of parameters is as follows. First replace the constants c_1 and c_2 by unknown functions of x, say A and B. That is, put

$$(3) \qquad\qquad y = A\varphi_1(x) + B\varphi_2(x),$$

where A and B should now be looked upon as two new dependent variables. Here A and B replace the parameters c_1 and c_2 of (2), and now A and B are being permitted to vary. That is where the method got its name.

Now three dependent variables, A, B, and y, are present. They must satisfy equations (1) and (3). But, in general, three variables can be made to satisfy three equations. Hence we are free to impose one more condition upon A, B, and y.

From (3) it follows that

$$(4) \qquad y' = A\varphi_1'(x) + B\varphi_2'(x) + A'\varphi_1(x) + B'\varphi_2(x).$$

Now let us impose a third condition by demanding that

$$(5) \qquad\qquad A'\varphi_1(x) + B'\varphi_2(x) = 0.$$

Then (4) becomes

$$(6) \qquad\qquad y' = A\varphi_1'(x) + B\varphi_2'(x),$$

from which

$$(7) \qquad y'' = A\varphi_1''(x) + B\varphi_2''(x) + A'\varphi_1'(x) + B'\varphi_2'(x),$$

involving nothing higher than first-order derivatives of A and B.

Finally, (3), (6), and (7) can be used to eliminate y from (1), and we can thus get an equation in A' and B' to go with (5). Thus A' and B' can be found, and then we can determine A and B by integration. Once A and B are known, equation (3) gives us the desired y. See the examples below.

The method is easily extended to equations of order higher than two, but no essentially new ideas appear and the details can get tedious. In this section, only second-order equations will be treated.

EXAMPLE (a): Solve the equation

$$(8) \qquad\qquad (D^2 + 1)y = \sec x \tan x.$$

Of course,

$$y_c = c_1 \cos x + c_2 \sin x.$$

Let us seek a particular solution by variation of parameters. Put

(9) $$y = A \cos x + B \sin x,$$

from which

$$y' = -A \sin x + B \cos x + A' \cos x + B' \sin x.$$

Next set

(10) $$A' \cos x + B' \sin x = 0,$$

so

$$y' = -A \sin x + B \cos x.$$

Then

(11) $$y'' = -A \cos x - B \sin x - A' \sin x + B' \cos x.$$

Next we eliminate y by combining equations (9) and (11) with the original equation (8). Thus we get the relation

(12) $$-A' \sin x + B' \cos x = \sec x \tan x.$$

From (12) and (10), A' is easily eliminated. The result is

$$B' = \tan x,$$

so

(13) $$B = \ln \sec x,$$

in which the arbitrary constant has been disregarded because we are seeking only a particular solution to add to our previously determined complementary function y_c.

From equations (12) and (10) it also follows easily that

$$A' = -\sin x \sec x \tan x,$$

or

$$A' = -\tan^2 x.$$

Then

$$A = -\int \tan^2 x \, dx = \int (1 - \sec^2 x) \, dx,$$

so

(14) $$A = x - \tan x,$$

again disregarding the arbitrary constant.

Returning to equation (9) with the known A from (14) and the known B from (13), we write the particular solution

$$y_p = (x - \tan x) \cos x + \sin x \ln \sec x,$$

or

$$y_p = x \cos x - \sin x + \sin x \ln \sec x.$$

Then the general solution of (8) is

(15) $y = c_1 \cos x + c_3 \sin x + x \cos x + \sin x \ln \sec x,$

where the term $(- \sin x)$ in y_p has been absorbed in the complementary function term $c_3 \sin x$, since c_3 is an arbitrary constant.

The solution (15) can, as usual, be verified by direct substitution into the original differential equation.

EXAMPLE (b): Solve the equation

(16) $$(D^2 - 3D + 2)y = \frac{1}{1 + e^{-x}}.$$

Here
$$y_c = c_1 e^x + c_2 e^{2x},$$
so we put

(17) $$y = A e^x + B e^{2x}.$$

Since
$$y' = A e^x + 2B e^{2x} + A' e^x + B' e^{2x},$$
we impose the condition

(18) $$A' e^x + B' e^{2x} = 0.$$

Then

(19) $$y' = A e^x + 2B e^{2x},$$

from which it follows that

(20) $$y'' = A e^x + 4B e^{2x} + A' e^x + 2B' e^{2x}.$$

Combining (17), (19), (20), and the original equation (16), we find that

(21) $$A' e^x + 2B' e^{2x} = \frac{1}{1 + e^{-x}}.$$

Elimination of B' from equations (18) and (21) yields

$$A' e^x = - \frac{1}{1 + e^{-x}},$$

$$A' = - \frac{e^{-x}}{1 + e^{-x}}.$$

Then
$$A = \ln (1 + e^{-x}).$$

Similarly,

$$B'e^{2x} = \frac{1}{1 + e^{-x}}$$

so

$$B = \int \frac{e^{-2x}}{1 + e^{-x}} \, dx = \int \left[e^{-x} - \frac{e^{-x}}{1 + e^{-x}} \right] dx,$$

or

$$B = -e^{-x} + \ln(1 + e^{-x}).$$

Then, from (17),

$$y_p = e^x \ln(1 + e^{-x}) - e^x + e^{2x} \ln(1 + e^{-x}).$$

The term $(-e^x)$ in y_p can be absorbed into the complementary function. The general solution of equation (16) is

$$y = c_3 e^x + c_2 e^{2x} + (e^x + e^{2x}) \ln(1 + e^{-x}).$$

Equation (16) can equally well be solved without variation of parameters by a judicious use of the exponential shift of Section 48.

81. Solution of $y'' + y = f(x)$

Consider next the equation

(1) $$(D^2 + 1)y = f(x),$$

in which all that we require of $f(x)$ is that it be integrable in the interval on which we seek a solution. For instance, $f(x)$ may be any continuous function or any function with only a finite number of finite discontinuities on the interval $a \leqq x \leqq b$.

The method of variation of parameters will now be applied to the solution of (1). Put

(2) $$y = A \cos x + B \sin x.$$

Then

$$y' = -A \sin x + B \cos x + A' \cos x + B' \sin x,$$

and if we choose

(3) $$A' \cos x + B' \sin x = 0,$$

we obtain

(4) $$y'' = -A \cos x - B \sin x - A' \sin x + B' \cos x.$$

From (1), (2), and (4) it follows that

(5) $$-A' \sin x + B' \cos x = f(x).$$

Equations (3) and (5) may be solved for A' and B', yielding

$$A' = -f(x) \sin x, \quad B' = f(x) \cos x.$$

We may now write

(6) $$A = - \int_a^x f(\beta) \sin \beta \, d\beta,$$

(7) $$B = \int_a^x f(\beta) \cos \beta \, d\beta,$$

for any x in $a \leqq x \leqq b$. It is here that we use the integrability of $f(x)$ on the interval $a \leqq x \leqq b$.

The A and B of (6) and (7) may be inserted in (2) to give us the particular solution

$$y_p = - \cos x \int_a^x f(\beta) \sin \beta \, d\beta + \sin x \int_a^x f(\beta) \cos \beta \, d\beta$$

$$= \int_a^x f(\beta)[\sin x \cos \beta - \cos x \sin \beta] \, d\beta.$$

Hence we have

(8) $$y_p = \int_a^x f(\beta) \sin (x - \beta) \, d\beta,$$

and we can now write the general solution of equation (1):

(9) $$y = c_1 \cos x + c_2 \sin x + \int_a^x f(\beta) \sin (x - \beta) \, d\beta.$$

See Section 68 for a simpler, but less elementary, method for obtaining the solution (9).

82. A general second-order linear equation

The method used in Section 80 applies equally well to the equation

(1) $$y'' + p(x)y' + q(x)y = f(x),$$

where $p(x)$ and $q(x)$ need not be constants, as long as we know two linearly independent solutions $y = y_1(x)$ and $y = y_2(x)$ of the corresponding homogeneous equation

(2) $$y'' + p(x)y' + q(x)y = 0.$$

Let the Wronskian (page 99) of $y_1(x)$ and $y_2(x)$ be denoted by $W(x)$,

(3) $$W(x) = \begin{vmatrix} y_1(x) & y_2(x) \\ y_1'(x) & y_2'(x) \end{vmatrix},$$

and let $W(x) \neq 0$ on the interval $a \leqq x \leqq b$. Then the method of variation of parameters yields the following particular solution of equation (1).

(4) $$y_p = \int_a^x \frac{f(\beta)[y_1(\beta)y_2(x) - y_1(x)y_2(\beta)]\,d\beta}{W(\beta)}.$$

The general solution of (1) is, of course,

(5) $$y = c_1 y_1(x) + c_2 y_2(x) + y_p(x).$$

Since we have as yet no methods for obtaining y_1 and y_2 unless equation (1) has constant coefficients, the solution (5) is at present of purely theoretical interest to us. In general, power series methods are used to find y_1 and y_2 when equation (1) has variable coefficients.

For the Wronskian (3) of any two linearly independent solutions y_1 and y_2 of equation (1), it is not difficult* to derive Abel's formula

(6) $$W(x) = c \exp\left[-\int p(x)\,dx\right],$$

where c is constant.

Exercises

In Exs. 1–20, use variation of parameters, Section 80.

1. $(D^2 + 1)y = \csc x \cot x.$
   ANS. $y = c_1 \cos x + c_2 \sin x - x \sin x - \cos x \ln \sin x.$
2. $(D^2 + 1)y = \cot x.$ ANS. $y = y_c - \sin x \ln (\csc x + \cot x).$
3. $(D^2 + 1)y = \sec x.$
   ANS. $y = c_1 \cos x + c_2 \sin x + x \sin x + \cos x \ln \cos x.$
4. $(D^2 + 1)y = \sec^2 x.$ ANS. $y = y_c - 1 + \sin x \ln (\sec x + \tan x).$
5. $(D^2 + 1)y = \sec^3 x.$ ANS. $y = y_c + \frac{1}{2} \sec x.$
6. $(D^2 + 1)y = \sec^4 x.$
   ANS. $y = y_c - \frac{1}{2} + \frac{1}{6} \sec^2 x + \frac{1}{2} \sin x \ln (\sec x + \tan x).$
7. $(D^2 + 1)y = \tan x.$ ANS. $y = y_c - \cos x \ln (\sec x + \tan x).$
8. $(D^2 + 1)y = \tan^2 x.$
   ANS. $y = y_1 - 1,$ where y_1 is the solution of Ex. 4 above.

* See, for example, E. D. Rainville, *Intermediate Differential Equations*, 2nd ed. (New York: The Macmillan Co., 1964), p. 274.

9. $(D^2 + 1)y = \sec x \csc x.$

   ANS. $y = y_c - \cos x \ln (\sec x + \tan x) - \sin x \ln (\csc x + \cot x).$

10. $(D^2 + 1)y = \sec^2 x \csc x.$ ANS. $y = y_c - \sin x \ln (\csc 2x + \cot 2x).$

11. $(D^2 - 2D + 1)y = e^{2x}(e^x + 1)^{-2}.$ ANS. $y = y_c + e^x \ln (1 + e^x).$

12. $(D^2 - 3D + 2)y = e^{2x}/(1 + e^{2x}).$

   ANS. $y = y_c + e^x \operatorname{Arctan} (e^{-x}) - \tfrac{1}{2}e^{2x} \ln (1 + e^{-2x}).$

13. $(D^2 - 3D + 2)y = \cos (e^{-x}).$ ANS. $y = y_c - e^{2x} \cos (e^{-x}).$

14. $(D^2 - 1)y = 2(1 - e^{-2x})^{-\frac{1}{2}}.$

   ANS. $y = c_1 e^x + c_2 e^{-x} - e^x \operatorname{Arcsin} (e^{-x}) - (1 - e^{-2x})^{\frac{1}{2}}.$

15. $(D^2 - 1)y = e^{-2x} \sin e^{-x}.$ ANS. $y = y_c - \sin e^{-x} - e^x \cos e^{-x}.$

16. $(D^2 - 5D + 4)y = 6/(1 + e^{-2x}).$

   ANS. $y = y_c + 2e^x \operatorname{Arctan} e^{-x} - e^{2x} + e^{4x} \ln (1 + e^{-2x}).$

17. $(D^2 - 1)y = (1 + e^{-x})^{-2}.$

   ANS. $y = y_c - 1 + xe^{-x} + e^{-x} \ln (1 + e^{-x}).$

18. $(D - 1)(D - 3)y = \cos e^{-x}.$

   ANS. $y = y_c + e^{3x} \sin e^{-x} - e^{2x} \cos e^{-x}.$

19. $(D^2 - 3D + 2)y = 15(1 + e^{-x})^{\frac{1}{2}}.$

   ANS. $y = c_1 e^x + c_2 e^{2x} + 4(e^x + e^{2x})(1 + e^{-x})^{\frac{3}{2}};$ or
   $$y = y_c + 4e^{2x}(1 + e^{-x})^{\frac{1}{2}}.$$

20. $(D^2 - 3D + 2)y = (1 + e^{-2x})^{-\frac{1}{2}}.$

   ANS. $y = y_c + e^x \ln [e^{-x} + (1 + e^{-2x})^{\frac{1}{2}}] - e^{2x}(1 + e^{-2x})^{\frac{1}{2}}.$

In Exs. 21–28 use the exponential shift once or twice, as needed, to solve the equation without variation of parameters.

21. Ex. 11.   **22.** Ex. 12.
23. Ex. 13.   **24.** Ex. 15.
25. Ex. 16.   **26.** Ex. 17.
27. Ex. 18.   **28.** Ex. 19.

29. Use variation of parameters to obtain the solution (4), Section 82.

30. Use variation of parameters to solve the equation

$$y'' + 4y' + 4y = f(x).$$

ANS. $y = c_1 e^{-2x} + c_2 x e^{-2x} + \displaystyle\int_0^x f(\beta)(x - \beta) \exp [-2(x - \beta)] \, d\beta.$

83. Reduction of order by using factors of the operator

Consider the equation

(1) $$(D - a)(D - b)y = R(x).$$

The change of dependent variable

(2) $(D - b)y = w$

leads us to the equation

(3) $(D - a)w = R(x),$

which is linear of the first order. Then (3) can be written in standard form (page 36)

$$dw - aw\,dx = R(x)\,dx$$

and so solved with the aid of the integrating factor e^{-ax}.

Once w is known we revert to equation (2) to find y. Equation (2) is also of the first order, so it can be solved just as (3) was solved.

The problem of solving the equation (1) of order two is thus replaced by a succession of two problems, each the solving of an equation of order one. In general this device permits us to replace a linear equation of order n (with constant coefficients) with n successive linear equations of order one. The only difficulty is that of performing the integrations. In practice, that difficulty is often quite serious.

EXAMPLE: Solve the equation

(4) $(D^2 - 1)y = \dfrac{2}{e^x + e^{-x}}.$

Thinking of equation (4) in the form

$$(D + 1)(D - 1)y = \frac{2}{e^x + e^{-x}},$$

we put

(5) $(D - 1)y = w.$

Then we need to solve

$$(D + 1)w = \frac{2}{e^x + e^{-x}},$$

which may be written

(6) $dw + w\,dx = \dfrac{2\,dx}{e^x + e^{-x}}.$

An integrating factor for (6) is e^x. Therefore

$$e^x\,dw + we^x\,dx = \frac{2e^x\,dx}{e^x + e^{-x}}$$

is exact. Hence

$$e^x w = \int \frac{2e^x \, dx}{e^x + e^{-x}} = \int \frac{2e^{2x}}{e^{2x} + 1} \, dx,$$

from which

$$e^x w = \ln (e^{2x} + 1),$$

the arbitrary constant being disregarded as usual when searching for a particular solution.

Next the expression for w is inserted in equation (5), which then becomes

$$(D - 1)y = e^{-x} \ln (e^{2x} + 1),$$

$$dy - y \, dx = e^{-x} \ln (e^{2x} + 1) \, dx.$$

Here an integrating factor is e^{-x}, so we write

$$e^{-x} \, dy - ye^{-x} \, dx = e^{-2x} \ln (e^{2x} + 1) \, dx,$$

$$e^{-x}y = \int e^{-2x} \ln (e^{2x} + 1) \, dx.$$

Integration by parts can be used to reduce the above to the form

(7) $$e^{-x}y = -\tfrac{1}{2}e^{-2x} \ln (e^{2x} + 1) + \int \frac{dx}{e^{2x} + 1}.$$

Then we write

$$e^{-x}y = -\tfrac{1}{2}e^{-2x} \ln (e^{2x} + 1) + \int \left[1 - \frac{e^{2x}}{e^{2x} + 1} \right] dx$$

and thus find that

$$e^{-x}y = -\tfrac{1}{2}e^{-2x} \ln (e^{2x} + 1) + x - \tfrac{1}{2} \ln (e^{2x} + 1),$$

(8) $$y = xe^x - \tfrac{1}{2}(e^x + e^{-x}) \ln (e^{2x} + 1).$$

Equation (8) is a particular solution of the original equation (4). The general solution of the differential equation (4) is therefore

$$y = c_1 e^x + c_2 e^{-x} + xe^x - \tfrac{1}{2}(e^x + e^{-x}) \ln (e^{2x} + 1).$$

84. A third method: change of dependent variable

Consider the general second-order linear equation

(1) $$y'' + py' + qy = R.$$

Suppose we know a solution $y = y_1$ of the corresponding homogeneous equation

(2) $$y'' + py' + qy = 0.$$

Then the introduction of a new dependent variable v by the substitution

(3) $$y = y_1 v$$

will lead to a solution of equation (1) in the following way.

From (3) it follows that

$$y' = y_1 v' + y_1' v,$$
$$y'' = y_1 v'' + 2y_1' v' + y_1'' v,$$

so substitution of (3) into (1) yields

$$y_1 v'' + 2y_1' v' + y_1'' v + py_1 v' + py_1' v + qy_1 v = R,$$

or

(4) $$y_1 v'' + (2y_1' + py_1)v' + (y_1'' + py_1' + qy_1)v = R.$$

But $y = y_1$ is a solution of (2). That is,

$$y_1'' + py_1' + qy_1 = 0$$

and equation (4) reduces to

(5) $$y_1 v'' + (2y_1' + py_1)v' = R.$$

Now let $v' = w$ so equation (5) becomes

(6) $$y_1 w' + (2y_1' + py_1)w = R,$$

a linear equation of the first order in w.

By the usual method (integrating factor) we can find w from (6). Then we can get v from $v' = w$ by an integration. Finally $y = y_1 v$.

Note that the method is not restricted to equations with constant coefficients. It depends only upon our knowing a particular solution of equation (2); that is, upon our knowledge of the complementary function. For practical purposes, the method depends also upon our being able to effect the integrations.

EXAMPLE: Solve the equation

(7) $$(D^2 + 1)y = \csc x.$$

The complementary function is

(8) $$y_c = c_1 \cos x + c_2 \sin x.$$

We may use any special case of (8) as the y_1 in the theory above. Let us then put

$$y = v \sin x.$$

We find that

$$y' = v' \sin x + v \cos x$$

and

$$y'' = v'' \sin x + 2v' \cos x - v \sin x.$$

The equation for v is

$$v'' \sin x + 2v' \cos x = \csc x,$$

or

(9) $$v'' + 2v' \cot x = \csc^2 x.$$

Put $v' = w$; then equation (9) becomes

$$w' + 2w \cot x = \csc^2 x,$$

or

$$dw + 2w \cot x \, dx = \csc^2 x \, dx,$$

for which an integrating factor is $\sin^2 x$. Thus

(10) $$\sin^2 x \, dw + 2w \sin x \cos x \, dx = dx$$

is exact. From (10) we get

$$w \sin^2 x = x,$$

seeking, as usual, only a particular solution.
    Then

$$w = x \csc^2 x$$

or

$$v' = x \csc^2 x.$$

Hence

$$v = \int x \csc^2 x \, dx,$$

or

$$v = -x \cot x + \ln \sin x,$$

a result easily obtained using integration by parts.
    Now

$$y = v \sin x,$$

so the particular solution which we sought is

$$y_p = -x \cos x + \sin x \ln \sin x.$$

Finally, the complete solution of (7) is seen to be

$$y = c_1 \cos x + c_2 \sin x - x \cos x + \sin x \ln \sin x.$$

Exercises

In Exs. 1–4, use the method of Section 83.

1. $(D^2 + 2D + 1)y = (e^x - 1)^{-2}$.

ANS. $y = e^{-x}[c_1 + c_2 x - \ln(1 - e^{-x})]$.

2. $(D^2 + 2D + 1)y = (e^x + 1)^{-2}$.

ANS. $y = e^{-x}[c_1 + c_2 x + \ln(1 + e^{-x})]$.

3. $(D - 1)(D - 3)y = \sin e^{-x}$.

ANS. $y = y_c - e^{2x} \sin e^{-x} - e^{3x} \cos e^{-x}$.

4. $(D^2 - 1)y = 2e^x(1 + e^x)^{-2}$.

ANS. $y = y_c + 1 + xe^x - (e^x + e^{-x}) \ln(1 + e^x)$.

In Exs. 5–9, use the method of Section 84.

5. Use the substitution $y = v \cos x$ to solve the equation of the example of Section 84.

6. $(D^2 + 1)y = \sec x$.   ANS.   See Ex. 3, page 256.

7. $(D^2 + 1)y = \sec^3 x$. Use $y = v \sin x$.   ANS.   See Ex. 5, page 256.

8. $(D^2 + 1)y = \csc^3 x$. Take a hint from Ex. 7. Use $y = v \cos x$, since $\cos x$ is complementary to $\sin x$ just as $\csc x$ is complementary to $\sec x$.

9. $(D^2 - 3D + 2)y = (1 + e^{-2x})^{-\frac{1}{2}}$.   ANS.   See Ex. 20, page 257.

10. $y'' + 4y' + 4y = x^{-2}e^{-2x}$. Use the exponential shift.

ANS. $y = e^{-2x}(c_1 + c_2 x - \ln x)$.

11. In the example of Section 83, perform the integration needed in equation (7) by using the trick below.

$$\int \frac{dx}{e^{2x} + 1} = \int \frac{e^{-2x}\, dx}{1 + e^{-2x}} = -\tfrac{1}{2} \ln(1 + e^{-2x}).$$

Thus obtain for equation (4) a particular solution in the form

$$y = -\tfrac{1}{2}e^{-x} \ln(e^{2x} + 1) - \tfrac{1}{2}e^x \ln(1 + e^{-2x})$$

and show that this solution is equivalent to that given in equation (8).

Miscellaneous Exercises

1. $(D^2 - 1)y = 2e^{-x}(1 + e^{-2x})^{-2}$.

ANS. $y = y_c - xe^{-x} - \tfrac{1}{2}e^{-x} \ln(1 + e^{-2x})$.

2. $(D^2 - 1)y = (1 - e^{2x})^{-\frac{1}{2}}$.   ANS. $y = y_c - (1 - e^{2x})^{\frac{1}{2}}$.

3. $(D^2 - 1)y = e^{2x}(3 \tan e^x + e^x \sec^2 e^x)$.   ANS. $y = y_c + e^x \ln \sec e^x$.

4. $(D^2 + 1)y = \sec^2 x \tan x$.

ANS. $y = y_c + \tfrac{1}{2} \tan x + \tfrac{1}{2} \cos x \ln(\sec x + \tan x)$.

5. Do Ex. 4 by another method.

6. $(D^2 + 1)y = \csc x$. Use variation of parameters.

ANS.   See the example of Section 84.

7. $(D^2 - 3D + 2)y = \sec^2 (e^{-x})$.

ANS. $y = c_1 e^x + c_2 e^{2x} + e^{2x} \ln \sec (e^{-x})$.

8. Do Ex. 7 by another method.

9. $(D^2 - 1)y = 2/(1 + e^x)$.

ANS. $y = y_c - 1 - xe^x + (e^x - e^{-x}) \ln (1 + e^x)$.

10. $(D^3 + D)y = \sec^2 x$. Hint: integrate once first.

ANS. $y = c_1 + c_2 \cos x + c_3 \sin x - \cos x \ln (\sec x + \tan x)$.

11. $(D^2 - 1)y = 2/(e^x - e^{-x})$.

ANS. $y = y_c - xe^{-x} + \frac{1}{2}(e^x - e^{-x}) \ln (1 - e^{-2x})$.

12. $(D^2 - 3D + 2)y = \sin e^{-x}$.   ANS. $y = y_c - e^{2x} \sin e^{-x}$.

13. $(D^2 - 1)y = 1/(e^{2x} + 1)$.   ANS. $y = y_c - \frac{1}{2} - \cosh x \operatorname{Arctan} e^{-x}$.

14. $y'' + y = \sec^3 x \tan x$.   ANS. $y = y_c + \frac{1}{6} \sec x \tan x$.

15. $y'' + y = \sec x \tan^2 x$. Verify your answer.

16. $y'' + 4y' + 3y = \sin e^x$.   ANS. $y = y_c - e^{-2x} \sin e^x - e^{-3x} \cos e^x$.

17. $y'' + y = \csc^3 x \cot x$.   ANS. $y = y_c + \frac{1}{6} \cot x \csc x$.

CHAPTER 17

The Existence of Solutions

85. Preliminary remarks

The methods of Chapter 2 are strictly dependent upon certain special properties (variables separable, exactness, etc.), which may or may not be possessed by an individual equation. It is intuitively plausible that no collection of methods can be found that would permit the explicit solution, in the sense of Chapter 2, of all differential equations. We may seek solutions in other forms, employing infinite series or other limiting processes; we may resort to numerical approximations.

Confronted with this situation, the pure mathematician frequently reacts by searching for what is known as an existence theorem. He seeks to determine conditions that are sufficient to insure the existence of a solution with certain properties. It may happen that in discovering such a theorem and a proof of it, the mathematician will hit upon a method, practical or not, for constructing a solution of the equation.

86. Nature of solutions of a particular equation

Before proceeding to a statement of an existence theorem, let us examine in some detail the solutions of a simple equation,

$$(1) \qquad 2y\,dx - x\,dy = 0.$$

Equation (1) has the general solution $y = cx^2$, including the solution $x = 0$ by our usual convention. This family of curves consists of the two axes and all parabolas that have the origin as vertex and have their foci on the y-axis, as shown in Figure 41, page 265.

Additional solutions of equation (1) may be formed by combining parts of different elements of the family of solutions given above. Since we need to retain continuity of y and dy/dx, we permit ourselves to pass from one element of the family to another only where the two intersect and have a common tangent. In this case the elements intersect only at the origin.

As an example, the curve defined by

$$y = x^2, \qquad 0 \leqq x,$$
$$y = -4x^2, \quad x < 0,$$

is a solution of equation (1). Note the continuity of its slope at the origin.

Given any point in the xy-plane, we can find a solution that passes through that point. If the given point is not the origin, then the solution that passes through the given point is unique in the vicinity of that point. See Section 33.

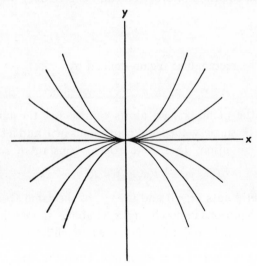

FIGURE 41

Now write equation (1) in the form

(2) $$\frac{dy}{dx} = \frac{2y}{x}.$$

The right member of equation (2) is discontinuous at each point where $x = 0$ and is continuous elsewhere. Through each point where the right member of equation (2) is continuous there is a solution unique near that point. At the origin, trouble is to be expected because of the clustering of solutions there as indicated earlier. In searching for solutions through a point $x = 0$, $y = y_0 \neq 0$, it is more natural to write equation (2) in the form

$$(3) \qquad \frac{dx}{dy} = \frac{x}{2y},$$

and to consider x as the dependent variable. Then the slope is dx/dy and it is continuous at $(0, y_0)$, $y_0 \neq 0$. Again a solution passing through the point in question exists and is unique near that point.

87. An existence theorem

We now state without proof an existence theorem for certain first-order equations. A proof of this theorem can be found in Ince.*

Consider the equation of order one and degree one,

$$(1) \qquad \frac{dy}{dx} = f(x, y).$$

Let T denote the rectangular region defined by

$$|x - x_0| \leq a, \quad |y - y_0| \leq b,$$

a region with the point (x_0, y_0) at its center. Let the function $f(x, y)$ in equation (1) be single-valued and continuous in T and let $f(x, y)$ satisfy the "Lipschitz condition" that there exists a constant K such that

$$|f(x, y_1) - f(x, y_2)| < K|y_1 - y_2|$$

for every pair of points (x, y_1) and (x, y_2), of the same abscissa, in T.

Under the conditions imposed on $f(x, y)$ above, there exists an interval about x_0, $|x - x_0| \leq h$, and a function $y(x)$ which has the properties:

(a) $y = y(x)$ is a solution of equation (1) on the interval $|x - x_0| \leq h$;

(b) On the interval $|x - x_0| \leq h$, $y(x)$ satisfies the inequality $|y(x) - y_0| \leq b$;

(c) At $x = x_0$, $y = y(x_0) = y_0$;

(d) $y(x)$ is unique on the interval $|x - x_0| \leq h$ in the sense that it is the only function that has all of the properties (a), (b), and (c).

---

* E. L. Ince, *Ordinary Differential Equations* (London: Longmans, Green and Co., 1927), pp. 62–66.

The interval $|x - x_0| \leqq h$ may or may not need to be smaller than the interval $|x - x_0| \leqq a$ over which conditions were imposed upon $f(x, y)$.

In rough language, the theorem states that if $f(x, y)$ is sufficiently well behaved near the point (x_0, y_0), then the differential equation

(1) $$\frac{dy}{dx} = f(x, y)$$

has a solution that passes through the point (x_0, y_0) and that solution is unique near (x_0, y_0).

It is important that the solution under discussion can actually be exhibited. The function $y(x)$ is the limit of a sequence of functions $y_n(x)$; $n = 1, 2, \cdots$, defined as follows:

$$y = y(x) = \operatorname*{Lim}_{n \to \infty} y_n(x),$$

where

$$y_1(x) = y_0 + \int_{x_0}^{x} f(t, y_0) \, dt,$$

$$y_2(x) = y_0 + \int_{x_0}^{x} f[t, y_1(t)] \, dt,$$

$$y_3(x) = y_0 + \int_{x_0}^{x} f[t, y_2(t)] \, dt,$$

. . .

$$y_n(x) = y_0 + \int_{x_0}^{x} f[t, y_{n-1}(t)] \, dt.$$

The student should use this process to construct a solution of the boundary value problem

(2) $$\frac{dy}{dx} = \frac{2y}{x} \; ; \text{ when } x = 1, \, y = 1.$$

It will be found that

$$y_1(x) = 1 + 2 \ln x,$$
$$y_2(x) = 1 + 2 \ln x + 2 \ln^2 x,$$
$$y_3(x) = 1 + 2 \ln x + 2 \ln^2 x + \tfrac{4}{3} \ln^3 x,$$

. . .

$$y_n(x) = 1 + \sum_{k=1}^{n} \frac{2^k \ln^k x}{k!},$$

and that

$$y = \exp(2 \ln x) = x^2.$$

CHAPTER 18

Equations of Order One
and Higher Degree

88. Factoring the left member

If an equation

(1) $$f(x, y, y') = 0$$

is of degree higher than one, it may be possible to factor the left member into parts, each of degree one. The problem of solving (1) is then replaced by two or more problems of simpler type. The latter may be capable of solution by the methods of Chapters 2 and 4.

Since y' will be raised to powers in the example and exercises, let us simplify the printing and writing by a common device, using p for y':

$$p = \frac{dy}{dx}.$$

EXAMPLE: Solve the differential equation

(2) $$xyp^2 + (x + y)p + 1 = 0.$$

The left member of equation (2) is readily factored. Thus (2) leads to

$$(xp + 1)(yp + 1) = 0,$$

from which it follows that either

(3) $$yp + 1 = 0$$

or

(4) $$xp + 1 = 0.$$

From equation (3) in the form

$$y\,dy + dx = 0$$

it follows that

(5) $$y^2 = -2(x - c_1).$$

Equation (4) may be written

$$x\,dy + dx = 0$$

from which, for $x \neq 0$,

$$dy + \frac{dx}{x} = 0,$$

so

(6) $$y = -\ln(c_2 x).$$

Equation (2) may be rewritten

$$xy(dy)^2 + (x + y)(dx)(dy) + (dx)^2 = 0,$$

in which form $x = 0$ is seen to be a solution. But (6) may be written in the form $x = c_3 e^{-y}$ where $c_3 = 1/c_2$. Then $x = 0$ is a special case of this latter solution and need not be listed separately.

We say, and it is very rough language, that the general solution of (2) is (5) and (6). Particular solutions may be made up from this general solution; they may be drawn from (5) alone, from (6) alone, or conceivably pieced together by using (5) in some intervals and (6) in others. At a point where a solution from (5) is to be joined with a solution from (6), the slope must remain continuous, so (see Ex. 21 below) the piecing together must take place along the line $y = x$. Note (see Ex. 23) that the second derivative, which does not enter the differential equation, need not be continuous.

The existence of these three sets of particular solutions of (2), that is, solutions from (5), from (6), or from (5) and (6), leads to an interesting phenomenon in boundary value problems. Consider the problem of finding a solution of (2) such that the solution passes through the point $(-\frac{1}{2}, 2)$.

If the result is to be valid for the interval $-1 < x < -\frac{1}{4}$, there are two answers, which will be found in Ex. 24, following. If the result is to be valid for $-1 < x < \frac{1}{2}$, there is only one answer (Ex. 25), one of the two answers to Ex. 24. If the result is to be valid in $-1 < x < 2$, there is only one answer (Ex. 26), and it is different from either of the answers to Ex. 24.

Exercises

In Exs. 1–18, find the general solution in the sense of (5) and (6) above.

1. $x^2 p^2 - y^2 = 0$.   ANS. $y = c_1 x$, $xy = c_2$.

2. $xp^2 - (2x + 3y)p + 6y = 0$.   ANS. $y = c_1 x^3$, $y = 2x + c_2$.

3. $x^2 p^2 - 5xyp + 6y^2 = 0$.   ANS. $y = c_1 x^2$, $y = c_2 x^3$.

4. $x^2 p^2 + xp - y^2 - y = 0$.   ANS. $y = c_1 x$, $x(y + 1) = c_2$.

5. $xp^2 + (1 - x^2 y)p - xy = 0$.

ANS. $y = c_1 \exp\left(\frac{1}{2}x^2\right)$, $y = -\ln(c_2 x)$.

6. $p^2 - (x^2 y + 3)p + 3x^2 y = 0$.   ANS. $y = 3x + c_1$, $x^3 = 3\ln(c_2 y)$.

7. $xp^2 - (1 + xy)p + y = 0$.   ANS. $y = \ln(c_1 x)$, $x = \ln(c_2 y)$.

8. $p^2 - x^2 y^2 = 0$.   ANS. $x^2 = 2\ln(c_1 y)$, $x^2 = -2\ln(c_2 y)$.

9. $(x + y)^2 p^2 = y^2$.   ANS. $x = y\ln(c_1 y)$, $y(2x + y) = c_2$.

10. $yp^2 + (x - y^2)p - xy = 0$.   ANS. $x^2 + y^2 = c_1^2$, $y = c_2 e^x$.

11. $p^2 - xy(x + y)p + x^3 y^3 = 0$.

ANS. $y(x^2 + c_1) = -2$, $x^3 = 3\ln(c_2 y)$.

12. $(4x - y)p^2 + 6(x - y)p + 2x - 5y = 0$.

ANS. $x + y = c_1$, $(2x + y)^2 = c_2(y - x)$.

13. $(x - y)^2 p^2 = y^2$.   ANS. $x = -y\ln(c_1 y)$, $y(2x - y) = c_2$.

14. $xyp^2 + (xy^2 - 1)p - y = 0$.   ANS. $y^2 = 2\ln(c_1 x)$, $x = -\ln(c_2 y)$.

15. $(x^2 + y^2)^2 p^2 = 4x^2 y^2$.   ANS. $y^2 - x^2 = c_1 y$, $y(3x^2 + y^2) = c_2$.

16. $(y + x)^2 p^2 + (2y^2 + xy - x^2)p + y(y - x) = 0$.

ANS. $y^2 + 2xy = c_1$, $y^2 + 2xy - x^2 = c_2$.

17. $xy(x^2 + y^2)(p^2 - 1) = p(x^4 + x^2 y^2 + y^4)$.

ANS. $y^2(y^2 + 2x^2) = c_1$, $y^2 = 2x^2\ln(c_2 x)$.

18. $xp^3 - (x^2 + x + y)p^2 + (x^2 + xy + y)p - xy = 0$.

ANS. $y = c_1 x$, $y = x + c_2$, $x^2 = 2(y - c_3)$.

Exs. 19–26 refer to the example of this section. There the differential equation

(2) $xyp^2 + (x + y)p + 1 = 0$

was shown to have the general solution

(5) $y^2 = -2(x - c_1)$

and

(6) $y = -\ln(c_2 x).$

19. Show that of the family (5) above, the only curve that passes through the point $(1, 1)$ is $y = (3 - 2x)^{\frac{1}{2}}$ and that this solution is valid for $x < \frac{3}{2}.$

20. Show that of the family (6) above, the only curve that passes through the point $(1, 1)$ is $y = 1 - \ln x$ and that this solution is valid for $0 < x.$

21. Show that if a solution of (2) is to be pieced together from (5) and (6), then the slopes of the curves must be equal where the pieces join. Show that the pieces must therefore be joined at a point on the line $y = x.$

FIGURE 42

22. Show that the curve determined by

$$y = (3 - 2x)^{\frac{1}{2}} \quad \text{for } x \leqq 1,$$
$$y = 1 - \ln x \quad \text{for } 1 \leqq x$$

is a solution of equation (2) and is valid for all x. The interesting portion of this curve is shown in Figure 42.

23. Show for the solution given in Ex. 22 that y'' is not continuous at $x = 1$. Show that as $x \to 1^-$, $y'' \to -1$, and as $x \to 1^+$, $y'' \to +1.$

24. Find those solutions of (2) which are valid in $-1 < x < -\frac{1}{4}$ and each of which has its graph passing through the point $(-\frac{1}{2}, 2)$.
    ANS. $y = (3 - 2x)^{\frac{1}{2}}$; and $y = 2 - \ln 2 - \ln(-x).$

25. Find that solution of (2) which is valid for $-1 < x < \frac{1}{2}$ and has its graph passing through the point $(-\frac{1}{2}, 2)$. ANS. $y = (3 - 2x)^{\frac{1}{2}}.$

26. Find that solution of (2) which is valid for $-1 < x < 2$ and has its graph passing through the point $(-\frac{1}{2}, 2)$.
    ANS. $y = (3 - 2x)^{\frac{1}{2}}$ for $x \leqq 1,$
    $y = 1 - \ln x$ for $1 \leqq x.$

89. Singular solutions

Let us solve the differential equation

(1) $$y^2 p^2 - a^2 + y^2 = 0.$$

Here

$$yp = \pm \sqrt{a^2 - y^2},$$

so we may write

(2) $$\frac{y\,dy}{\sqrt{a^2 - y^2}} = dx,$$

or

(3) $$-\frac{y\,dy}{\sqrt{a^2 - y^2}} = dx,$$

or (if the division by $\sqrt{a^2 - y^2}$ cannot be effected)

(4) $$a^2 - y^2 = 0.$$

From (2) it follows that

(5) $$x = c_1 - \sqrt{a^2 - y^2},$$

while from (3) that

(6) $$x = c_2 + \sqrt{a^2 - y^2},$$

and from (4) that

(7) $$y = a \quad \text{or} \quad y = -a.$$

Graphically, the solutions (5) are left-hand semicircles with radius a and centered on the x-axis; the solutions (6) are right-hand semicircles of radius a, centered on the x-axis. We may combine (5) and (6) into

(8) $$(x - c)^2 + y^2 = a^2,$$

which is called the general solution of (1).

From either of equations (7) we get $p = 0$, so they too satisfy the differential equation (1). But neither of equations (7) is a special case of (8). Then $y = a$ and $y = -a$ are called singular solutions.

A *singular solution* of a nonlinear first-order differential equation is any solution that

(a) is not a special case of the general solution, and

(b) is, at each of its points, tangent to some element of the one-parameter family that is the general solution.

A linear equation cannot have a singular solution.

FIGURE 43

Figure 43 shows several elements of the family of circles given by equation (8) and also shows the two lines representing $y = a$ and $y = -a$. At each point of either line, the line is tangent to an element of the family of circles. A curve which at each of its points is tangent to an element of a one-parameter family of curves is called an *envelope* of that family.

90. The c-discriminant equation

Consider the differential equation of the first order,

$$(1) \qquad f(x, y, p) = 0; \quad p = \frac{dy}{dx},$$

in which the left member is a polynomial in x, y, and p. It may not be possible to factor the left member into factors which are themselves polynomials in x, y, and p. Then the equation is said to be irreducible.

The general solution of (1) will be a one-parameter family of curves,

$$(2) \qquad \varphi(x, y, c) = 0.$$

A singular solution, if it exists, for equation (1) must be an envelope of the family (2). Each point on the envelope is a point of tangency of the envelope with some element of the family (2) and is determined by the value of c that identifies that element of the family. Then the envelope has parametric equations, $x = x(c)$ and $y = y(c)$, with the c of equation (2) as the parameter. The functions $x(c)$ and $y(c)$ are as yet unknown to us. But the x and y of the point of contact must also satisfy equation (2), from which we get, by differentiation with respect to c, the equation

$$(3) \qquad \frac{\partial \varphi}{\partial x} \frac{dx}{dc} + \frac{\partial \varphi}{\partial y} \frac{dy}{dc} + \frac{\partial \varphi}{\partial c} = 0.$$

The slope of the envelope and the slope of the family element concerned must be equal at the point of contact. That slope can be determined by differentiating equation (2) with respect to x, keeping c constant. Thus it follows that

$$(4) \qquad \frac{\partial \varphi}{\partial x} + \frac{\partial \varphi}{\partial y} \frac{dy}{dx} = 0.$$

Equations (3) and (4) both hold at the point of contact and from them it follows that

$$(5) \qquad \frac{\partial \varphi}{\partial c} = 0.$$

We now have two equations, $\varphi = 0$ and $\dfrac{\partial \varphi}{\partial c} = 0$, which must be satisfied by x, y, and c. These two equations may be taken as the desired parametric equations. They contain any envelope which may exist for the original family of curves, $\varphi = 0$. Fortunately, there is no need for us to put these equations into the form $x = x(c)$, $y = y(c)$.

The equation that results from the elimination of c from the equations $\varphi = 0$ and $\dfrac{\partial \varphi}{\partial c} = 0$ is called the *c-discriminant equation** of the family $\varphi = 0$. It is a necessary and sufficient condition that the equation

$$(2) \qquad \varphi(x, y, c) = 0,$$

considered as an equation in c, have at least two of its roots equal.

There is nothing in our work to guarantee that the c-discriminant equation, or any part of it, will be a solution of the differential equation. To get the c-discriminant equation we need the general solution. During the process of obtaining the general solution, we find also the singular solution, if there is one.

91. The p-discriminant equation

Suppose that in the irreducible differential equation

$$(1) \qquad f(x, y, p) = 0$$

the polynomial f is of degree n in p. There will be n roots of equation (1),

---

* The c-discriminant equation may contain a locus of cusps of the elements of the general solution and a locus of nodes of those elements, as well as the envelope which aroused our interest in it.

each yielding a result of the form

$$(2) \qquad\qquad p = g(x, y).$$

If at a point (x_0, y_0) the equation (1) has, as an equation in p, all its roots distinct, then near (x_0, y_0) there will be n distinct equations of the type of equation (2). Near (x_0, y_0) the right members of these n equations will be single-valued and may satisfy the conditions of the existence theorem described in Chapter 17. But if at (x_0, y_0) equation (1) has at least two of its roots equal, then at least two of the n equations like (2) will have right members assuming the same value at (x_0, y_0). For such equations there is no region, no matter how small, surrounding (x_0, y_0) in which the right member is single-valued. Hence the existence theorem of Chapter 17 cannot be applied when equation (1) has two or more equal roots as an equation in p. Therefore we must give separate consideration to the locus of points (x, y) for which (1) has at least two of its roots equal.

The condition that equation (1) have at least two equal roots as an equation in p is that both $f = 0$ and $\dfrac{\partial f}{\partial p} = 0$. These two equations in the three variables x, y, and p are parametric equations of a curve in the xy-plane with p playing the role of parameter. The equation that results when p is eliminated from the parametric equations $f = 0$ and $\dfrac{\partial f}{\partial p} = 0$ is called the *p-discriminant equation*.

If an envelope of the general solution of $f = 0$ exists, it will be contained in the p-discriminant equation. No proof is included here.* For us the p-discriminant equation is useful in two ways. When a singular solution is obtained in the natural course of solving an equation, as occurs in Sections 92–94, the p-discriminant equation furnishes us with a check. If none of our methods of attack leads to a general solution, then the p-discriminant equation offers curves which may be particular (including singular) solutions of the differential equation. Then the p-discriminant equation should be tested for possible solutions of the differential equation. Such particular solutions make, of course, no contribution toward finding the general solution.

The p-discriminant equation may contain singular solutions, solutions that are not singular, and curves that are not solutions at all.

---

* For more detail on singular solutions and the discriminants see E. L. Ince, *Ordinary Differential Equations* (London: Longmans, Green and Co., 1927), pp. 82–92.

Exercises

1. For the quadratic equation

$$f = Ap^2 + Bp + C = 0,$$

with A, B, C functions of x and y, show that the p-discriminant obtained by eliminating p from $f = 0$ and $\dfrac{\partial f}{\partial p} = 0$ is the familiar equation

$$B^2 - 4AC = 0.$$

2. For the cubic $p^3 + Ap + B = 0$, show that the p-discriminant equation is $4A^3 + 27B^2 = 0$.

3. For the cubic $p^3 + Ap^2 + B = 0$, show that the p-discriminant equation is $B(4A^3 + 27B) = 0$.

4. Set up the condition that the equation $x^3p^2 + x^2yp + 4 = 0$ (Ex. 1, page 287) have equal roots as a quadratic in p. Compare with the singular solution $xy^2 = 16$.

5. Show that the condition that the equation $xyp^2 + (x + y)p + 1 = 0$ of the example of Section 88 have equal roots in p is $(x - y)^2 = 0$ and that the latter equation does not yield a solution of the differential equation. Was there a singular solution?

6. For the equation $y^2p^2 - a^2 + y^2 = 0$ of Section 89, find the condition for equal roots in p and compare with the singular solution.

7. For the differential equation of Ex. 6 show that the curve defined by

$$y = [a^2 - (x + 2a)^2]^{\frac{1}{2}} \quad \text{for } -3a < x \le -2a,$$
$$y = a \qquad\qquad\qquad \text{for } -2a \le x \le 2a,$$
$$y = [a^2 - (x - 2a)^2]^{\frac{1}{2}} \quad \text{for } \quad 2a \le x < 3a,$$

is a solution. Sketch the curve and show how it was pieced together from the general solution and the singular solution given in equations (5), (6), and (7) of Section 89.

In Ex. 8–16, obtain (a) the p-discriminant equation and (b) those solutions of the differential equation that are contained in the p-discriminant.

8. $xp^2 - 2yp + 4x = 0$.   ANS. (a) $y^2 - 4x^2 = 0$;
(b) $y = 2x$, $y = -2x$.

9. $3x^4p^2 - xp - y = 0$.   ANS. (a) $x^2(1 + 12x^2y) = 0$;
(b) $x = 0$, $12x^2y = -1$.

10. $p^2 - xp - y = 0$.   ANS. (a) $x^2 + 4y = 0$; (b) None.

11. $p^2 - xp + y = 0$.   ANS. (a) $x^2 - 4y = 0$; (b) $x^2 - 4y = 0$.

12. $p^2 + 4x^5p - 12x^4y = 0$.   ANS.   (a) $x^4(x^6 + 3y) = 0$; (b) $3y = -x^6$.

13. $4y^3p^2 - 4xp + y = 0$.   ANS.   (a) $(y^2 - x)(y^2 + x) = 0$;
    (b) Same as (a).

14. $4y^3p^2 + 4xp + y = 0$. See also Ex. 13.
    ANS.   (a) $(y^2 - x)(y^2 + x) = 0$;
    (b) None.

15. $p^3 + xp^2 - y = 0$.   ANS.   (a) $y(4x^3 - 27y) = 0$; (b) $y = 0$.

16. $y^4p^3 - 6xp + 2y = 0$.   ANS.   (a) $y^8(y^2 - 2x)(y^4 + 2xy^2 + 4x^2) = 0$;
    (b) $y = 0$, $y^2 = 2x$.

17. For the differential equation of Ex. 4 above, the general solution will
    be found to be $cxy + 4x + c^2 = 0$. Find the condition that this
    quadratic equation in c have equal roots. Compare that condition
    with the singular solution.

18. For the general solution

$$(x^2 - 1)c^2 - 2xyc + y^2 - 1 = 0$$

of Example (b), Section 93, find the condition that the equation have
equal roots when considered as a quadratic in c. Compare that condition with the singular solution given in that example.

19. Consider the differential equation $xp^2 - 3yp + 9x^2 = 0$ of Example
    (a), Section 92. Verify that the singular solution $y^2 = 4x^3$ is the
    envelope of the family of curves given by the general solution

$$x^3 = c(y - c).$$

That is, show that the last two equations have the common solution
$x = c^{\frac{1}{3}}, y = 2c$, counted twice. Then obtain the slopes of the two curves
at the point of intersection. Each slope turns out to be $3c^{\frac{1}{3}}$.

92. Eliminating the dependent variable

Suppose the equation

(1) $$f(x, y, p) = 0; p = \frac{dy}{dx},$$

is of a form such that we can readily solve it for the dependent variable y
and write

(2) $$y = g(x, p).$$

We can differentiate equation (2) with respect to x and, since $\frac{dy}{dx} = p$,
get an equation

$$(3) \qquad h\left(x, p, \frac{dp}{dx}\right) = 0$$

involving only x and p. If we can solve equation (3), we will have two equations relating x, y, and p, namely, equation (2) and the solution of (3). These together form parametric equations of the solution of (1) with p now considered a parameter. Or, if p be eliminated between (2) and the solution of (3), then a solution in the nonparametric form is obtained.

EXAMPLE (a): Solve the differential equation

$$(4) \qquad xp^2 - 3yp + 9x^2 = 0.$$

Rewrite (4) as

$$(5) \qquad 3y = xp + 9x^2/p.$$

Then differentiate both members of (5) with respect to x, using the fact that $\dfrac{dy}{dx} = p$, thus getting

$$3p = p + \frac{18x}{p} + \left(x - \frac{9x^2}{p^2}\right)\frac{dp}{dx},$$

or

$$(6) \qquad 2p\left(1 - \frac{9x}{p^2}\right) = x\left(1 - \frac{9x}{p^2}\right)\frac{dp}{dx}.$$

From (6) it follows that either

$$(7) \qquad 1 - \frac{9x}{p^2} = 0$$

or

$$(8) \qquad 2p = x\frac{dp}{dx}.$$

First consider (8), which leads to

$$2\frac{dx}{x} = \frac{dp}{p}$$

so

$$(9) \qquad p = cx^2.$$

Therefore equations (4) and (9), with p as a parameter, constitute a solution of (4) looked upon as a differential equation with $p = dy/dx$.

In this example it is easy to eliminate p from equations (4) and (9), so we perform that elimination. The result is

$$x \cdot c^2x^4 - 3y \cdot cx^2 + 9x^2 = 0.$$

Disregarding for the moment the possibility that $x = 0$, we can write our solution as

$$c^2x^3 - 3cy + 9 = 0,$$

or

$$3cy = c^2x^3 + 9.$$

Now put $c = 3k$ to get

(10) $$ky = k^2x^3 + 1.$$

Equation (10) with k as an arbitrary constant is called the general solution of the differential equation (4).

It can be seen, rewriting (4) in the form

$$x(dy)^2 - 3y(dy)(dx) + 9x^2(dx)^2 = 0,$$

that $x = 0$ is also a solution of the differential equation. This solution can be fitted into the general solution by a simple device. In equation (10) replace k by $1/c_1$, thus obtaining

(11) $$c_1y = x^3 + c_1^2.$$

Putting $c_1 = 0$ in (11) yields the solution $x = 0$.

We have yet to deal with equation (7). Note that (7) is an algebraic relation between x and p in contrast to the differential relation (8) which we have already used. We reason that the elimination of p from (7) and (4) may lead to a solution of the differential equation (4) and that the solution will not involve an arbitrary constant. From (7) it is seen that $p = 3x^{\frac{1}{2}}$ or $p = -3x^{\frac{1}{2}}$. Either of these expressions for p may be substituted into (4) and will lead to

(12) $$y^2 = 4x^3.$$

It is not difficult to show that equation (12) is a solution of the differential equation. This solution is not a special case of the general solution (10) or (11). It is a singular solution. Equation (12) has for its graph the envelope of the family of curves given by equation (11). The solution (12) is also easily obtained from the p-discriminant equation.

EXAMPLE (b): Solve the differential equation

(13) $$xp^2 - yp - x = 0.$$

The equation is readily solved for y, yielding

$$y = xp - \frac{x}{p}.$$

Then differentiation with respect to x gives

$$p = p - \frac{1}{p} + \left(x + \frac{x}{p^2}\right)\frac{dp}{dx},$$

or

$$\frac{1}{p} = x\left(1 + \frac{1}{p^2}\right)\frac{dp}{dx}.$$

Thus we are led to the differential equation

$$\frac{dx}{x} = \frac{p^2 + 1}{p}\,dp,$$

from which

$$\ln x = \tfrac{1}{2}p^2 + \ln p + \ln c,$$

or

(14) $$x = cp \exp\left(\tfrac{1}{2}p^2\right).$$

From equation (13) we get

$$y = x(p^2 - 1)/p.$$

Therefore, using (14), we find y in the form

(15) $$y = c(p^2 - 1)\exp\left(\tfrac{1}{2}p^2\right).$$

Equations (14) and (15) are parametric equations of the general solution of the original differential equation. In sketching a curve of the family of solutions, for each value of p inserted in (14) and (15) a pair of values x and y is obtained. Thus for each p used we get a point on the desired curve.

The parameter p could have been eliminated by solving the quadratic (13) for p and substituting in (14). The result would be more difficult to sketch than the same curve in parametric form, (14) and (15).

The student should use the p-discriminant equation to show that equation (13) has no singular solution.

It frequently happens, as exhibited in answers to some of the exercises below that it is inconvenient, even out of the question, to obtain y in terms of p and c alone. It may be best to leave the solution in the form

(16) $$\varphi(x, p) = 0$$

and

(17) $$y = g(x, p).$$

Then, in computation we would choose p and determine x from equation (16), after which y would be found from equation (17), using the values of both x and p.

93. Clairaut's equation

Any differential equation of the form

(1) $$y = px + f(p),$$

where $f(p)$ contains neither x nor y explicitly, can be solved at once by the method of Section 92. Equation (1) is called *Clairaut's equation*.

Let us differentiate both members of (1) with respect to x, thus getting

$$p = p + [x + f'(p)]p',$$

(2) $$[x + f'(p)] \frac{dp}{dx} = 0.$$

Then either

(3) $$\frac{dp}{dx} = 0$$

or

(4) $$x + f'(p) = 0.$$

The solution of the differential equation (3) is, of course, $p = c$, where c is an arbitrary constant. Returning to the differential equation (1), we can now write its general solution as

(5) $$y = cx + f(c),$$

a result easily verified by direct substitution into the differential equation (1). Note that (5) is the equation of a family of straight lines.

Now consider equation (4). Since $f(p)$ and $f'(p)$ are known functions of p, equations (4) and (1) together constitute a set of parametric equations giving x and y in terms of the parameter p. Indeed, from equation (4) it follows that

(6) $$x = -f'(p),$$

which, combined with equation (1), yields

(7) $$y = f(p) - pf'(p).$$

If $f(p)$ is not a linear function of p and not a constant, it can be shown (Exs. 1 and 2 below) that (6) and (7) are parametric equations of a non-linear solution of the differential equation (1). Since the general solution (5) represents a straight line for each value of c, the solution (6) and (7) cannot be a special case of (5); it is a singular solution.

EXAMPLE (a): Solve the differential equation

(8) $$y = px + p^3.$$

Since (8) is a Clairaut equation, we can write its general solution

$$y = cx + c^3$$

at once.

Then using (6) and (7) we obtain the parametric equations

(9) $$x = -3p^2, \; y = -2p^3,$$

of the singular solution. The parameter p may be eliminated from equa-

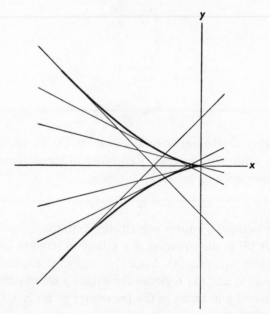

FIGURE 44

tions (9), yielding the form

(10) $$27y^2 = -4x^3$$

for the singular solution. See Figure 44.

EXAMPLE (b): Solve the differential equation

(11) $$(x^2 - 1)p^2 - 2xyp + y^2 - 1 = 0.$$

Rewrite (11) as

$$x^2p^2 - 2xyp + y^2 - 1 - p^2 = 0.$$

Then it is clear that the equation is of the form

(12) $$(y - xp)^2 - 1 - p^2 = 0$$

and so could be broken up into two equations, each of Clairaut's form. Then the general solution of (11) is obtained by replacing p everywhere in it by an arbitrary constant c. That is,

(13) $$(x^2 - 1)c^2 - 2xyc + y^2 - 1 = 0$$

is the general solution of (11). The solution (13) is composed of two families of straight lines,

(14) $$y = c_1x + \sqrt{1 + c_1{}^2}$$

and

(15) $$y = c_2x - \sqrt{1 + c_2{}^2}.$$

From the p-discriminant equation for (11) we obtain at once the singular solution

(16) $$x^2 + y^2 = 1.$$

Exercises

1. Let α be a parameter and prove that if $f''(\alpha)$ exists, then

   (17) $$x = -f'(\alpha),\ y = f(\alpha) - \alpha f'(\alpha)$$

   is a solution of the differential equation $y = px + f(p)$. Hint: use dx and dy to get p in terms of α and then show that $y - px - f(p)$ vanishes identically.

2. Prove that if $f''(\alpha) \neq 0$, then (17) above is not a special case of the general solution $y = cx + f(c)$. Hint: show that the slope of the graph of one solution depends upon x whereas the slope of the graph of the other does not depend upon x.

In Exs. 3–30, find the general solution and also the singular solution, if it exists.

3. $p^2 + x^3p - 2x^2y = 0$.   ANS. $c^2 + cx^2 = 2y$; sing. sol., $8y = -x^4$.

4. $p^2 + 4x^5p - 12x^4y = 0.$

ANS. $12y = c(c + 4x^3)$; sing. sol., $3y = -x^6.$

5. $2xp^3 - 6yp^2 + x^4 = 0.$ ANS. $2c^3x^3 = 1 - 6c^2y$; sing. sol., $2y = x^2.$

6. $p^2 - xp + y = 0.$ ANS. $y = cx - c^2$; sing. sol., $x^2 = 4y.$

7. $y = px + kp^2.$ ANS. $y = cx + kc^2$; sing. sol., $x^2 = -4ky.$

8. $x^8p^2 + 3xp + 9y = 0.$

ANS. $x^3(y + c^2) + c = 0$; sing. sol., $4x^6y = 1.$

9. $x^4p^2 + 2x^3yp - 4 = 0.$ ANS. $x^2(1 + cy) = c^2.$

10. $xp^2 - 2yp + 4x = 0.$

ANS. $x^2 = c(y - c)$; sing. sol., $y = 2x$ and $y = -2x.$

11. $3x^4p^2 - xp - y = 0.$ ANS. $xy = c(3cx - 1)$; sing. sol., $12x^2y = -1.$

12. $xp^2 + (x - y)p + 1 - y = 0.$

ANS. $xc^2 + (x - y)c + 1 - y = 0$; sing. sol., $(x + y)^2 = 4x.$

13. $p(xp - y + k) + a = 0.$

ANS. $c(xc - y + k) + a = 0$; sing. sol., $(y - k)^2 = 4ax.$

14. $x^6p^3 - 3xp - 3y = 0.$ ANS. $3xy = c(xc^2 - 3)$; sing. sol., $9x^3y^2 = 4.$

15. $y = x^6p^3 - xp.$ ANS. $xy = c(c^2x - 1)$; sing. sol., $27x^3y^2 = 4.$

16. $xp^4 - 2yp^3 + 12x^3 = 0.$

ANS. $2c^3y = c^4x^2 + 12$; sing. sol., $3y^2 = \pm 8x^3.$

17. $xp^3 - yp^2 + 1 = 0.$

ANS. $xc^3 - yc^2 + 1 = 0$; sing. sol., $4y^3 = 27x^2.$

18. $y = px + p^n$, for $n \neq 0$, $n \neq 1.$

ANS. $y = cx + c^n$; sing. sol., $\left(\dfrac{x}{n}\right)^n = -\left(\dfrac{y}{n - 1}\right)^{n-1}.$

19. $p^2 - xp - y = 0.$ ANS. $3x = 2p + cp^{-\frac{1}{2}}$ and $3y = p^2 - cp^{\frac{1}{2}}.$

20. $2p^3 + xp - 2y = 0.$ ANS. $x = 2p(3p + c)$ and $y = p^2(4p + c).$

21. $2p^2 + xp - 2y = 0.$ ANS. $x = 4p \ln (pc)$ and $y = p^2[1 + 2 \ln (pc)].$

22. $p^3 + 2xp - y = 0.$

ANS. $4x = -3p^2 + cp^{-2}$ and $2y = -p^3 + cp^{-1}.$

23. $4xp^2 - 3yp + 3 = 0.$

ANS. $2x = 3p^{-2} + cp^{-4}$ and $3y = 9p^{-1} + 2cp^{-3}.$

24. $p^3 - xp + 2y = 0.$ ANS. $x = p(c - 3p)$ and $2y = p^2(c - 4p).$

25. $5p^2 + 6xp - 2y = 0.$ ANS. $p^3(x + p)^2 = c$ and $2y = 6xp + 5p^2.$

26. $2xp^2 + (2x - y)p + 1 - y = 0.$

ANS. $p^2x = (1 + p)^{-1} + \ln [c(1 + p)]$ and
$py = 1 + (1 + p)^{-1} + 2 \ln [c(1 + p)].$

27. $5p^2 + 3xp - y = 0.$ ANS. $p^3(x + 2p)^2 = c$ and $y = 3xp + 5p^2.$

28. $p^2 + 3xp - y = 0.$ ANS. $p^3(5x + 2p)^2 = c$ and $y = 3xp + p^2.$

29. $y = xp + x^3p^2.$ ANS. $x^2 = cp^{-\frac{1}{3}} - 2p^{-1}$ and $y = xp + x^3p^2.$

30. $8y = 3x^2 + p^2.$ ANS. $(p - 3x)^3 = c(p - x)$ and $8y = 3x^2 + p^2.$

94. Eliminating the independent variable

Suppose that a differential equation

$$(1) \qquad f(x, y, p) = 0; \; p = \frac{dy}{dx},$$

can readily be solved for the independent variable x. Then we can proceed very much as we did in Section 92, but this time differentiating with respect to y and using the fact that

$$\frac{dx}{dy} = \frac{1}{p}.$$

This is, of course, nothing new at all. Since (1) is a first-order equation, the roles of independent and dependent variable can be interchanged at will using the relation

$$\frac{dy}{dx} = \left(\frac{dx}{dy} \right)^{-1}.$$

EXAMPLE: Solve the differential equation

$$(2) \qquad yp^2 - xp + 2y = 0.$$

First solve for x, obtaining

$$(3) \qquad x = yp + \frac{2y}{p},$$

and then differentiate both members of equation (3) with respect to y. The resulting relation is

$$\frac{1}{p} = p + \frac{2}{p} + \left(y - \frac{2y}{p^2} \right) \frac{dp}{dy}$$

or

$$\frac{1}{p} + p + y \left(1 - \frac{2}{p^2} \right) \frac{dp}{dy} = 0.$$

Therefore we are led to the equation

$$(4) \qquad \frac{dy}{y} + \frac{p^2 - 2}{p(1 + p^2)} dp = 0,$$

from which

$$\frac{dy}{y} + \frac{3p \, dp}{1 + p^2} - \frac{2 \, dp}{p} = 0.$$

Hence
$$\ln y = -\tfrac{3}{2} \ln (1 + p^2) + 2 \ln p + \ln c,$$
so

(5)
$$y = cp^2(1 + p^2)^{-\frac{3}{2}}.$$

From equation (3) it follows that
$$x = p^{-1}y(p^2 + 2).$$

Therefore, using (5) we may write

(6)
$$x = cp(p^2 + 2)(1 + p^2)^{-\frac{3}{2}}.$$

Equations (5) and (6) are a set of parametric equations for the general solution of (2). There is no singular solution of (2).

Exercises

In Exs. 1–10, find the general solution and the singular solution in non-parametric form. That is, eliminate the parameter after obtaining the solutions in parametric form.

1. $xp^2 + yp = 3y^4$.   ANS. $3y = c(1 + cxy)$; sing. sol., $12xy^2 = -1$.
2. $9x^2p^2 + 3yp + y^8 = 0$. ANS. $c^2xy^3 + c + y^3 = 0$; sing. sol., $4xy^6 = 1$.
3. $p^2 + xy^2p + y^3 = 0$.   ANS. $cy(x - c) = 1$; sing. sol., $x^2y = 4$.
4. $4xp^2 + 4yp - y^4 = 0$.   ANS. $y(c^2x - 1) = 2c$; sing. sol., $xy^2 = -1$.
5. $4yp^2 - 2xp + y = 0$.   ANS. $cx = y^2 + c^2$; sing. sols., $x = \pm 2y$.
6. $9p^2 + 12xy^4p + 4y^5 = 0$.

   ANS. $c^2y^3 + 4cxy^3 + 4 = 0$; sing. sol., $x^2y^3 = 1$.
7. $2xy^2p^2 - y^3p - 1 = 0$.   ANS. $2c^2x = cy^2 + 1$; sing. sol., $y^4 = -8x$.
8. $p^2 + 2xy^3p + y^4 = 0$.   ANS. $4cy^2(x - c) = 1$; sing. sol., $xy = -1$.
9. $9y^2p^2 - 3xp + y = 0$.   ANS. $y^3 = c(x - c)$; sing. sol., $x^2 = 4y^3$.
10. $y^4p^3 - 6xp + 2y = 0$. ANS. $y^3 = 18c(x - 6c^2)$; sing. sol., $y^2 = 2x$.

In Exs. 11–15, find the general solution in parametric form.

11. $xp^2 - yp - y = 0$.   ANS. $x = c(p + 1)e^p$ and $y = cp^2e^p$.
12. $y^2p^3 - xp + y = 0$.   ANS. $y = cp^{-1} - \tfrac{1}{4}p^{-3}$ and $px = y(yp^3 + 1)$.
13. $yp^2 - xp + y = 0$.

   ANS. $x = c(p^{-2} + 1)e^{-1/(2p^2)}$ and $y = cp^{-1}e^{-1/(2p^2)}$.
14. $yp^3 - 3xp + 3y = 0$.

   ANS. $\ln y = c - p^{-3} - 2\ln p$ and $3px = y(p^3 + 3)$.
15. $y^3p^3 - xp + y = 0$.

   ANS. $5y^2 = cp^{-\frac{5}{2}} - 2p^{-3}$ and $5px = y(3 + cp^{\frac{5}{2}})$.

Miscellaneous Exercises

1. $x^3p^2 + x^2yp + 4 = 0$. ANS. $cxy + 4x + c^2 = 0$; sing. sol., $xy^2 = 16$.

2. $6xp^2 - (3x + 2y)p + y = 0$. ANS. $y^3 = c_1x$, $2y = x + c_2$.

3. $9p^2 + 3xy^4p + y^5 = 0$. ANS. $cy^3(x - c) = 1$; sing. sol., $x^2y^3 = 4$.

4. $4y^3p^2 - 4xp + y = 0$. ANS. $y^4 = 4c(x - c)$; sing. sol., $y^2 = x$.

5. $x^6p^2 - 2xp - 4y = 0$. ANS. $x^2(y - c^2) = c$; sing. sol., $4x^4y = -1$.

6. $5p^2 + 6xp - 2y = 0$. ANS. $x = cp^{-\frac{3}{2}} - p$ and $2y = 6cp^{-\frac{1}{2}} - p^2$.

7. Do Ex. 6 by another method.

8. $y^2p^2 - y(x + 1)p + x = 0$. ANS. $x^2 - y^2 = c_1$, $y^2 = 2(x - c_2)$.

9. $4x^5p^2 + 12x^4yp + 9 = 0$. ANS. $x^3(2cy - 1) = c^2$; sing. sol., $x^3y^2 = 1$.

10. $4y^2p^3 - 2xp + y = 0$.

ANS. $y^2 = 2c(x - 2c^2)$; sing. sol., $8x^3 = 27y^4$.

11. $p^4 + xp - 3y = 0$. ANS. $5x = 4p^3 + cp^{\frac{1}{2}}$ and $15y = 9p^4 + cp^{\frac{3}{2}}$.

12. Do Ex. 11 by another method.

13. $xp^2 + (k - x - y)p + y = 0$, the equation of Ex. 5, p. 13.

ANS. $xc^2 + (k - x - y)c + y = 0$;

sing. sol., $(x - y)^2 - 2k(x + y) + k^2 = 0$.

14. $x^2p^3 - 2xyp^2 + y^2p + 1 = 0$.

ANS. $x^2c^3 - 2xyc^2 + y^2c + 1 = 0$; sing. sol., $27x = -4y^3$.

15. $16xp^2 + 8yp + y^6 = 0$. ANS. $y^2(c^2x + 1) = 2c$; sing. sol., $xy^4 = 1$.

16. $xp^2 - (x^2 + 1)p + x = 0$. ANS. $x^2 = 2(y - c_1)$, $y = \ln(c_2x)$.

17. $p^3 - 2xp - y = 0$. ANS. $8x = 3p^2 + cp^{-\frac{3}{2}}$ and $4y = p^3 - cp^{\frac{1}{2}}$.

18. Do Ex. 17 by another method.

19. $9xy^4p^2 - 3y^5p - 1 = 0$. ANS. $cy^3 = c^2x - 1$; sing. sol., $y^6 = -4x$.

20. $x^2p^2 - (2xy + 1)p + y^2 + 1 = 0$.

ANS. $x^2c^2 - (2xy + 1)c + y^2 + 1 = 0$; sing. sol., $4x^2 - 4xy - 1 = 0$.

21. $x^6p^2 = 8(2y + xp)$. ANS. $c^2x^2 = 8(2x^2y - c)$; sing. sol., $x^4y = -1$.

22. $x^2p^2 = (x - y)^2$. ANS. $x(x - 2y) = c_1$, $y = -x \ln(c_2x)$.

23. $xp^3 - 2yp^2 + 4x^2 = 0$. See Ex. 10 above.

ANS. $x^2 = 4c(y - 8c^2)$; sing. sol., $8y^3 = 27x^4$.

24. $(p + 1)^2(y - px) = 1$.

ANS. $(c + 1)^2(y - cx) = 1$; sing. sol., $4(x + y)^3 = 27x^2$.

25. $p^3 - p^2 + xp - y = 0$.

ANS. $y = cx + c^3 - c^2$; sing. sol. with parametric equations,

$x = 2\alpha - 3\alpha^2$ and $y = \alpha^2 - 2\alpha^3$.

26. $xp^2 + y(1 - x)p - y^2 = 0$. ANS. $xy = c_1$, $x = \ln(c_2y)$.

27. $yp^2 - (x + y)p + y = 0$.

ANS. $py = c \exp(p^{-1})$ and $px = y(p^2 - p + 1)$; sing. sol., $y = x$.

CHAPTER 19

Special Equations of Order Two

95. Dependent variable missing

Consider a second-order equation,

$$(1) \qquad f(x, y', y'') = 0,$$

which does not contain the dependent variable y explicitly. Let us put

$$y' = p.$$

Then

$$y'' = \frac{dp}{dx}$$

and equation (1) may be replaced by

$$(2) \qquad f\left(x, p, \frac{dp}{dx}\right) = 0,$$

an equation of order one in p. If we can find p from equation (2), then y can be obtained from $y' = p$ by an integration.

EXAMPLE: Solve the equation

$$(3) \qquad xy'' - (y')^3 - y' = 0$$

of Example (b), page 13.

Since y does not appear explicitly in the differential equation (3), put $y' = p$. Then

$$y'' = \frac{dp}{dx},$$

so equation (3) becomes

$$x\frac{dp}{dx} - p^3 - p = 0.$$

Separation of variables leads to

$$\frac{dp}{p(p^2 + 1)} = \frac{dx}{x}$$

or

$$\frac{dp}{p} - \frac{p\,dp}{p^2 + 1} = \frac{dx}{x},$$

from which

(4) $$\ln p - \tfrac{1}{2}\ln(p^2 + 1) + \ln c_1 = \ln x$$

follows.

Equation (4) yields

(5) $$c_1 p(p^2 + 1)^{-\frac{1}{2}} = x,$$

which we wish to solve for p. From (5) we conclude that

$$c_1{}^2 p^2 = x^2(1 + p^2),$$

$$p^2 = \frac{x^2}{c_1{}^2 - x^2}.$$

But $p = y'$, so we have

(6) $$dy = \pm\frac{x\,dx}{\sqrt{c_1{}^2 - x^2}}.$$

The solution of (6) is

$$y - c_2 = \mp(c_1{}^2 - x^2)^{\frac{1}{2}},$$

or

(7) $$x^2 + (y - c_2)^2 = c_1{}^2.$$

Equation (7) is the desired general solution of the differential equation (3). Note that in dividing by p early in the work we might have discarded the solutions $y = k\,(p = 0)$, where k is constant. But (7) can be put in the form

(8) $$c_3(x^2 + y^2) + c_4 y + 1 = 0,$$

with new arbitrary constants c_3 and c_4. Then the choice $c_3 = 0, c_4 = -1/k$ yields the solution $y = k$.

96. Independent variable missing

A second-order equation

$$(1) \qquad\qquad f(y, y', y'') = 0$$

in which the independent variable x does not appear explicitly can be reduced to a first-order equation in y and y'. Put

$$y' = p,$$

then

$$y'' = \frac{dp}{dx} = \frac{dy}{dx}\frac{dp}{dy} = p\frac{dp}{dy},$$

so equation (1) becomes

$$(2) \qquad\qquad f\left(y, p, p\frac{dp}{dy}\right) = 0.$$

We try to determine p in terms of y from equation (2) and then substitute the result into $y' = p$.

EXAMPLE: Solve the equation

$$(3) \qquad\qquad yy'' + (y')^2 + 1 = 0$$

of Ex. 8, page 14.

Since the independent variable does not appear explicitly in equation (3), we put $y' = p$ and obtain

$$y'' = p\frac{dp}{dy}$$

as before. Then equation (3) becomes

$$(4) \qquad\qquad yp\frac{dp}{dy} + p^2 + 1 = 0,$$

in which the variables p and y are easily separated.

From (4) it follows that

$$\frac{p\,dp}{p^2 + 1} + \frac{dy}{y} = 0,$$

from which

$$\tfrac{1}{2}\ln(p^2 + 1) + \ln y = \ln c_1,$$

so

$$(5) \qquad\qquad p^2 + 1 = c_1{}^2 y^{-2}.$$

We solve equation (5) for p and find that

$$p = \pm \frac{(c_1{}^2 - y^2)^{\frac{1}{2}}}{y}.$$

Therefore

$$\frac{dy}{dx} = \pm \frac{(c_1{}^2 - y^2)^{\frac{1}{2}}}{y}$$

or

$$\pm y(c_1{}^2 - y^2)^{-\frac{1}{2}}\, dy = dx.$$

Then

$$\mp (c_1{}^2 - y^2)^{\frac{1}{2}} = x - c_2.$$

from which we obtain the final result

$$(x - c_2)^2 + y^2 = c_1{}^2.$$

Exercises

1. $y'' = x(y')^3$.   ANS. $x = c_1 \sin (y + c_2)$.

2. $x^2 y'' + (y')^2 - 2xy' = 0$; when $x = 2$, $y = 5$ and $y' = -4$.
     ANS. $y = \frac{1}{2}x^2 + 3x - 3 + 9 \ln (3 - x)$.

3. $x^2 y'' + (y')^2 - 2xy' = 0$; when $x = 2$, $y = 5$ and $y' = 2$.
     ANS. $x^2 = 2(y - 3)$.

4. $yy'' + (y')^2 = 0$.   ANS.   See Ex. 20, page 14.

5. $y^2 y'' + (y')^3 = 0$.   ANS. $x = c_1 y - \ln (c_2 y)$.

6. $(y + 1)y'' = (y')^2$.   ANS. $y + 1 = c_2 e^{c_1 x}$.

7. $2ay'' + (y')^3 = 0$.   ANS. $(y - c_2)^2 = 4a(x - c_1)$.

8. Do Ex. 7 by another method.

9. $xy'' = y' + x^5$; when $x = 1$, $y = \frac{1}{2}$ and $y' = 1$.
     ANS. $24y = x^6 + 9x^2 + 2$.

10. $xy'' + y' + x = 0$; when $x = 2$, $y = -1$ and $y' = -\frac{1}{2}$.
     ANS. $y = -\frac{1}{4}x^2 + \ln (\frac{1}{2}x)$.

11. $y'' = 2y(y')^3$.   ANS. $y^3 = 3(c_2 - x - c_1 y)$.

12. $yy'' + (y')^3 - (y')^2 = 0$.   ANS. $x = y - c_1 \ln (c_2 y)$.

13. $y'' + \beta^2 y = 0$. Check your result by solving the equation in two ways.

14. $yy'' + (y')^3 = 0$.   ANS. $x = c_1 + y \ln (c_2 y)$.

15. $y'' \cos x = y'$.   ANS. $y = c_2 + c_1 \ln (1 - \sin x)$.

16. $y'' = x(y')^2$; when $x = 2$, $y = \frac{1}{4}\pi$ and $y' = -\frac{1}{4}$.   ANS. $x = 2 \cot y$.

17. $y'' = x(y')^2$; when $x = 0$, $y = 1$ and $y' = \frac{1}{2}$.
     ANS. $y = 1 + \frac{1}{2} \ln \dfrac{2 + x}{2 - x}.$

18. $y'' = -e^{-2y}$; when $x = 3$, $y = 0$ and $y' = 1$.   ANS. $y = \ln (x - 2)$.

19. $y'' = -e^{-2y}$; when $x = 3$, $y = 0$ and $y' = -1$.

ANS. $y = \ln (4 - x)$.

20. $2y'' = \sin 2y$; when $x = 0$, $y = \pi/2$ and $y' = 1$.

ANS. $x = -\ln (\csc y + \cot y)$.

21. $2y'' = \sin 2y$; when $x = 0$, $y = -\pi/2$ and $y' = 1$.

ANS. $x = \ln (-\csc y - \cot y)$.

22. Show that if you can perform the integrations encountered, then you can solve any equation of the form $y'' = f(y)$.

23. $x^3 y'' - x^2 y' = 3 - x^2$.   ANS. $y = x^{-1} + x + c_1 x^2 + c_2$.

24. $y'' = (y')^2$.   ANS. $y = -\ln [c_2(c_1 - x)]$; or $x = c_1 + c_3 e^{-y}$.

25. $y'' = e^x (y')^2$.   ANS. $c_1 y + c_2 = -\ln (c_1 e^{-x} - 1)$.

26. $2y'' = (y')^3 \sin 2x$; when $x = 0$, $y = 1$ and $y' = 1$.

ANS. $y = 1 + \ln (\sec x + \tan x)$.

27. $x^2 y'' + (y')^2 = 0$.   ANS. $c_1^2 y = c_1 x + \ln [c_2(c_1 x - 1)]$.

28. $y'' = 1 + (y')^2$.   ANS. $e^y \cos (x + c_1) = c_2$.

29. Do Ex. 28 by another method.

30. $y'' = [1 + (y')^2]^{\frac{3}{2}}$. Solve in three ways, by considering the geometric significance of the equation, and by the methods of this chapter.

31. $yy'' = (y')^2[1 - y' \sin y - yy' \cos y]$.   ANS. $x = c_1 \ln (c_2 y) - \cos y$.

32. $(1 + y^2)y'' + (y')^3 + y' = 0$.

ANS. $x = c_2 + c_1 y - (1 + c_1^2) \ln (y + c_1)$.

33. $[yy'' + 1 + (y')^2]^2 = [1 + (y')^2]^3$.   ANS. $(y - c_1)^2 + (x - c_2)^2 = c_1^2$.

34. $x^2 y'' = y'(2x - y')$; when $x = -1$, $y = 5$ and $y' = 1$.

ANS. $2y - 1 = (x - 2)^2 + 8 \ln (x + 2)$.

35. $x^2 y'' = y'(3x - 2y')$.   ANS. $2y = x^2 + c_2 - c_1 \ln (x^2 + c_1)$.

36. $xy'' = y'(2 - 3xy')$.   ANS. $3y = c_2 + \ln (x^3 + c_1)$.

37. $x^4 y'' = y'(y' + x^3)$; when $x = 1$, $y = 2$ and $y' = 1$.

ANS. $y = 1 + x^2 - \ln \left(\dfrac{1 + x^2}{2} \right)$.

38. $y'' = 2x + (x^2 - y')^2$.   ANS. $3y = x^3 + c_2 - 3 \ln (x + c_1)$.

39. $(y'')^2 - 2y'' + (y')^2 - 2xy' + x^2 = 0$; when $x = 0$, $y = \frac{1}{2}$ and $y' = 1$.

ANS. $2y = 1 + x^2 + 2 \sin x$.

40. $(y'')^2 - xy'' + y' = 0$.

ANS.   General solution: $2y = c_1 x^2 - 2c_1^2 x + c_2$;
family of singular solutions: $12y = x^3 + k$.

41. $(y'')^3 = 12y'(xy'' - 2y')$.

ANS.   General solution: $y = c_1(x - c_1)^3 + c_2$;
family of singular solutions: $9y = x^4 + k$.

42. $3yy'y'' = (y')^3 - 1$.   ANS. $27c_1(y + c_1)^2 = 8(x + c_2)^3$.

43. $4y(y')^2 y'' = (y')^4 + 3$.   ANS. $256c_1(y - c_1)^3 = 243(x - c_2)^4$.

97. The catenary

Let a cable of uniformly distributed weight w (lb. per ft.) be suspended between two supports at points A and B as indicated in Figure 45. The cable will sag and there will be a lowest point V as indicated in the figure. We wish to determine the curve formed by the suspended cable. That curve is called the *catenary*.

FIGURE 45

Choose coordinate axes as shown in Figure 46, the y-axis vertical through the point V and the x-axis horizontal and passing at a distance y_0 (to be chosen later) below V. Let s represent length (ft.) of the cable

FIGURE 46

measured from V to the variable point P with coordinates (x, y). Then the portion of the cable from V to P is subject to the three forces shown in Figure 46. Those forces are: (a) the gravitational force ws (lb.) acting downward through the center of gravity of the portion of the cable from V to P, (b) the tension T_1 (lb.) acting tangentially at P, and (c) the tension T_2 (lb.) acting horizontally (again tangentially) at V. The tension T_1 is a variable; the tension T_2 is constant.

Since equilibrium is assumed, the algebraic sum of the vertical components of these forces is zero and the algebraic sum of the horizontal components of these forces is also zero. Therefore, if θ is the angle of inclination, from the horizontal, of the tangent to the curve at the point (x, y), we have

(1) $$T_1 \sin \theta - ws = 0$$

and

(2) $$T_1 \cos \theta - T_2 = 0.$$

But tan θ is the slope of the curve of the cable, so

(3) $$\tan \theta = \frac{dy}{dx}.$$

We may eliminate the variable tension T_1 from equations (1) and (2) and obtain

(4) $$\tan \theta = \frac{ws}{T_2}.$$

The constant T_2/w has the dimension of a length. Put $T_2/w = a$ (ft.). Then equation (4) becomes

(5) $$\tan \theta = \frac{s}{a}.$$

From equations (3) and (5) we see that

(6) $$\frac{s}{a} = \frac{dy}{dx}.$$

Now we know from calculus that since s is the length of arc of the curve, then

(7) $$\frac{ds}{dx} = \sqrt{1 + \left(\frac{dy}{dx}\right)^2}.$$

From (6) we get $\dfrac{1}{a}\dfrac{ds}{dx} = \dfrac{d^2y}{dx^2}$, so the elimination of s yields the differential equation

(8) $$\frac{d^2y}{dx^2} = \frac{1}{a}\sqrt{1 + \left(\frac{dy}{dx}\right)^2}.$$

The desired equation of the curve assumed by the suspended cable is that solution of the differential equation (8) which also satisfies the boundary conditions

(9)   when $x = 0$, $y = y_0$ and $\dfrac{dy}{dx} = 0$.

Equation (8) fits into either of the types studied in this chapter. It is left as an exercise for the student to solve the differential equation (8) with the conditions (9) and arrive at the result

(10) $y = a \cosh \dfrac{x}{a} + y_0 - a.$

Then, of course, the sensible choice $y_0 = a$ is made, so the equation of the desired curve (the catenary) is

$$y = a \cosh \frac{x}{a}.$$

Index

Index

$$100 \cancel{} 15$$

15 سمتین

$$100 \underline{\cancel{15}}^{3}$$
$$90 \quad 96$$
$$\overline{\sim 100}$$

کیل

وریل

اسل

١ر ٦٧
30
داحی ٦ر 60
90

15
7³
─────
105